GALAXY

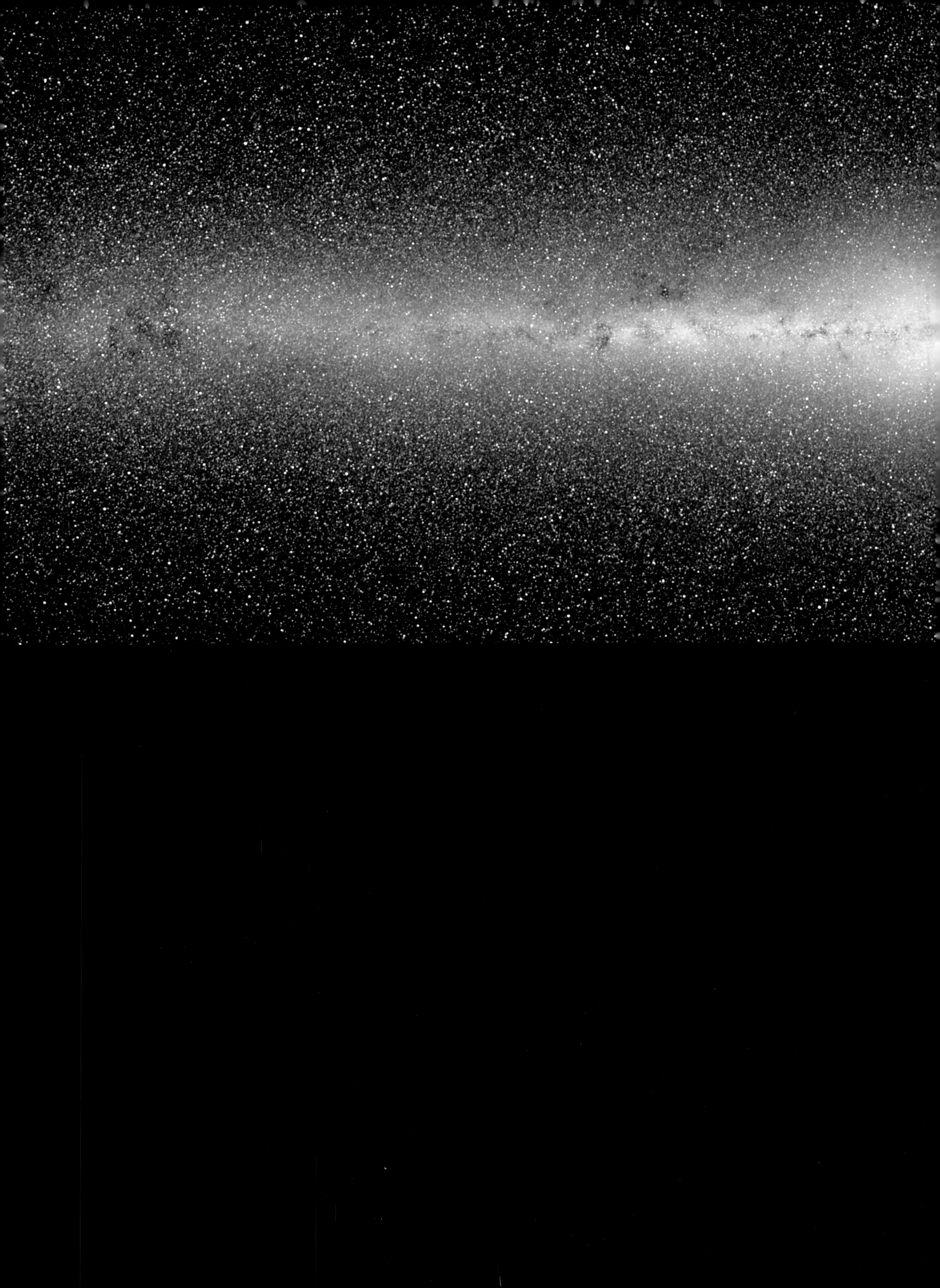

GALAXY

EXPLORING THE MILKY WAY

STUART CLARK

FALL RIVER PRESS

CONTENTS_

Introduction 6

THE COSMIC LANDSCAPE 8

Our Place in the Cosmos 10
The Cosmos at 13 billion light years 12
The Cosmos at 5 billion light years 14
The Cosmos at 1 billion light years 16
The Cosmos at 200 million light years 18
The Cosmos at 100 million light years 20
Galaxy classification 22
Spiral galaxies 24
Barred spiral galaxies 26
Lenticular galaxies 28
Elliptical galaxies 30
Irregular galaxies 32
The Cosmos at 5 million light years 34
The Cosmos at 500,000 light years 38

THE MILKY WAY 46

Anatomy of a Galaxy 48
The Milky Way: a bird's eye view 50
The Milky Way: in profile 52
Spiral arms 56
Dust clouds 58
The galactic core 64
The dark heart of the galaxy 66
The Milky Way and dark matter 68

STARS 70

Star Life 72
The stellar life cycle 74

Birth 76
Dark clouds and emission nebulae 78

Maturity 104
Young stars 106
Open clusters 110
Globular clusters 112
Stellar mergers 114
Stellar classification 116

Old Age and Death 118
Planetary nebulae 120
White dwarfs 130
Supergiant stars 132
Supernovae 136
Stellar corpses 138

Rebirth 142

SOLAR SYSTEMS 148

Planets 150
Building a solar system 152

Our Solar System 154
Sun 156
Solar activity 158

Rocky Worlds 160
Mercury 162
Venus 164
Geology of Venus 166
Venusian weather 168
Earth 170
A restless planet 172
Wind and weather 174
Life on Earth 176
Moon 178
Near side 180
Far side 181
Human lunar exploration 182
Mars 184
Martian moons 185
Martian volcanoes 186
Valles Marineris 188
Martian weather 190
Icy plains and polar caps 192
Water on Mars 194
The Asteroid belt 196

Gas Giants 200
Jupiter 202
The Jovian atmosphere 204
The moons of Jupiter 206
Saturn 214
Rings 216
The moons of Saturn 218
Uranus 232
The moons of Uranus 234
Neptune 236
The moons of Neptune 238

Outer Limits 240
The Kuiper belt 242
The Oort cloud 244

What next? 248

Glossary 250
Index 253
Credits 256

INTRODUCTION_

The Sun, Earth and Moon make up a tiny, tiny part of a much larger celestial object known as the Galaxy. Also called the Milky Way, this vast collection of stars is a microcosm, if the word can be applied on such a large scale, of what is happening across the Universe as a whole.

Our Galaxy is just one of a great many others. Astronomers estimate there could be 125 billion galaxies. Some are clustered nearby, most are flung across the very depths of space that together make the Universe.

Our route to knowledge about such far-flung realms is through observation. For most of human history, astronomers relied on nothing but their own eyes. Then Galileo pointed a newly invented telescope at the night sky in 1610 and saw planets and stars in detail, the like of which had never been imagined before.

His observation of the mountains on the Moon, the faint stars of the Milky Way and his discovery of four large moons surrounding Jupiter, caused a revolution in the way astronomy was practised. From that moment on, the telescope became the essential weapon in an astronomer's arsenal.

Telescopes have grown larger and better throughout the centuries. Whereas Galileo's telescope was a few centimetres or so across, telescopes today reach ten metres in diameter. Instruments dissect light into its constituent colours and record the results on computers, providing astronomers with a wealth of detail about their targets.

In addition, astronomers have become so sophisticated that they no longer need to rely on ordinary light alone. There are other forms of 'light' invisible to human eyes. These go by names such as gamma rays, X-rays, ultraviolet light, infrared light, microwaves and radio waves. Although they sound completely different from one another, they are all related – their individual characteristics being determined by their wavelengths. The shortest wavelengths belong to the gamma rays, the longest to the radio waves. Collectively they are known as the electromagnetic spectrum.

Atoms and other particles produce these emissions and can also absorb them. By observing the Universe at different wavelengths, astronomers gain an insight into not only its chemical composition but also the physical processes that are taking place amongst its atoms. This allows them to build up detailed pictures of what must be happening inside very distant objects.

Studying light also gives astronomers another powerful diagnostic tool. They call it look-back time and it is based on the fact that light travels at a finite speed across space. That speed is extremely fast, crossing nearly 300 million metres every second, and on everyday scales light seems to make its journeys instantaneously. On an astronomical scale, however, the same is not true. It takes light a long time to cross the vast swathes of space that separate celestial objects.

Astronomers call the distance that light can travel in a year, a light year. It is approximately 9.5 trillion kilometres. In the Universe at large, with its distances measured in millions and even billions of light years, it means that the images astronomers make of these distant realms also show them what those celestial objects looked like in the past. This is the look-back time. For example, a galaxy located 100 million light years away, appears to us as it was 100 million years ago because that's how long its light has taken to reach us across space.

This book concentrates on our Galaxy. Spanning just 100,000 light years, our Galaxy is a tiny speck in the cosmic landscape yet it contains a marvellously rich variety of objects and phenomena. As bewildering in number as these bodies seem to be, with astronomers' catalogues now containing thousands upon thousands of items, it is important to remember that they are just a mere sampling of the true number of celestial objects.
In this book the location icons associated with each featured galactic body bring this point home.

Only a centimetre across, a single millimetre on the location icon [1] spans 10,000 light years in space and when plotted most of this book's celestial wonders appear to cluster around the location of our Sun, even though they are thousands or ten of thousands of light years away in reality. This does not reflect any grand astronomical design, just the fact that astronomers tend to concentrate on the largest, nearest examples because these are the ones they can see in the most detail. As bigger and bigger telescopes are built, so astronomers look further afield.

Doing this allows them to understand more about the way celestial objects interact with each other and their environments. Although it is impossible to see our Galaxy as a whole, because we are so deeply embedded within it, astronomers can look outwards into the Universe and see a plethora of other galaxies in their entirety. By studying these, astronomers can fit their knowledge of the detailed workings of individual objects into a picture of what our Galaxy must look like from outside.

The Galaxy is our celestial home, and an amazing home it turns out to be. At first sight, it is a dizzying panorama of exotica that defies description. Yet, with painstaking research covering centuries, the astronomers have marshalled their facts and built a strong edifice of understanding. This has done nothing to diminish the wonder of the night sky. If anything, it serves to enhance the extraordinary power of nature and highlight the fragile cocoon of our own existence.

As you will discover within these pages, our Galaxy – our home – is a beautiful place of awesome spectacle.

[1] Galaxy location icon
• Object location
• Sun

From the surface of the Earth, we look up into the Universe. The band of light across the night sky is the Milky Way, our first hint as to the structure of the galaxy in which we live. Astronomers have become adept at reading these visual clues and translating them into testable, scientific theory about the nature of space and the celestial objects it contains. As a result, our knowledge of the Universe now seems more robust than ever, but there is still much to discover and define.

01

THE COSMIC LANDSCAPE_

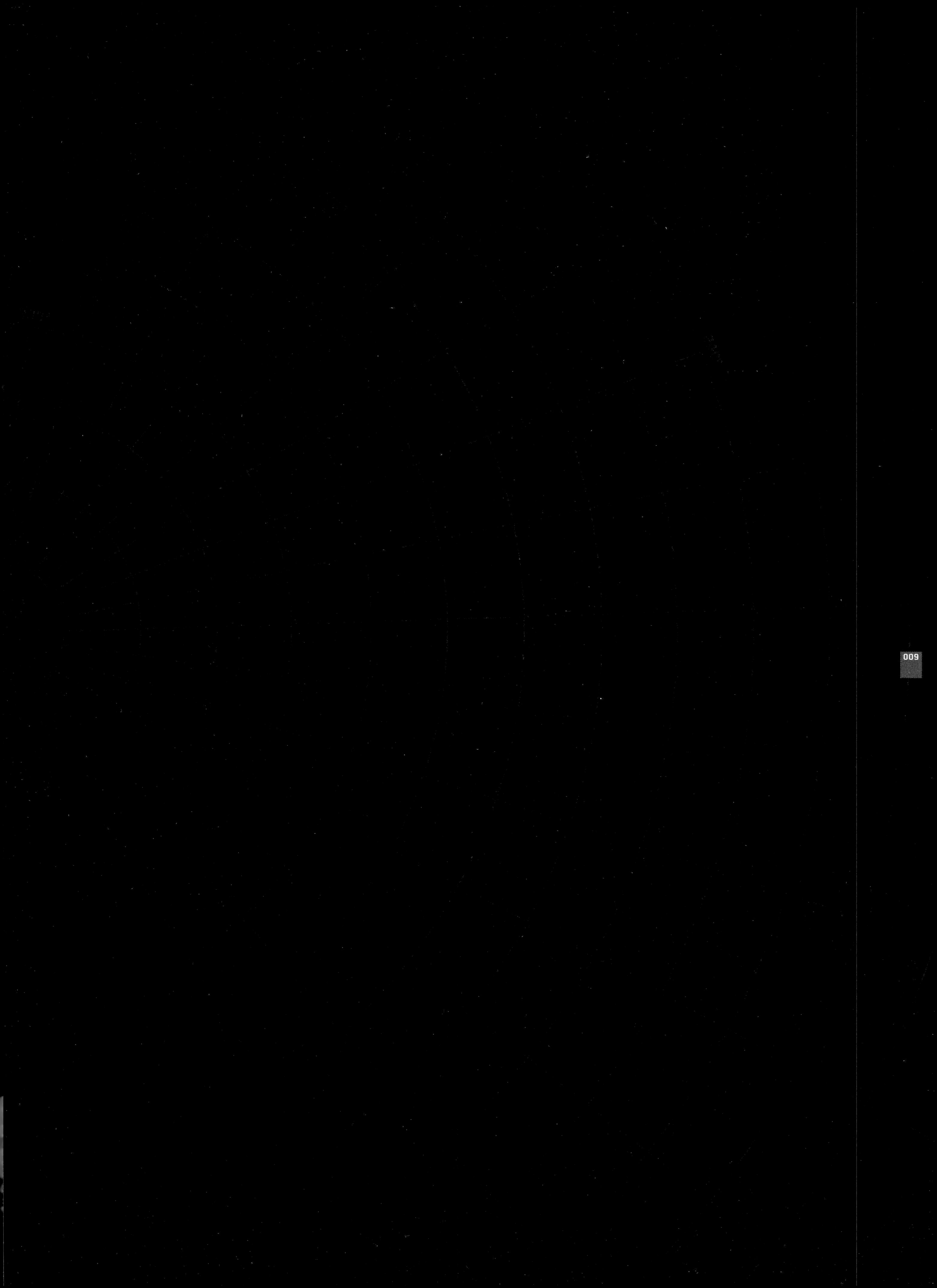

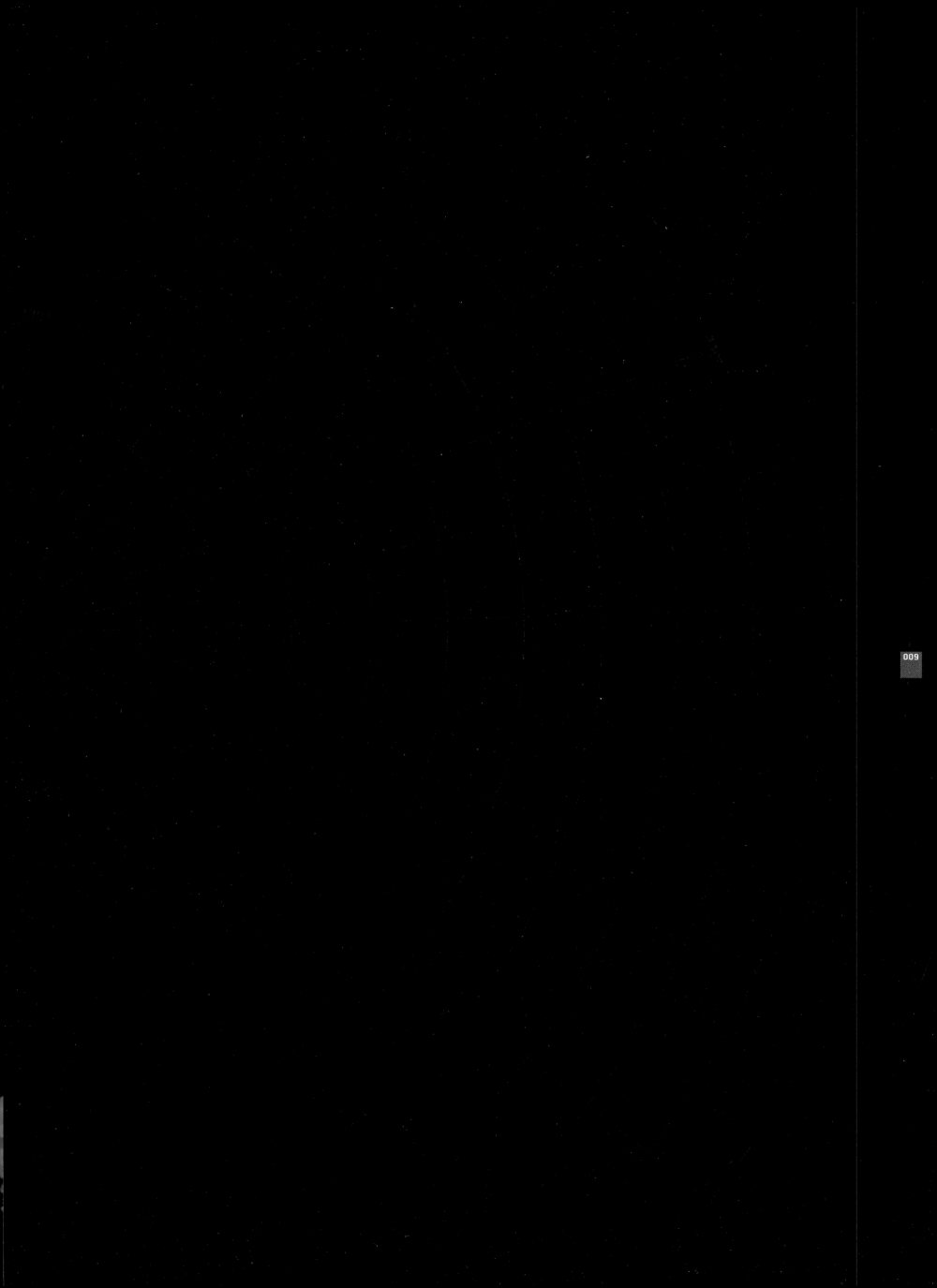

OUR PLACE IN THE COSMOS_

Astronomy can often feel like an exercise in ever expanding scales. Every time we change scale, so we change the type of celestial objects at which we are looking. On the smallest astronomical scales, the dominant celestial objects are the planets and their attendant retinues of moons. Beyond them lies the realm of the stars, each one burning brightly into the night sky; some with their own suite of planets. Taken as a whole, the collection makes up our galaxy, the Milky Way.

Our galaxy is an enormous spiral swirl of stars that stretches through space. Containing some 200 billion stars, it forms an almost self-contained astronomical system, interacting only with the family of satellite galaxies that gather around it.

Beyond these galactic environs, other large galaxies come into view and the Milky Way begins to look just like one more member of a vast population. The galaxies cluster together in smaller groups and larger clusters that then accumulate into superclusters that spread through space in long filaments and sheets.

This celestial arrangement is the product of the origin and subsequent evolution of the Universe. The moment of creation is known as the Big Bang. It happened some 13.4 billion years ago according to modern estimates and brought into being everything there ever has been and everything there ever will be in the Universe.

The Big Bang

The concept of the Big Bang as the origin of the Universe came from the discovery during the 1920s that the Universe was expanding. The reasoning went that if the Universe is expanding now, it must have been smaller in the past. Perhaps it was once a 'primeval atom' that exploded outwards, a celestial seed from which everthing in today's cosmos grew.

The scenario now envisaged is that atoms formed first, accumulating into giant gas clouds that then fragmented to become galaxies. Within them, stars formed and the Universe lit up under the release of the first starlight.

On the scale of the Milky Way galaxy, where most objects are within 10,000 light years of the Sun, look-back time does not help that much because the phases in stellar lifetimes tend to be measured in hundreds of thousands, if not millions of years. So astronomers take a different tack. They collect together large numbers of observations of different celestial objects and then attempt to rearrange them in order of age. This is rather like taking a snapshot of a busy street and trying to work out the phases of the human lifespan by comparing different individuals.

Although this led to a few false starts, astronomers are now confident that they understand the process of stellar birth, life and death in reasonable detail. Perhaps the most uncertain of these phases remains the very birth of stars because the entire process takes place inside giant dusty incubators drifting through space. Another area of uncertainty is the birth of planets, because telescopes cannot yet resolve small enough details to really see this happening.

Today, computer simulations play an important role in an astronomer's analysis of space. They can be used to work through the complex physical equations that describe the behaviour of matter and energy, in order to predict observational properties of celestial objects, such as the amount of light and other radiation that each object releases into space. They have delivered some remarkable insights.

For example, stars have not always been the same throughout cosmic history. In the earliest phases of the Universe when there were no heavier elements, just hydrogen and helium, the stars are predicted to have been gigantic monsters containing perhaps a thousand times

The Hubble Space Telescope orbits the Earth and, although it is not a particularly large telescope by modern standards at just 2.4 metres across, it provides stunning images and information. This is because it is above the distorting blankets of air that mar the view from ground level.

Hubble's unique vantage point allowed it to take this image, the deepest view of the cosmos ever obtained. Known as the Hubble Ultra Deep Field, it is the product of an 11.5-day exposure on a tiny patch of sky. It reveals around ten thousand galaxies, some of them the first galaxies to form in the Universe.

more mass than a star like the Sun. At the present time, the influence of the heavier elements limits a star to about 100 times or so the mass of the Sun.

The dark side

To truly know our place in the Universe, astronomers have become adept at estimating the distance to the variety of celestial objects. Each class of object requires a different method, as do the progressive depths to which astronomers look. For the nearest stars, the method of parallax can be employed. This involves precisely measuring the position of a star twice and then comparing the difference.

Each measurement is taken six months apart, when the Earth is on opposite sides of its orbit and so looking at the star from slightly different directions. This causes the star to appear to change location with respect to the more distant stars. From this tiny change, astronomers can calculate a precise distance to the star.

On the largest scale, astronomers use the fact that the expansion of the Universe stretches the light from celestial objects, turning them redder in colour. Measuring this redshift, as it is known, enables astronomers to estimate a distance.

In addition to these two principal methods, astronomers have evolved numerous other techniques to bridge the gap. The panoply is called the cosmological distance ladder.

Throughout human history, first philosophers and then astronomers have believed in the presence of an all-pervading medium that fills space. This has gone under a number of names, perhaps most famously being called the ether. Although the ether was discredited in the early 20th century, a new form of 'invisible' substance has arisen to dominate astronomers' thinking: dark matter.

Dark matter is suspected to exist throughout the Universe in vast quantities. It hardly interacts at all with the surrounding, normal matter made from atoms, except through the force of gravity. Because it interacts so poorly with electromagnetic radiation, dark matter does not give out or absorb any light, rendering it invisible to telescopes.

Yet the movement of celestial objects on the large scale seems to indicate that much more gravity is being generated inside celestial objects than the bright, atomic matter can muster. So, whilst the planets in our Solar System move, based on Isaac Newton's law of gravity, as we expect them to, the Galaxy as a whole rotates differently. In galaxy clusters, the individual galaxies orbit as if they are being pulled by more mass than can be seen. This persuades many astronomers that there must be dark matter. Spread thinly through space, it builds up as the volumes being examined enlarge and eventually becomes a noticeable force.

Estimates surprisingly suggest that there may be around ten times more dark matter than atomic matter in the Universe. And this is not the only dark substance that astronomers believe exists in the Universe. In the late 1990s, the expansion of the Universe was discovered to be accelerating. As yet astronomers have no front-running explanation for what might be causing this, just a number of competing theories that suggest it may be a previously undiscovered form of energy or a new force of nature.

They have called this new ingredient in the Universe 'dark energy'. Most extraordinarily, the dark energy is estimated to make up about 70 percent of the Universe. What with the dark energy and the dark matter, astronomers are currently forced to believe that the atomic matter, making up all the visible objects in space, is nothing more than a small residue, comprising perhaps a few percent of the contents of the Universe.

The Cosmos at 13 billion light years: the cosmic web

On the very largest scale the Universe possesses a foamy structure, reminiscent of the fibrous skeleton in a natural sponge [opposite]. This heavenly web-work represents the distribution of matter throughout space. At this level, entire clusters of galaxies are no more than celestial pinpricks.

This overarching large-scale structure was revealed by surveys during the late 20th century. Until that time, astronomers had assumed that first clusters and then superclusters of galaxies were distributed randomly through space.

The discovery of dark energy has added a new colour to the Universal palette because it works against gravity and so must help sculpt the Universe into this extraordinary configuration.

Celestial blueprint

[1] Around 400,000 years after the Big Bang, the Universe had cooled sufficiently to allow atoms to form. This was a significant moment in celestial history and the evidence for it can still be seen today. The Universe is filled with radiation, generated in the Big Bang and now present as microwaves, carrying the imprint of the birth of atoms. Patches of slightly higher and lower temperature are coded here as differently coloured regions. The cooler regions, shown as blue, represent slightly denser regions of space; the hotter pink regions are less dense patches. Over the next several billion years, these regions developed into the filamentary structure we see in the Universe today. Although gravity is thought to be the driving force in this process, astronomers are still debating how this blueprint was superimposed on the Universe.

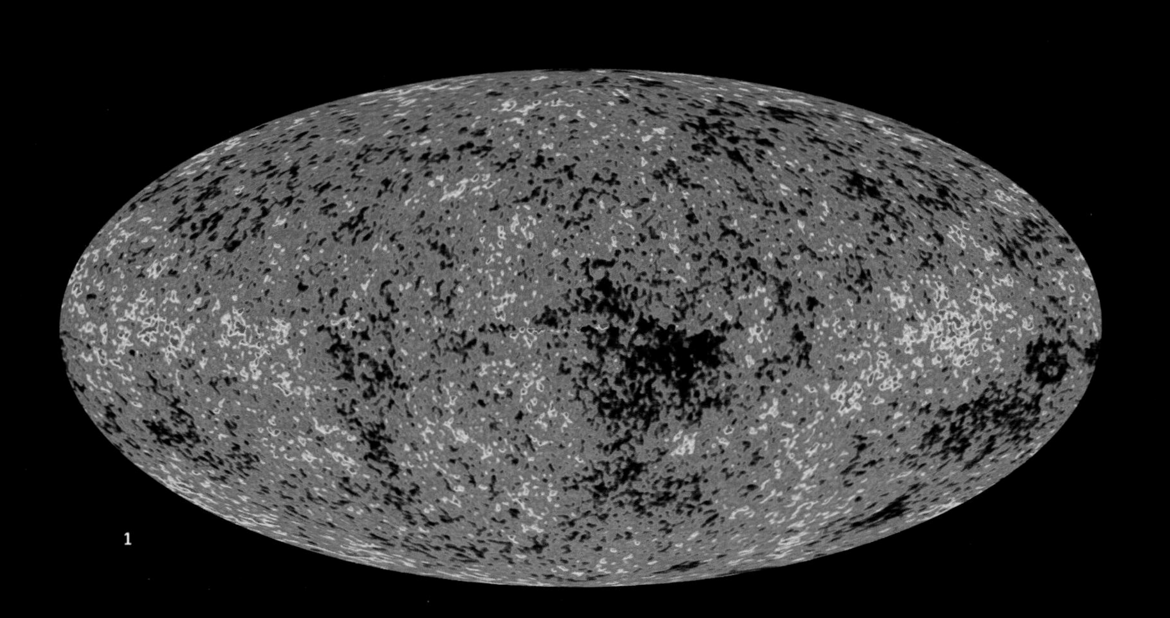

1

SDSS J1004+4112 GALAXY CLUSTER ▶
Gravity can fool the unwary by creating celestial mirages. Surrounding the centre-most orange galaxy are four bright star-like points. These are all images of the same background object. Lying some 3 billion light years behind the central galaxy is an energetic galaxy called a quasar. The gravity of the orange galaxy has split the quasar's light into four images and amplified it to boot. In effect, Nature has provided a zoom lens into the distant Universe for this image.

DISTANCE 7 BILLION LY

SIZE 0.6 MILLION LY

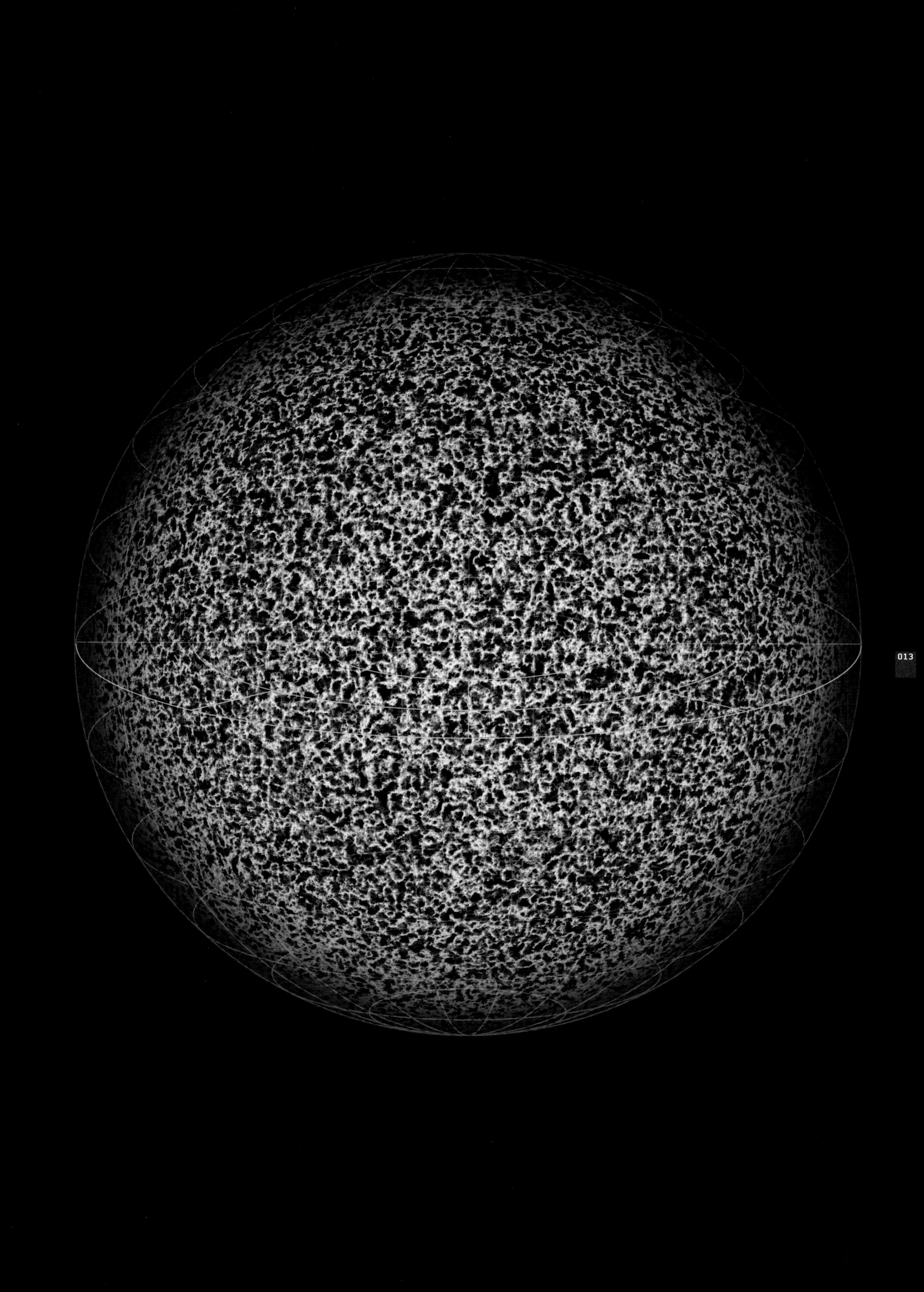

The Cosmos at 5 billion light years: filaments and voids

At this scale, supercomputers can be used to simulate the way that the Universe has evolved as a result of gravity pulling on the galaxies. Although these supercomputers employ 10 billion 'particles' of matter, each particle has to represent a whole cluster of galaxies.

Obvious on this scale [opposite] are the giant voids that punctuate space like vast bubbles. The galaxies are spread around the exterior surfaces of these bubbles making huge conglomerations in the zones where several void surfaces come together. The voids do still contain matter but not in anything like the quantity that the filaments do.

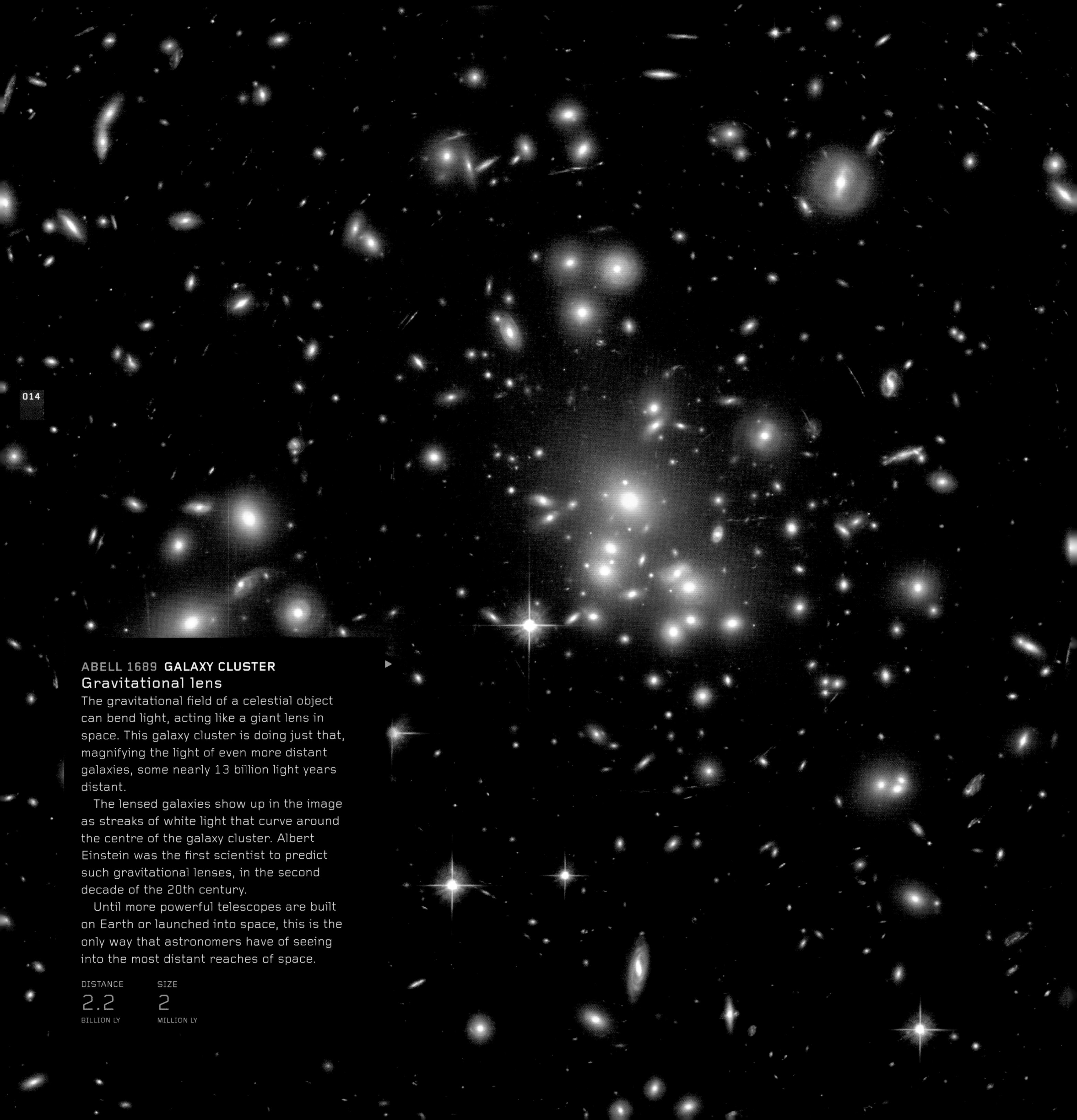

ABELL 1689 **GALAXY CLUSTER**

Gravitational lens

The gravitational field of a celestial object can bend light, acting like a giant lens in space. This galaxy cluster is doing just that, magnifying the light of even more distant galaxies, some nearly 13 billion light years distant.

The lensed galaxies show up in the image as streaks of white light that curve around the centre of the galaxy cluster. Albert Einstein was the first scientist to predict such gravitational lenses, in the second decade of the 20th century.

Until more powerful telescopes are built on Earth or launched into space, this is the only way that astronomers have of seeing into the most distant reaches of space.

DISTANCE 2.2 BILLION LY

SIZE 2 MILLION LY

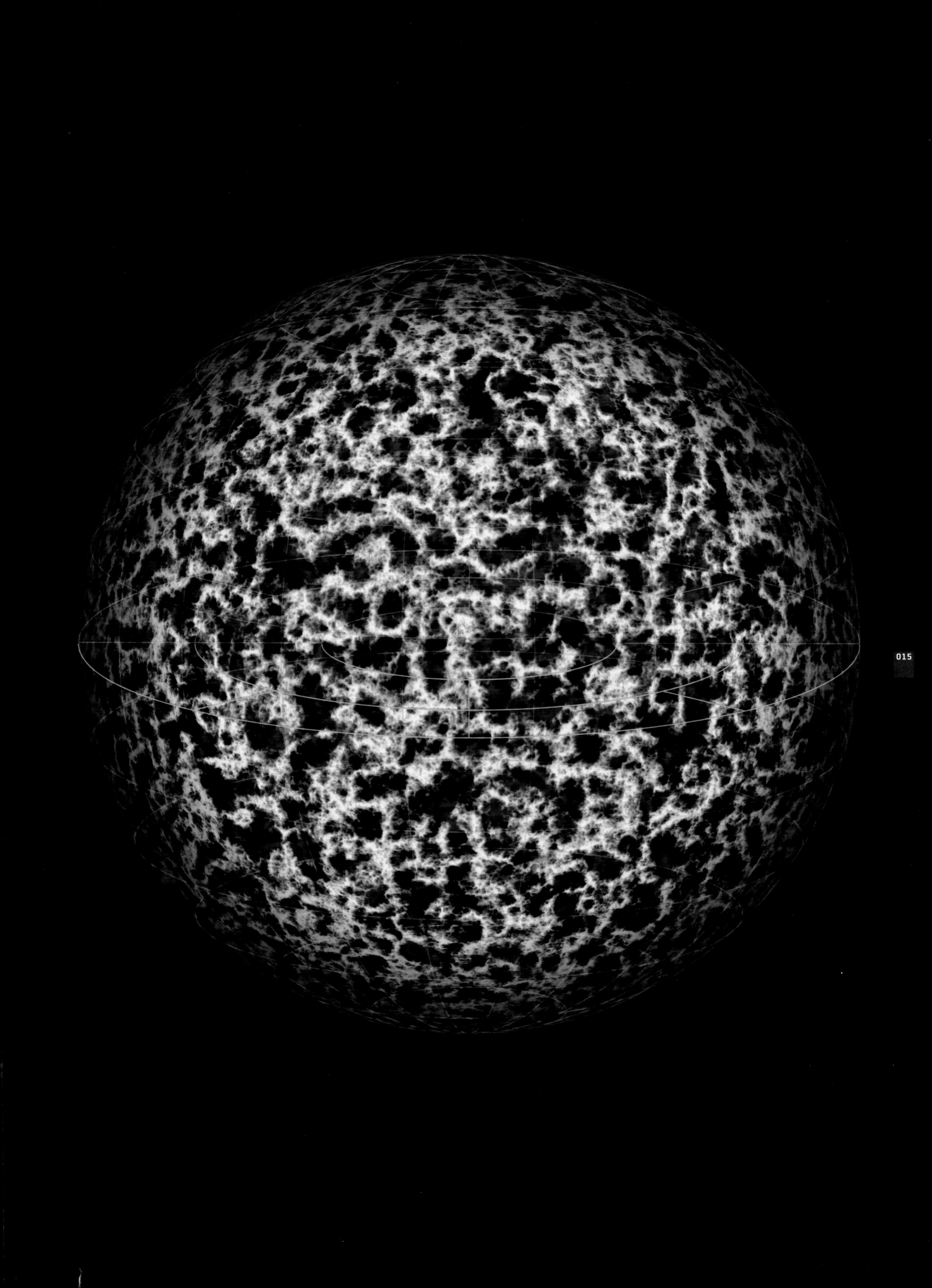

The Cosmos at 1 billion light years: superclusters

Galactic superclusters dominate space at this scale. The larger scale sheets and filaments of galaxies are now breaking up into enormous conglomerations of galaxy clusters, spanning hundreds of millions of light years [opposite].

There are currently estimated to be some 10 million superclusters in the Universe. They were probably some of the first structures to form. As they became discrete – even if gigantic – pockets of mass held together by gravity, so they fragmented inside into smaller pockets of mass that went on to become clusters of galaxies. In a supercluster, each galactic cluster is still associated through gravity with the others in its supercluster.

Mixed in with the clusters and groups of galaxies in a supercluster are a number of isolated galaxies. These are called field galaxies and make up just five percent of the galaxy population.

[1] ABELL 1656 **GALAXY CLUSTER**

The Coma Cluster

Thousands of galaxies comprise the Coma Supercluster of galaxies. It contains two clusters, the Coma cluster (shown here) and the Leo cluster. Coma is a rich cluster, packed with galaxies and, in common with most rich clusters, its central regions are mostly packed with elliptical galaxies. The fragile spiral galaxies circle the outskirts of the cluster.

The Coma Supercluster was one of the first 'clusters of clusters' to be identified in the sky. It showed astronomers that there is a larger hierarchy of structures in the Universe than just clusters of galaxies.

DISTANCE 300 MILLION LY

SIZE 20 MILLION LY

[2] ABELL 2151 **GALAXY CLUSTER**

The Hercules Cluster

Clusters of galaxies appear to be broadly similar, no matter where they are located in space. If anything sets Hercules apart, it is the fact that it is rich in spiral galaxies and relatively poor in ellipticals. As elliptical galaxies are thought to be forged in the collision of spiral galaxies, this may indicate that Hercules has enjoyed a relatively quiet history. The Hercules Cluster is part of the larger Hercules Supercluster, which is itself part of the 'Great Wall', which at 500 million light years long, 300 million light years wide and 15 million light years thick, is the second largest known superstructure in the Universe.

DISTANCE 470 MILLION LY

SIZE 15 MILLION LY

1 2

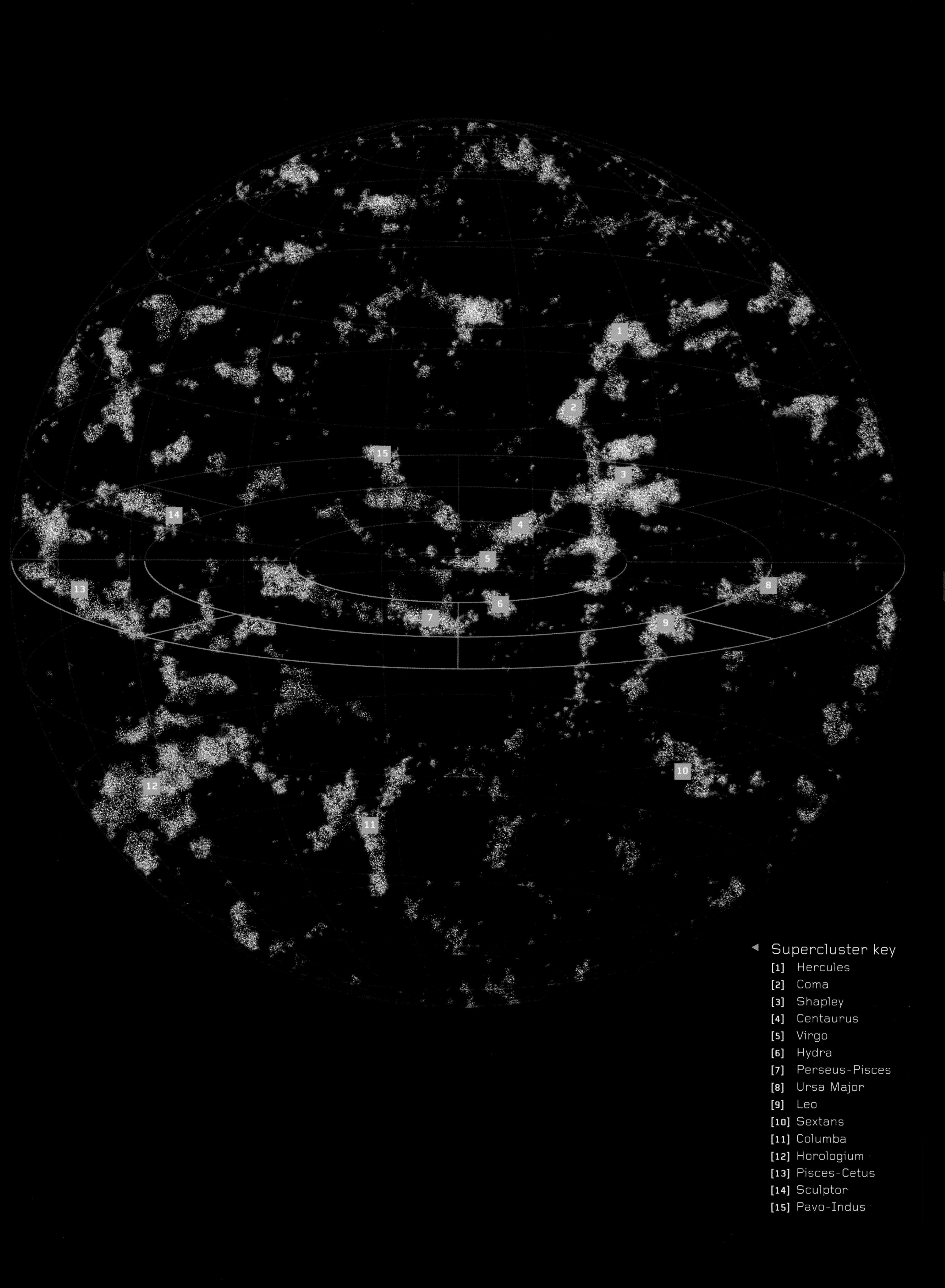
Supercluster key
[1] Hercules
[2] Coma
[3] Shapley
[4] Centaurus
[5] Virgo
[6] Hydra
[7] Perseus-Pisces
[8] Ursa Major
[9] Leo
[10] Sextans
[11] Columba
[12] Horologium
[13] Pisces-Cetus
[14] Sculptor
[15] Pavo-Indus

The Cosmos at 200 million light years: the Local Supercluster

Within our own supercluster [opposite], there is a collection of clusters and voids. Our own modest local family of galaxies, so small it is called a group rather than a cluster, is by no means the dominant member. The Local Supercluster is centred on the Virgo Cluster, a large cluster of galaxies some 60 million light years away.

The overall expansion of space on these scales is slow enough that the gravitational pull of the local cluster masses becomes noticeable. This gives rise to a mystery that humans may never be able to solve. Something is pulling the clusters that comprise the Local Supercluster in a specific direction.

This 'object' is most likely to be a particularly massive galaxy cluster, lying somewhere between 150 million and 250 million light years away in the direction of the constellations of Hydra and Centaurus. However, because the great mass of stars that forms our own galaxy, the Milky Way, lies in the same direction, we can never see this section of space. Hence, we may never know for sure the identity of this 'Great Attractor'.

ABELL 3627 **GALAXY CLUSTER**

The Norma Cluster

Hidden in this section of space lies the Great Attractor but the great density of stars in our own Galaxy creates a nearly impenetrable mass known as the zone of avoidance.

The Norma Cluster itself is a massive conglomeration of galaxies, close to the calculated central position of the Great Attractor. It almost certainly contributes to the anomalous gravitational pull that distorts the expansion of the Universe.

DISTANCE	SIZE
250 MILLION LY	30 MILLION LY

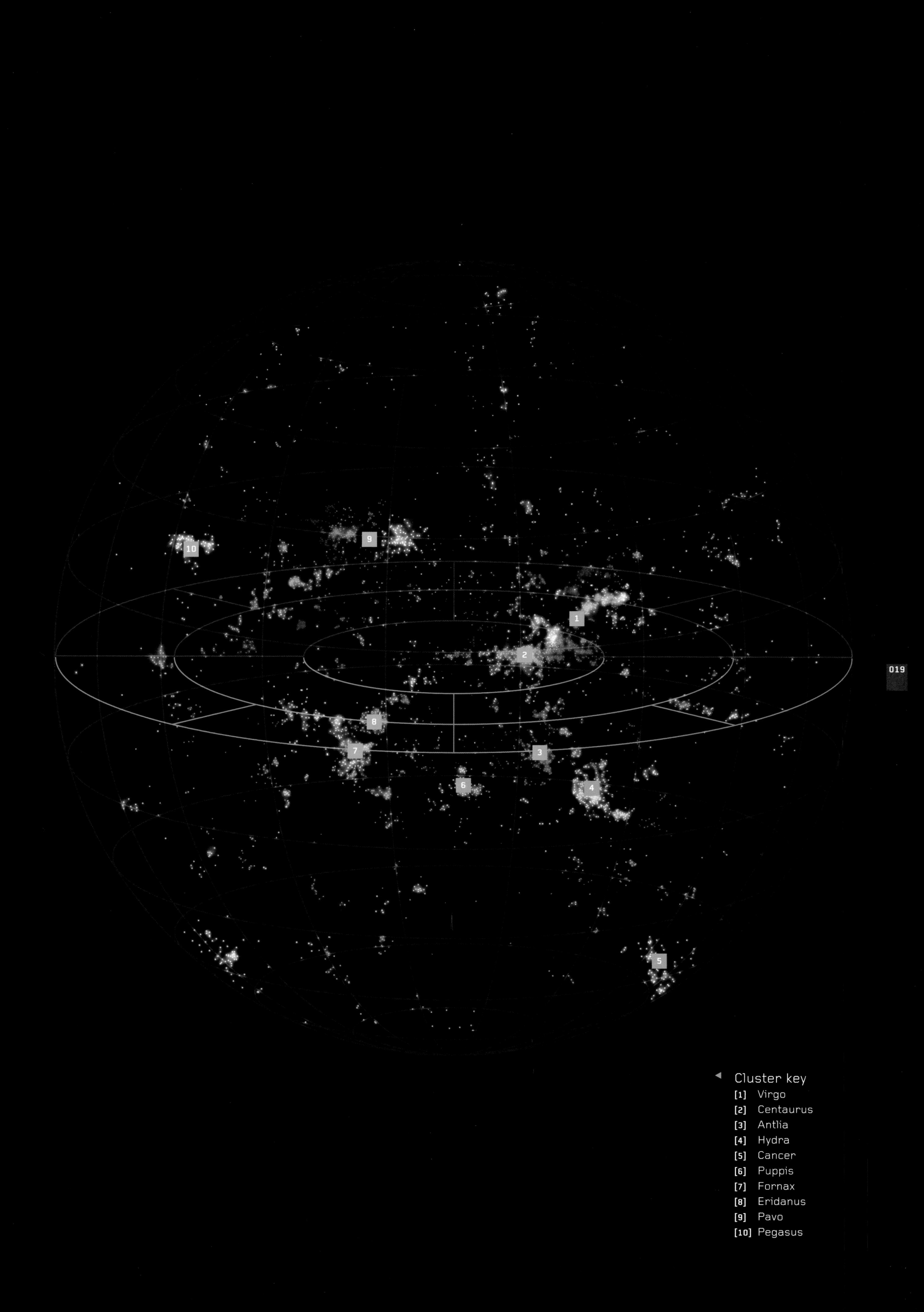
1
2
3
4
5
6
7
8
9
10
Cluster key
[1] Virgo
[2] Centaurus
[3] Antlia
[4] Hydra
[5] Cancer
[6] Puppis
[7] Fornax
[8] Eridanus
[9] Pavo
[10] Pegasus

The Cosmos at 100 million light years: the Virgo Cluster

Closing in on the Local Group [opposite], other nearby groups of galaxies come into focus. Groups of galaxies can contain up to about 50 galaxies, spread in a spherical region of up to 7 million light years. Gravitationally, they are dominated by whatever cluster of galaxies is nearby. In the case of our own region of space, that means the Virgo Cluster. The Local Group is being slowed in its passage through space by Virgo's gravity. Eventually, in tens or hundreds of billions of years, it will probably begin falling into the Virgo Cluster.

Groups and clusters are filled not only with galaxies but also with hot gas. It may be that there is as much hot gas in a galaxy cluster as there is locked up in stars in the visible galaxies. The hot gas shines mostly with X-rays that cannot pass through the Earth's atmosphere. So, only space telescopes can measure them.

GALAXY CLUSTER

The Virgo Cluster

The heart of the Local Supercluster, the Virgo cluster contains more than 1300 individual galaxies. Elliptical galaxies and spirals are distributed fairly randomly throughout the Virgo cluster, although there are some sub-groupings where large elliptical galaxies hold sway.

DISTANCE 52 MILLION LY

SIZE 20 MILLION LY

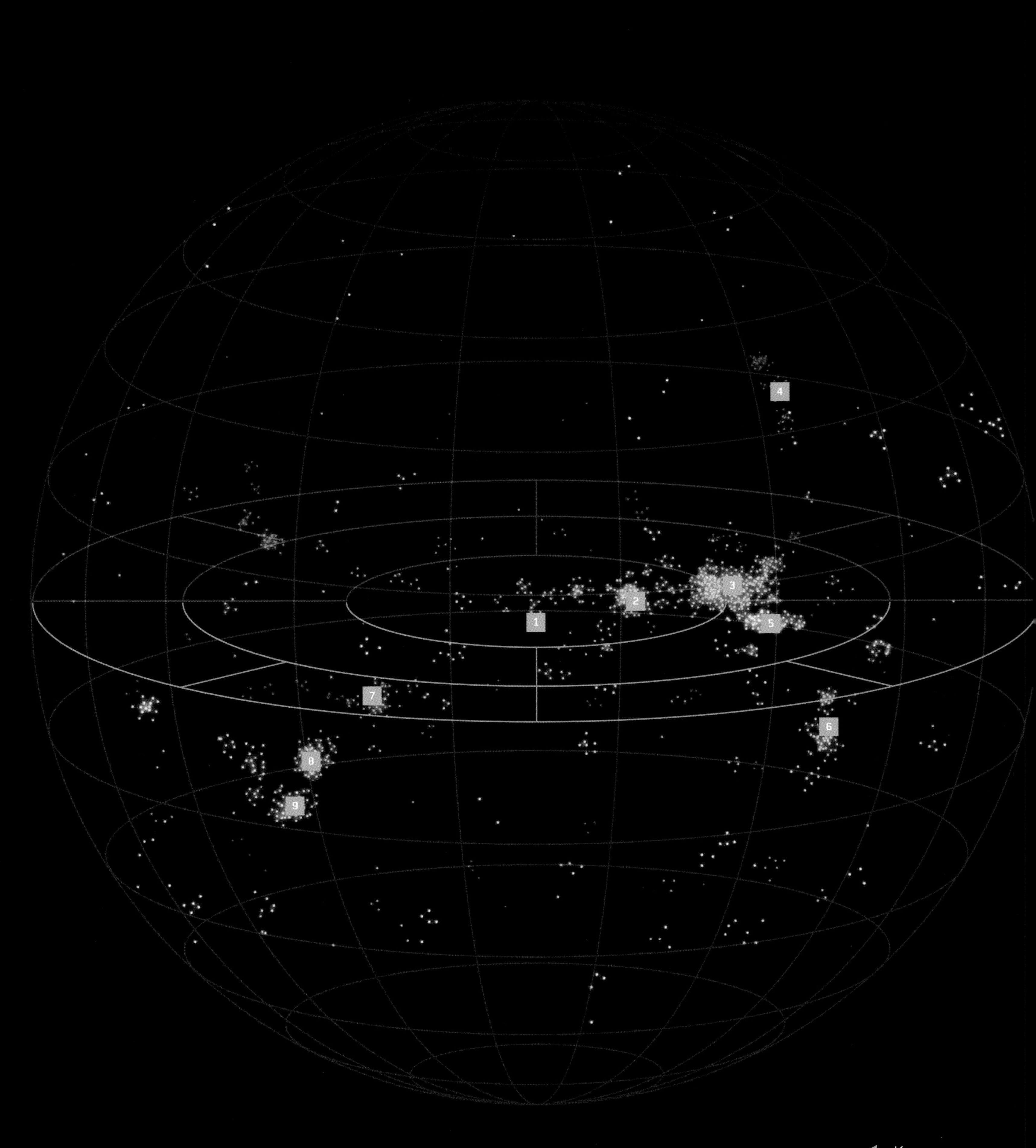

Key

[1] Local Group
[2] Canes groups
[3] Virgo Cluster
[4] Virgo III groups
[5] Ursa Major grou
[6] Leo II groups
[7] Dorado

Galaxy classification

What appears at first to be a bewildering array of galaxies, can be simplified into a straightforward classification scheme.

merican astronomer Edwin Hubble undertook is pioneering work in the 1920s. Poring over nage after image, he determined that there re three main categories of galaxy: ellipticals, pirals and barred spirals.

Ellipticals are round masses of stars that an be any shape from spherical to flattened. Spirals have sweeping arms of stars that wrap round a central bulge of stars. The barred pirals are similar except that their spiral rms are joined to the centre by a straight ar of stars.

Two subgroups also exist. The lenticular alaxies are spiral without spiral arms and hen there is the group of irregular galaxies 1] that includes everything that will not fit nto the scheme.

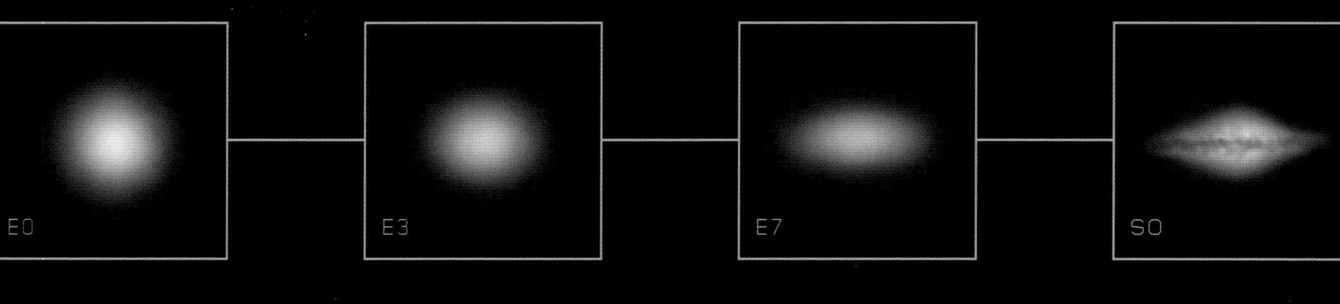

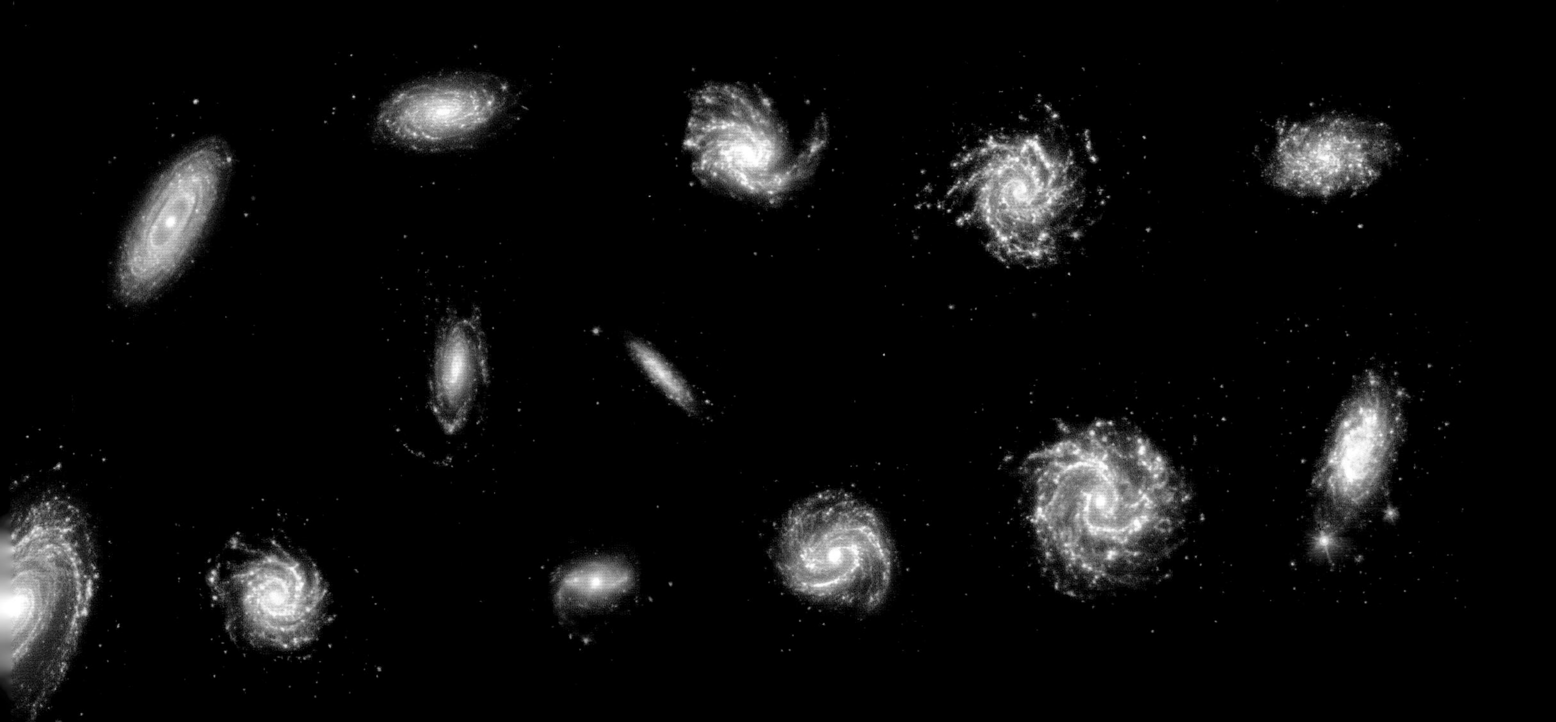

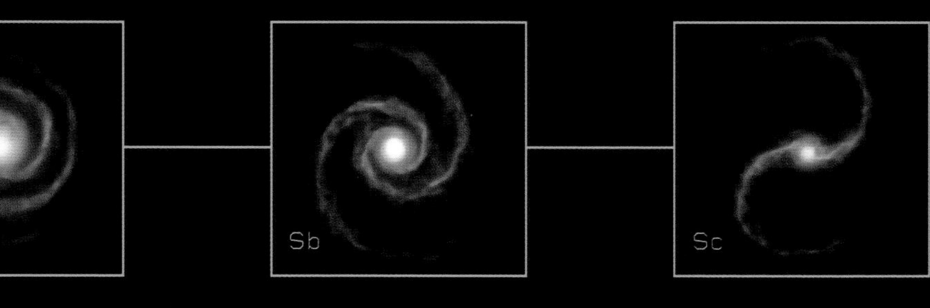

Sa
Sb
Sc

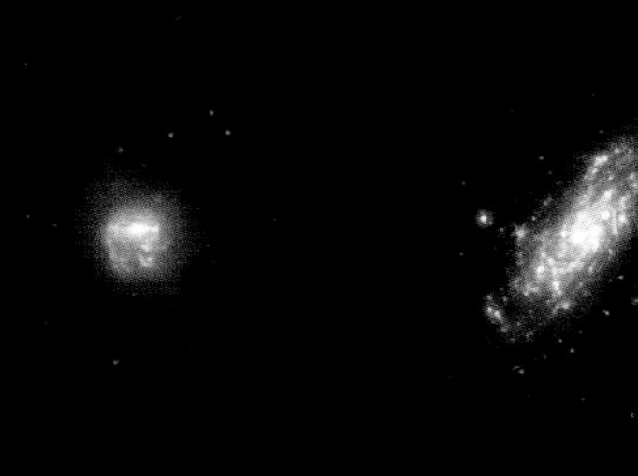

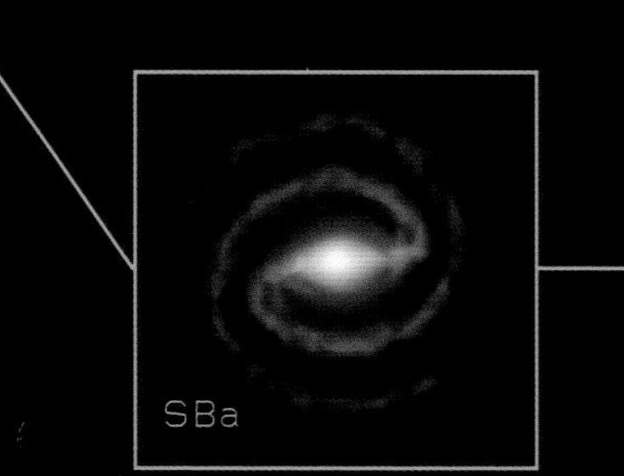

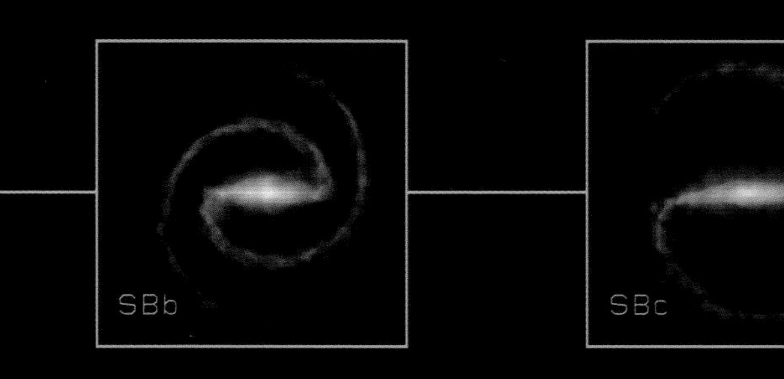

SBa
SBb
SBc

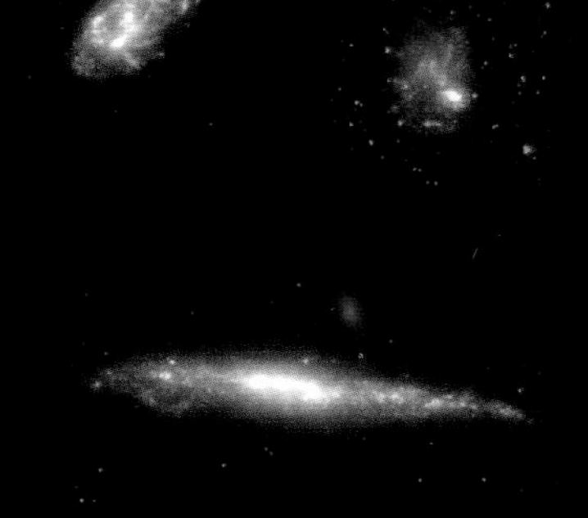

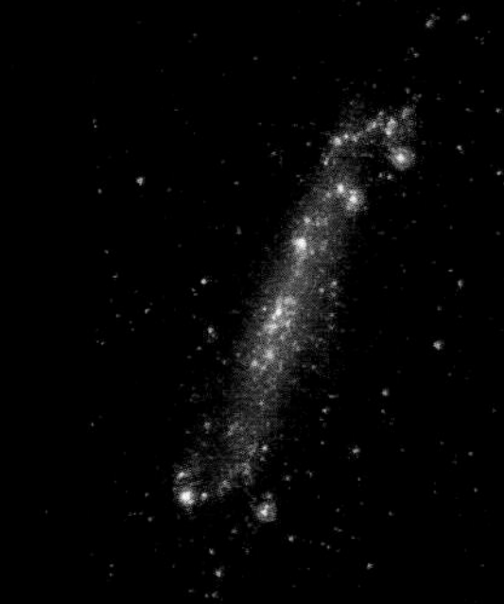

Spiral galaxies

Spiral galaxies embody celestial grace with their sweeping arms of short-lived stars that curl round to embrace the galaxy's central region. These inner realms are home to crowds of long-lived stars, dating from the very origin of the galaxy.

[1] M74 (NGC 628) SPIRAL GALAXY
The inner regions of spiral galaxy M74 show that the spiral structure, denoted most clearly here by the dark dust lanes, extends down into the very heart of the galaxy.

DISTANCE 32 MILLION LY
SIZE 90 THOUSAND LY

[2] NGC 4013 SPIRAL GALAXY
Viewed from the side, a spiral galaxy's tremendous swirl of stars is revealed as an almost flat disc. The clouds of dust that lace the galaxy absorb the starlight, creating the dark bands.

DISTANCE 55 MILLION LY
SIZE 80 THOUSAND LY

[3] M51 (NGC 5194) SPIRAL GALAXY
The Whirlpool Galaxy
Perhaps the classic example of a spiral galaxy, M51's spiral appearance was first noted by William Parsons, the third earl of Rosse, in 1845. It took another 80 years before the 'spiral nebulae' were recognized as being vast collections of stars, situated at large distances from the Earth.
In this image, red clouds of glowing hydrogen have been digitally enhanced to highlight the areas of prominent star formation. These celestial nurseries keep the spiral arms stocked with new stars.

DISTANCE 37 MILLION LY
SIZE 100 THOUSAND LY

1

2

1

Barred spiral galaxies

Closely related to the spiral galaxies are the barred spiral galaxies. As the name suggests, these display a straight bar of many stars that emanate from the central nucleus before transforming into the spiral arms.

3

[1] NGC 1300 BARRED SPIRAL GALAXY
NGC 1300 is a prime example of a barred spiral galaxy. The straight bar of stars is dominated by the yellow glow of long-lived stars, threaded by dark twists of dust. Following the dust lanes into the centre of the galaxy reveals a tight, inner spiral swirl.

DISTANCE 69 MILLION LY
SIZE 150 THOUSAND LY

[2] M81 SPIRAL GALAXY
Bode's Galaxy
M81 is a spiral galaxy where the spiral arms are less prominent than the nucleus, as can be seen in the visible light image. Switching to infrared wavelengths [3] literally shows M81 in a different light and the dust lanes become bright. This is because the dust absorbs starlight and heats up. It then radiates that heat at infrared wavelengths.

DISTANCE 12 MILLION LY
SIZE 70 THOUSAND LY

[4] NGC 1350 BARRED SPIRAL GALAXY
The faint outer arms of this galaxy emanate from a complete ring of stars that surrounds the galactic nucleus. The elongated nucleus marks NGC 1350 out as a barred spiral galaxy even though the bars are not prominently visible.

DISTANCE 85 MILLION LY
SIZE 130 THOUSAND LY

[5] M83 SPIRAL/BARRED SPIRAL GALAXY
Pinwheel Galaxy
Radio waves given out by hydrogen gas are shown here in red and reveal that the spiral arms of a galaxy can extend dramatically into space, beyond its visible confines. The blue swirl in the centre of the image is the visible extent of the galaxy.

DISTANCE 15 MILLION LY
SIZE 140 THOUSAND LY

4

5

Lenticular galaxies

These are best described as spiral galaxies that have lost their spiral arms. Viewed edge-on they appear to be lens-shaped collections of stars, hence the term lenticular galaxy.

M104 SPIRAL/LENTICULAR GALAXY

The Sombrero Galaxy

The Sombrero Galaxy is officially classified as a spiral galaxy with tightly wound arms. However, it looks extremely similar to many lenticular galaxies. Built up of a staggeringly large number of stars, astronomers estimate 800 billion, most of them are crowded into a central lens-shaped region spanning nearly 50,000 light years.

At infrared wavelengths [1], the dust becomes the most luminous component of the galaxy whereas at X-ray wavelengths [2], the hot gas surrounding the galaxy becomes visible.

The Sombrero Galaxy is the dominant member of the M104 group, shepherding at least seven other galaxies.

DISTANCE	SIZE
28 MILLION LY	50 THOUSAND LY

1

Elliptical galaxies

Perhaps not as pretty as the spiral galaxies, the elliptical galaxies are the true monsters of the Universe. They are formed by the collision of smaller galaxies. In these cosmic smash-ups, the colliding galaxies lose their own configurations and merge to become a single, giant mess of stars.

[1] NGC 1316 ELLIPTICAL GALAXY
Most elliptical galaxies do not contain much dust or other star forming materials. NGC 1316 is different, as can be seen from the dusty silhouettes in this image. This elliptical is the result of the collision of two spirals and, although this ignited a wave of star formation that tore through the merging galaxies, it somehow failed to use up all the available fuel.

DISTANCE 75 MILLION LY
SIZE 60 THOUSAND LY

[2] NGC 1132 ELLIPTICAL GALAXY
NGC 1132 is a vast elliptical galaxy containing a trillion stars. The already large galaxy is surrounded by an even larger cloud of hot gas. This appears at X-ray wavelengths and, in the inset image [3], the gas has been superimposed in purple on the underlying optical image. To be so surrounded is unusual for a single galaxy. Such hot gas is usually found binding groups of galaxies together.

It is possible that NGC 1132 was once a number of galaxies that orbited each other in a small group. Over billions of years, they have fallen together and coalesced into a single object, leaving behind the hot gas.

DISTANCE 318 MILLION LY
SIZE 120 THOUSAND LY

3

2

Irregular galaxies

These are usually galaxies caught in the transition from one type to another. The transformation is usually the result of either a collision with another galaxy or a near miss. In the latter case, the gravitational pull of the other galaxy distorts its counterpart. If the two galaxies are similar sizes, this can be a mutual process with both galaxies pulling the other out of shape.

[1] NGC 1427 IRREGULAR GALAXY
This small galaxy is being pulled through space by the combined gravitational force of all the galaxies in the Fornax cluster of galaxies. They have already accelerated it to 600 kilometres per second and are gradually elongating it as the back of the galaxy lags behind the front. Eventually, the galaxy will be pulled apart completely.

DISTANCE 62 MILLION LY
SIZE 20 THOUSAND LY

[2] NGC 1569 IRREGULAR GALAXY
Episodic bursts of star formation are driving this small galaxy out of shape. The current episode of furious activity is estimated to have begun 20 million years ago.

DISTANCE 8 MILLION LY
SIZE 10 THOUSAND LY

[3] NGC 4214 IRREGULAR GALAXY
The bright blob at the centre of this irregular galaxy is a cluster of stars. Over a hundred huge stars crowd inside, each one 10,000 times brighter than the Sun.

DISTANCE 13 MILLION LY
SIZE 22 THOUSAND LY

[4] M82 IRREGULAR GALAXY
The Cigar Galaxy
Two enormous fountains of hydrogen gas have been pulled out of this galaxy by the gravitational strength of an enormous nearby galaxy. This hydrogen glows as streamers of red in the image and is now raining back down onto the cigar-shaped mass of stars making up the underlying galaxy. M82 has been completely remodelled by the near miss and is now forming ten times more stars than our own galaxy.

DISTANCE 12 MILLION LY
SIZE 30 THOUSAND LY

1
2
3

The Cosmos at 5 million light years: the Local Group

On the size scale of five million light years, our view of the cosmos has shrunk to encompass only the Local Group of galaxies [opposite]. There are more than 35 galaxies in the Local Group and these are dominated by the gravitational influence of its two largest members: our own galaxy, the Milky Way, and the Andromeda Galaxy.

The Milky Way and Andromeda are currently far apart but they are orbiting ever closer. In approximately three billion years' time they will collide and form a single elliptical galaxy.

[1] M31 SPIRAL GALAXY

The Andromeda Galaxy

The nearest large spiral galaxy to our own is the mighty Andromeda Galaxy. It is truly revealed by the different wavelengths it emits. In the visible light image, two distinct stellar populations are apparent. Short-lived blue stars swirl in giant loops around the central bulge of long-lived yellow stars.

At infrared wavelengths, [2] the dust lanes shine brightly. Inside them, hidden from view, young stars are readying themselves to burst onto the cosmic scene.

Stars can also emit infrared radiation. This has been isolated in the image [3] and then removed from the overall infrared picture [4], to leave the true contribution from dust visible.

Visible in all images is the tilt of Andromeda's inner regions, compared to the outer ring of stars. This deformation is caused by the gravity of Andromeda's satellite galaxies. One such satellite galaxy is visible below Andromeda in the main image.

DISTANCE
2.5
MILLION LY

SIZE
140
THOUSAND LY

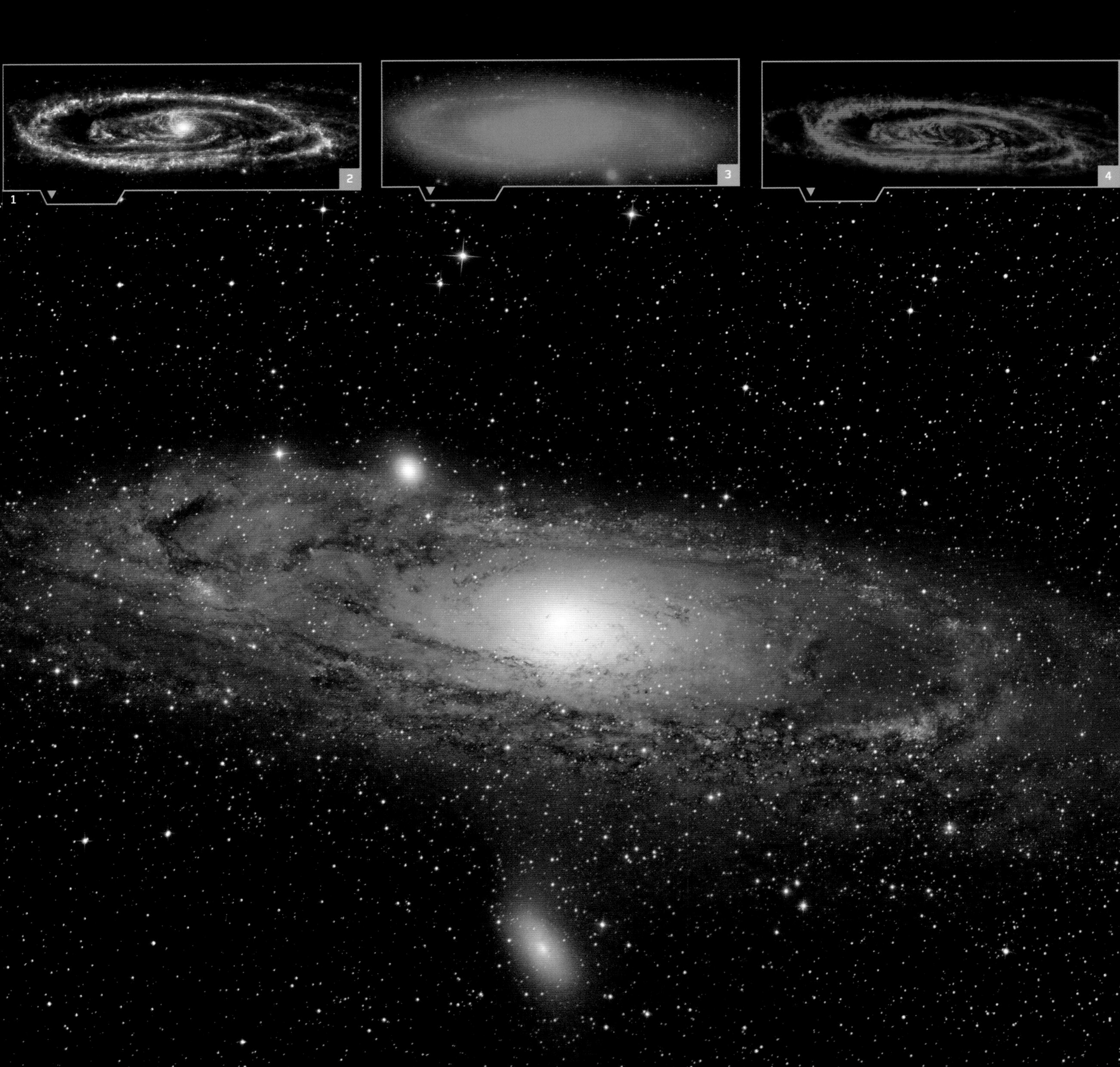

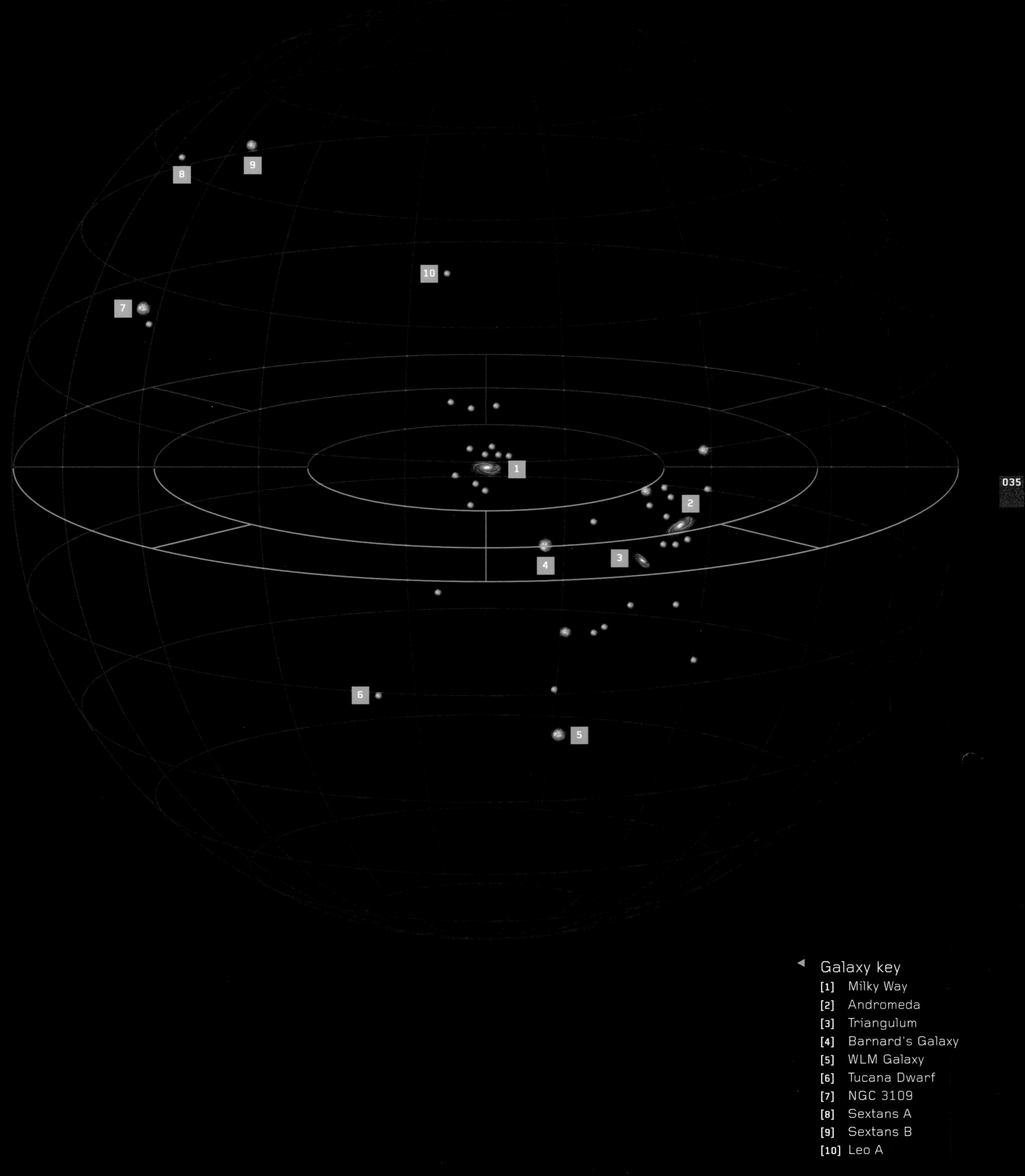

Galaxy key

[1] Milky Way
[2] Andromeda
[3] Triangulum
[4] Barnard's Galaxy
[5] WLM Galaxy
[6] Tucana Dwarf
[7] NGC 3109
[8] Sextans A
[9] Sextans B
[10] Leo A

1
2
2

[1] M33 SPIRAL GALAXY
The Triangulum Galaxy

M33 is the third spiral galaxy in the Local Group. Smaller than the Milky Way and much smaller than the Andromeda Galaxy, it still takes up as much space in the sky as several full Moons but is too faint to be seen with the unaided eye. The red patches across the galaxy are star forming regions, including the gigantic star-forming factory NGC 604 [2].

Spanning 1.3 light years, NGC 604 is a gigantic region of star formation. It is the home of thousands of freshly minted stars; several hundred of them are giant stars with up to 100 times the mass of the Sun. The ultraviolet light they emit into space is causing the surrounding hydrogen gas to glow.

Radio telescopes show [3] the delicate filigree of hydrogen gas that threads the galaxy and these can be superimposed upon optical image [4] to show how everything fits together. In doing this, it is obvious that hydrogen arms extend beyond the stellar arms of the galaxy. In addition, the radio waves can be analysed for movement to show us how the galaxy is rotating. [5] The side of the galaxy that is rotating towards us is shown as blue and the side that is rotating away is shown as red.

DISTANCE	SIZE
2.9 MILLION LY	50 THOUSAND LY

[6] NGC 6822 IRREGULAR GALAXY
Barnard's Galaxy

Many members of the Local Group are irregular galaxies. NGC 6822 is a prime example of a smaller, irregular mass of stars. To the top right of the galaxy, just in its fainter outer reaches, is a conspicuous bubble-shaped star-forming region.

DISTANCE	SIZE
1.8 MILLION LY	10 THOUSAND LY

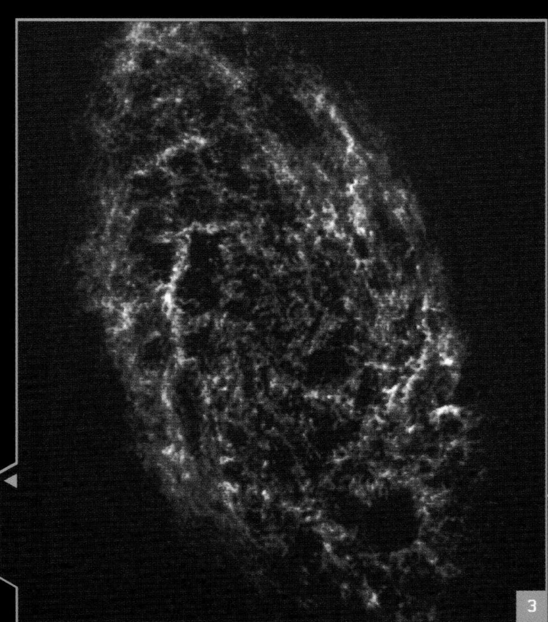

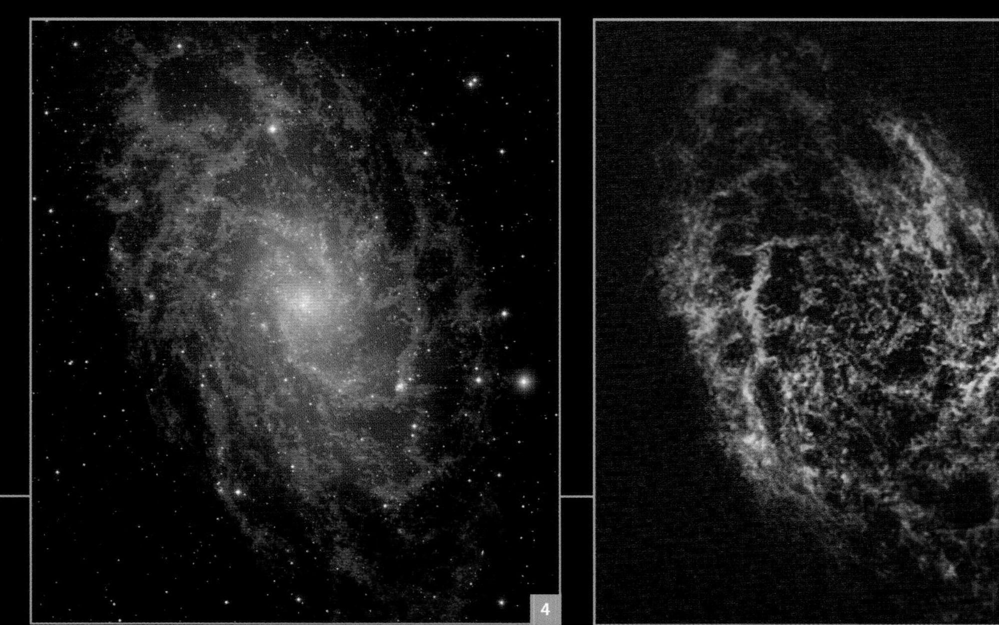

The Cosmos at 500,000 light years: satellite galaxies

Orbiting the Milky Way are a number of satellite galaxies. Of these, two are significant, the Large and Small Magellanic Clouds. These are probably galaxies that are caught in a final orbital dance before they merge with our Galaxy. This process may already be happening as astronomers have discovered streams of gas being pulled out of the Magellanic Clouds by the gravity of the Milky Way. Alternatively, other astronomers think that the Magellanic Clouds will escape our Galaxy's gravitational clutches because they are travelling too fast to be captured.

Numerous dwarf and satellite galaxies attend the magnificent spiral of the Milky Way. Each one is orbiting the centre of our Galaxy.

As well as studying the Magellanic Clouds, astronomers have recently begun to recognise slight 'over-densities' of stars in the sky that signal the presence of nearby dwarf galaxies. Named after the constellations where they are found, they are all in the process of being consumed by the Milky Way.

ESO 594-4 **DWARF GALAXY**

The Sagittarius Dwarf Irregular Galaxy

This faint smudge shows how hard it is to recognize nearby dwarf galaxies and this one is about ten times further away than some of those recently identified near the Milky Way. When brought much closer, the stars will appear even more spread out and it becomes almost impossible to recognize it as an individual galaxy except with the aid of computer analysis.

DISTANCE	SIZE
3.5 MILLION LY	1.5 THOUSAND LY

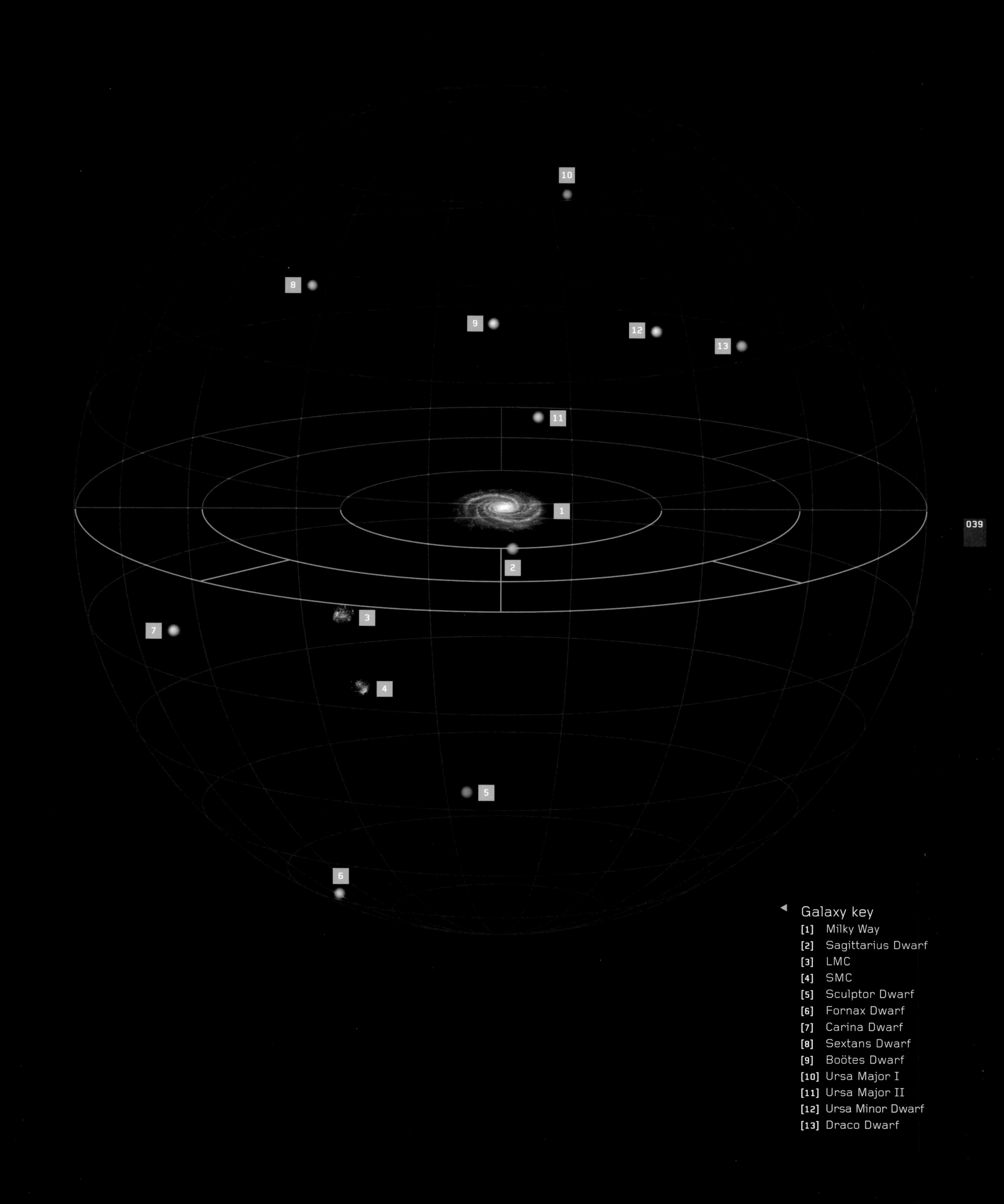
10
8
9
12
13
11
1
2
3
7
4
5
6
Galaxy key
[1] Milky Way
[2] Sagittarius Dwarf
[3] LMC
[4] SMC
[5] Sculptor Dwarf
[6] Fornax Dwarf
[7] Carina Dwarf
[8] Sextans Dwarf
[9] Boötes Dwarf
[10] Ursa Major I
[11] Ursa Major II
[12] Ursa Minor Dwarf
[13] Draco Dwarf

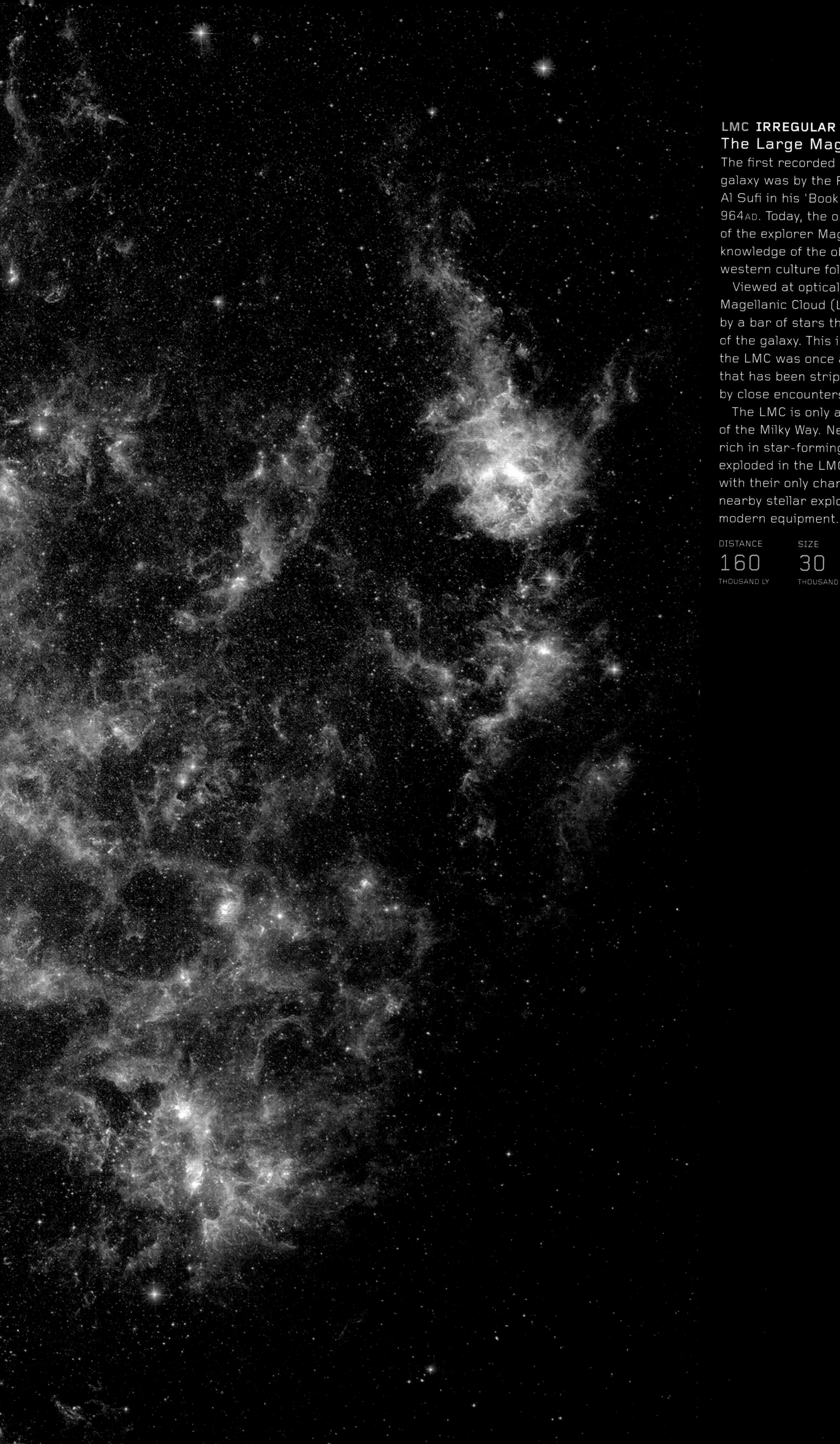

LMC **IRREGULAR GALAXY**

The Large Magellanic Cloud

The first recorded mention of this satellite galaxy was by the Persian astronomer Al Sufi in his 'Book of Fixed Stars' around 964AD. Today, the object bears the name of the explorer Magellan, who brought knowledge of the object into mainstream western culture following his voyage of 1519.

Viewed at optical wavelengths, the Large Magellanic Cloud (LMC) is characterized by a bar of stars that runs across the centre of the galaxy. This indicates that perhaps the LMC was once a barred spiral galaxy that has been stripped of its spiral arms by close encounters with the Milky Way.

The LMC is only about one tenth the mass of the Milky Way. Nevertheless, it is a system rich in star-forming activity. In 1987, a star exploded in the LMC, providing astronomers with their only chance so far to study a nearby stellar explosion with relatively modern equipment.

DISTANCE	SIZE
160 THOUSAND LY	30 THOUSAND LY

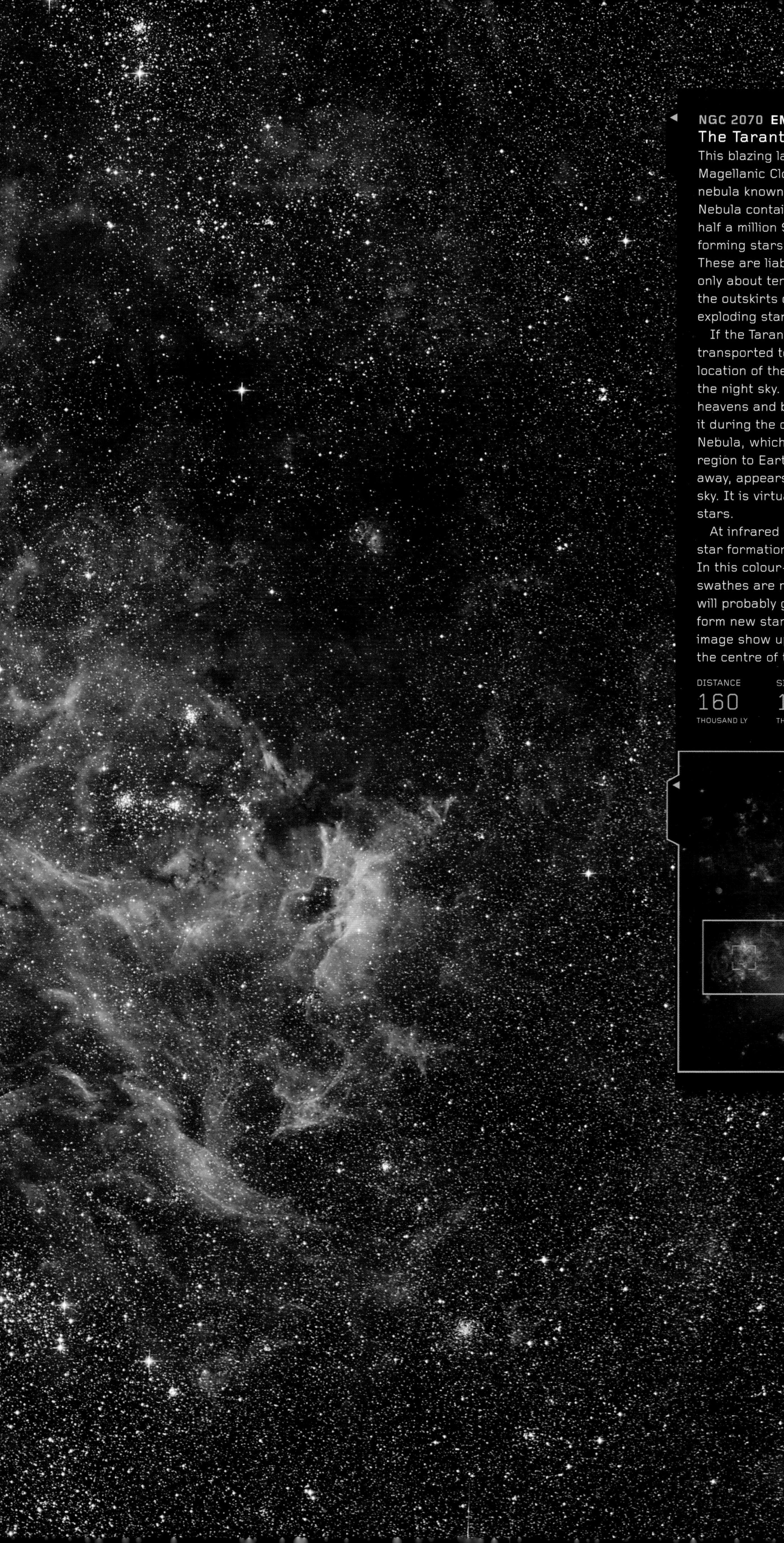

NGC 2070 **EMISSION NEBULA**

The Tarantula Nebula

This blazing labyrinth of gas within the Large Magellanic Cloud [1] is the largest emission nebula known to astronomers. The Tarantula Nebula contains enough dust and gas to make half a million Sun-like stars. It is constantly forming stars, some of them very massive. These are liable to explode after short lives of only about ten million years. Indeed, it was in the outskirts of the Tarantula Nebula that the exploding star of 1987 went off.

If the Tarantula Nebula could be magically transported to our Galaxy and situated at the location of the Orion Nebula, it would dominate the night sky. It would fill a quarter of the heavens and be so bright that you could see it during the daytime. In contrast, the Orion Nebula, which is our nearest star-forming region to Earth and located 1500 light years away, appears to us as only a dot in the night sky. It is virtually indistinguishable from the stars.

At infrared wavelengths [1], it seems that star formation in the LMC is far from complete. In this colour-coded image, the large green swathes are reservoirs of dust and gas that will probably go on to collapse together and form new stars. The existing stars in this image show up mostly a faint blue glow across the centre of the image.

DISTANCE	SIZE
160 THOUSAND LY	1 THOUSAND LY

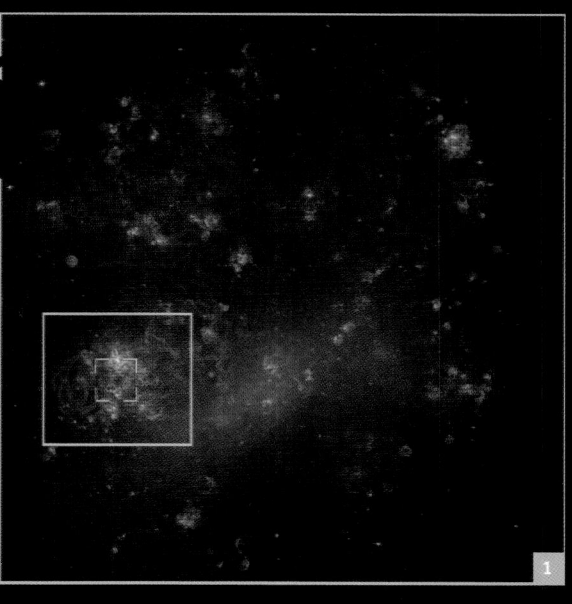
1

[1] SMC IRREGULAR GALAXY
The Small Magellanic Cloud

Like its larger cousin, the Small Magellanic Cloud is an irregular fuzz of stars, only visible in southern skies. It contains several hundred million stars compared with our Galaxy's 100 billion stars. Although it is clearly much smaller, its gravity combined with that of the Large Magellanic Cloud is pulling our Galaxy out of shape. Star formation takes place in the SMC, in regions such as NGC 346 [3].

DISTANCE 210 THOUSAND LY
SIZE 10 THOUSAND LY

[2] N90/NGC 602 STAR CLUSTER

The light and the sub-atomic particles given out by this tight cluster of new stars are blowing a cavity in the surrounding gases of the Small Magellanic Cloud. The 'trunks' of dark gas that point towards the stars are areas of denser material that the stars are finding harder to erode.

DISTANCE 210 THOUSAND LY
SIZE 50 LIGHT YEARS

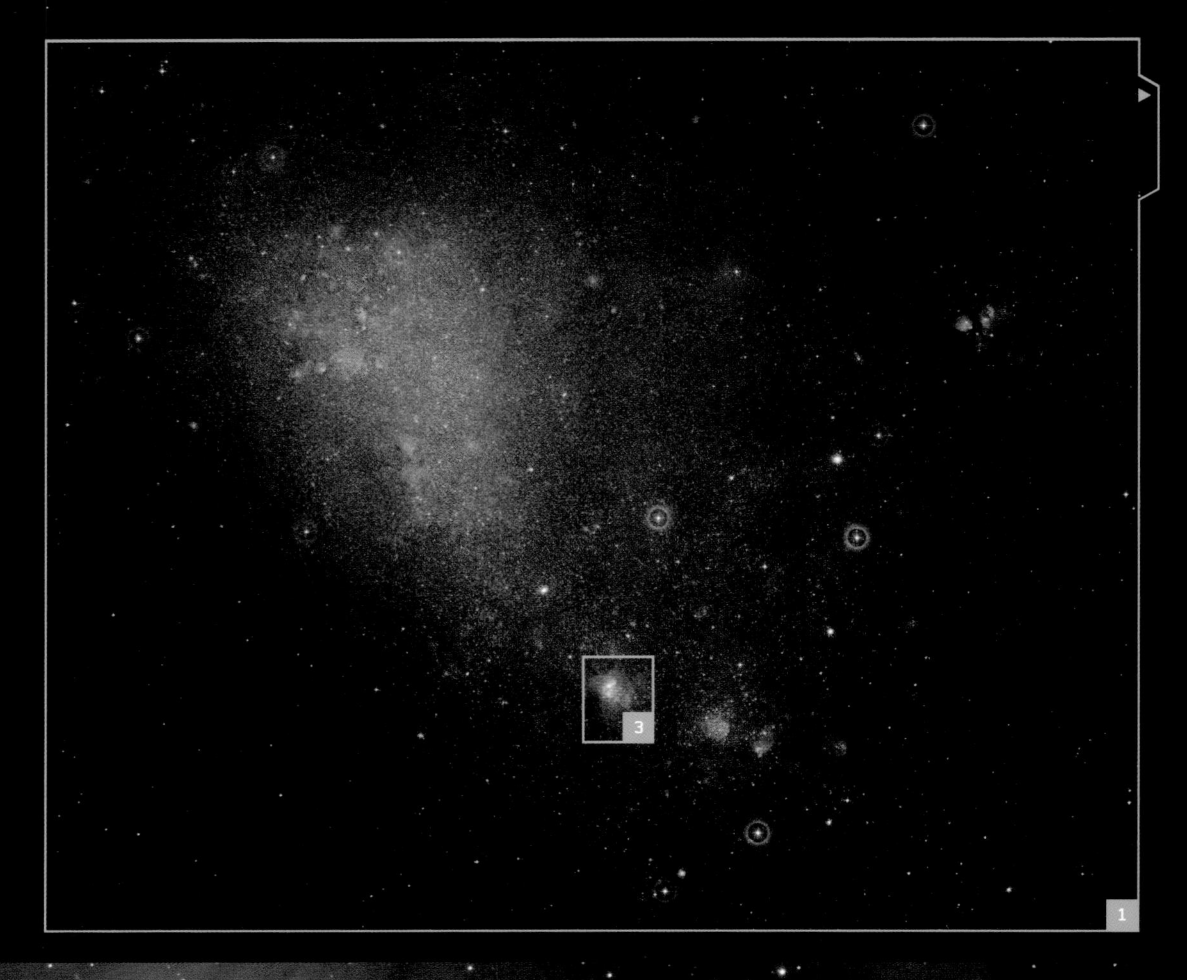

[3] NGC 346 **STAR CLUSTER**
Around 2500 newly created stars light up this massive star-forming region in the Small Magellanic Cloud. Such prodigious star formation in such a small galaxy may be the result of our Galaxy's gravitational forces compressing the gas clouds and accelerating their collapse into individual stars. The blue glow in this image is the light given out by the stars as it is scattered off the remaining dust particles.

DISTANCE
210
THOUSAND LY

SIZE
200
LIGHT YEARS

02

THE MILKY WAY_

240°

ANATOMY OF A GALAXY_

Our Galaxy is often called the Milky Way. This name was first used to describe the faint band of light that stretches across a dark sky. It derives from Greek mythology, where it was said that milk spilling from the goddess Hera's breasts created this path across the sky.

Other cultures have their own stories. In Armenia, they call it the Straw Thief's Way because legend has it that the god Vahagn stole straw from the Assyrian king Barsham to bring to Armenia during a cold winter. As the god fled across the heavens, he dropped some of the straw along the way.

Galileo Galilei revealed the truth in 1609 when he turned his telescope onto the Milky Way and saw it resolve into countless stars. Since that time, astronomers have devoted a substantial fraction of their efforts to mapping our Galaxy in order to understand its shape, extent and composition.

We now know that the Milky Way is a large spiral galaxy stretching 100,000 light years in diameter and containing around 200 billion stars. In keeping with other spiral galaxies, these are distributed in a flat disc of stars surrounding a central bulge of stars, often called the galaxy's nucleus.

The spiral arms in the disc region are formed by the accumulation of hot, short-lived stars. These shine a brilliant blue light into space but last only a few tens of millions of years. They are born on the leading edges of the spiral arms where waves of denser material pile up, triggering the formation of stars. The stars then lag behind as this material continues in its orbit around the centre of the Galaxy, giving the spiral arms their width.

As these stars live such short lives on astronomical timescales, they die before the next spiral arm catches up with them. This means that the Galaxy never develops a continuous disc of blue stars, but constantly maintains the appearance of a number of spiral arms.

The blue stars are the most massive stars and only occur in limited numbers, whereas many more lower mass stars form. These exist for much longer and do spread out to create a disc of brilliant stars stretching around the Galaxy. They shine with a yellow-red hue but cannot usually be seen in photographs because they are so much fainter than the blue stars.

The nucleus of the Galaxy is the place to view these stars, however. Formed when the Galaxy was very young, the central hub of the Milky Way has by and large stopped forming new stars, although a few pockets of activity remain. Mostly it is the combined light of billions of older stars that radiates away into space.

Lurking at the very heart of the galactic core, astronomers believe there lies a supermassive black hole. This is the inevitable consequence of the Galaxy's formation. As matter fell together in the very earliest eras of the Universe to form the Galaxy, so it naturally became densest at the centre. Early in the process, it passed a critical density and became a black hole. Nowadays, anything falling into the very centre of the Galaxy will be eaten by this central object and never seen again. Remarkably some stars have been found in close orbits around the black hole, dicing with death. One small deviation in their orbit and they will plunge to their doom.

Although stars are the most obvious component of the Galaxy, the space between the stars is far from empty. Much of our Galaxy's space is filled with atomic and molecular gas, primarily hydrogen and helium. There is also a proportion of tiny particles or dust, composed mainly of carbon, silicon and oxygen. These are the raw constituents of stars and planets and it is this material

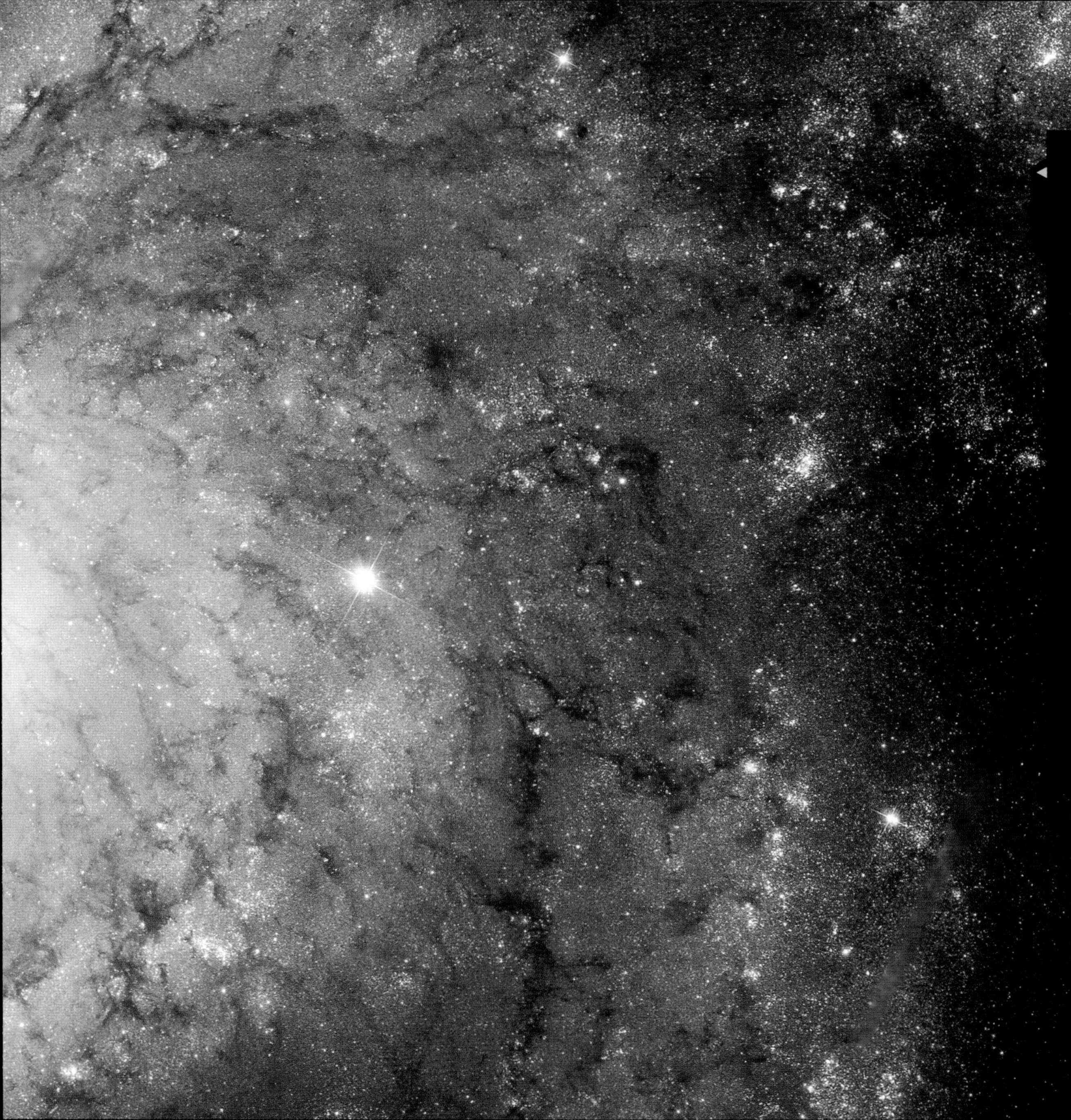

◄ M101 **SPIRAL GALAXY**
The Pinwheel Galaxy
The Pinwheel Galaxy is the archetypal spiral galaxy with its brilliant arms of blue stars winding around the inner nucleus of yellow stars. The arms are threaded with dust lanes and jewelled with star clusters. The galaxy's dramatic face-on appearance is due to a chance alignment with our own Galaxy.

This is roughly how our own galaxy would appear if we could look down upon it. Despite M101 being almost twice the size of the Milky Way, the only really noticeable difference would be that our Galaxy has a short bar of stars linking the central nucleus to the spiral arms.

In the background of this image, other galaxies can also be seen. They appear tiny in comparison to M101 because they are much further away.

DISTANCE 27 MILLION LY

SIZE 170 THOUSAND LY

that is transformed by its passage through the spiral arms.

Whilst the vast majority of matter in the Milky Way is confined to the disc region, there is a proportion that lies within a spherical bubble surrounding the Galaxy. Here are tenuous clouds of hydrogen and other gases, scattered stars and a number of globular star clusters.

As the name suggests, the globular star clusters are approximately spherical collections of a few million stars. All of them are ancient, with stars estimated to be some 10 billion years old. Like the black hole at the centre of the Galaxy, the globular clusters are thought to have formed as the Milky Way's original gas cloud coalesced. These collections of stars now orbit the centre of the Galaxy at highly inclined angles and this means that they occasionally crash through the disc region. Being gravitationally bound together, each globular cluster emerges from its disc crossing relatively unscathed.

The spherical bubble surrounding a galaxy is often called the halo and, as well as containing the globular clusters, gas clouds and the odd star, it is also thought to be home to a vast fog of dark matter. This mysterious substance has never been detected but astronomers think it may be needed to hold a galaxy together.

Placing the Sun
Our own location in the Milky Way was a subject that exercised astronomers for centuries. Some clung tenaciously to the old idea that the Sun and the Earth must somehow be at the centre of the Universe and so the vast array of stars we see in the Milky Way was distributed more or less evenly around the Sun. However, this is not the case.

The key to the Sun's location came from what at first appeared to be two entirely disconnected observations. It was noticed that irregularly shaped clusters of stars, so-called open clusters, are mostly distributed in the plane of the Milky Way, whereas the spherical globular clusters are generally seen far above or below the plane. In 1914, American astronomer Harlow Shapley began a detailed study into this distribution.

He reasoned that the globular clusters should be in orbit around the centre of the Galaxy and began plotting their locations. From his plots, he could see that they were strongly grouped in the southern part of the sky. If the Sun had been at the centre of the Galaxy, the globular clusters would have been arrayed more or less evenly across the sky.

As they were not, Shapley calculated how far away from the centre of the Galaxy the Sun must be to see them crowded into the southern sky. The figure he ended up with showed that the Sun was a long way out.

As a result, we know that our home and vantage point is in the outskirts of the Galaxy, a suburb some 26,000 light years from its central hub. This also means that the parts of the Galaxy directly behind the galactic centre are forever blocked from our view.

The Milky Way: a bird's-eye view

From above, our Galaxy would show its true size and shape. It is thought to be one of the Universe's largest spiral galaxies and its shape is that of a barred-spiral galaxy. However, the bar of stars is not as dramatic as in some galaxies.

Looking down on the Milky Way would be a glorious sight. In this artist's impression, the sweeping arms mark out our Galaxy as a grand design spiral with the Sun located at the centre of the grid, some 26,000 light years from the galactic core. The various arms are named after the constellations that they appear to pass through in our sky. From our vantage point, inside the Orion spur, they appear to blur into the Milky Way, the continuous band of light that stretches across the sky.

Only through careful analysis, of the distances to many stars and the observed motion of giant gas clouds, have astronomers deduced the three-dimensional structure of the Galaxy.

A recent revelation has been the bar of stars in the centre. For most of the last century, astronomers had assumed that the Milky Way was a straightforward spiral. The information about the bar has only been gleaned from deep studies of stellar motion near the nucleus of the Galaxy.

Two populations of stars are obvious. The population II stars are the old, long-lived stars that originated at the time of the Galaxy's original formation, some 10 billion years ago or more. These stars are found predominantly within the central bulge and shine with a yellow colour.

In the spiral arms are the population I stars. Characterized by their brilliant blue light, these are massive but short-lived stars. Longer lived population II stars are also present but they are outshone by the blue stars. Chemically, the two populations are distinct; the population II stars have fewer heavier chemicals in them.

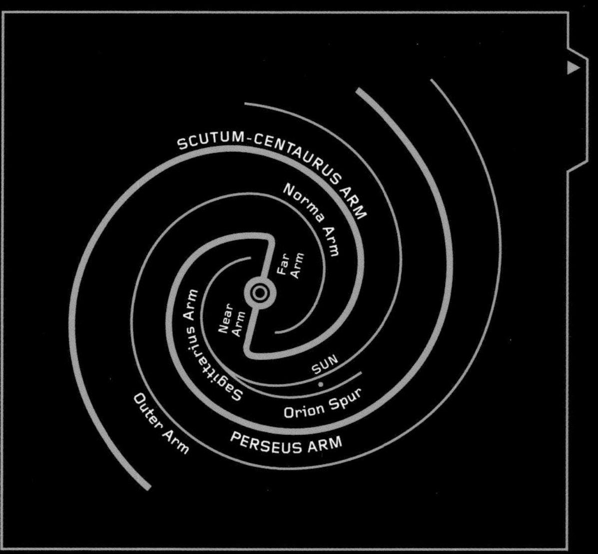

0°
75,000LY
60,000LY
30°
60°
90°

40,000LY
15,000LY
30,000LY
270°
240°
150°
120°

In this orientation, the Milky Way would more closely resemble the Milky Way we see stretching across the night sky: a stream of stars that widens into a bulge across the galactic centre before thinning out again.

Seen from edge-on, the Milky Way would look very different. This artist's impression shows the disc of stars as just a thin band, much more reminiscent of the Milky Way that we see in the night sky. Considering the 100,000 light year diameter of the Galaxy, the disc is thin, only 1000 light years in diameter. This is because the stars in this region orbit mainly in the same restricted plane. This is thought to be a symptom of the fact that the Galaxy formed from a collapsing cloud of gas. As the cloud drew itself together through gravity, so the outer sections pancaked into a flat spinning disc. Thus, the stars that have subsequently formed here have retained this motion.

Seen from this angle, the appearance of the spiral arms is lost but the dust embedded in them continues to be visible, threaded across the expanse of the disc. The older population II stars cluster in the middle of the Galaxy [1], forming the central nucleus. The round bulk of the nucleus is formed because stars here have orbits that are tilted at random to one another.

Surrounding the Galaxy is a large spherical region called the halo. This does contain stars but is much less dense than the disc and nucleus of the Galaxy. The only objects that can be seen in the halo are globular clusters of stars. As the name suggests, these are tightly packed, spherical collections of stars.

Our Sun lies on the disc halfway between the core and the edge of the galaxy [2].

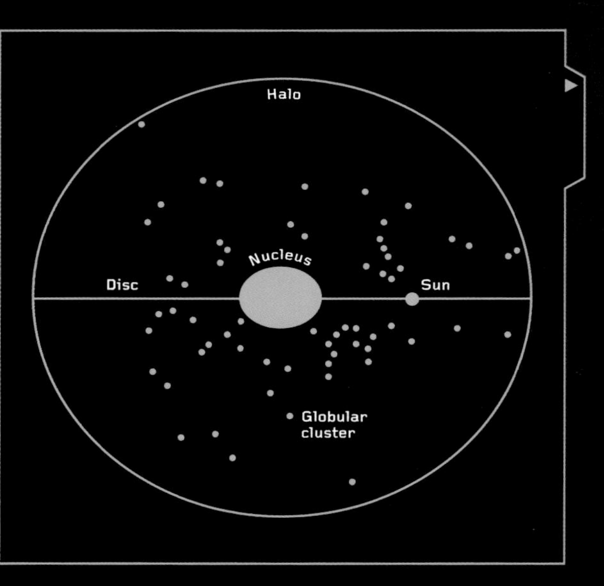

1
2
30,000
20,000
10,000
0
10,000
20,000
25,000

Stars like grains of sand

Stars are the most obvious component of the Milky Way. Covering an area of the sky equivalent to your fist held out at arm's length, this view contains 10 million stars The reddened area towards the upper right of the image marks the centre of the Galaxy Dark dust lanes also criss-cross the image.

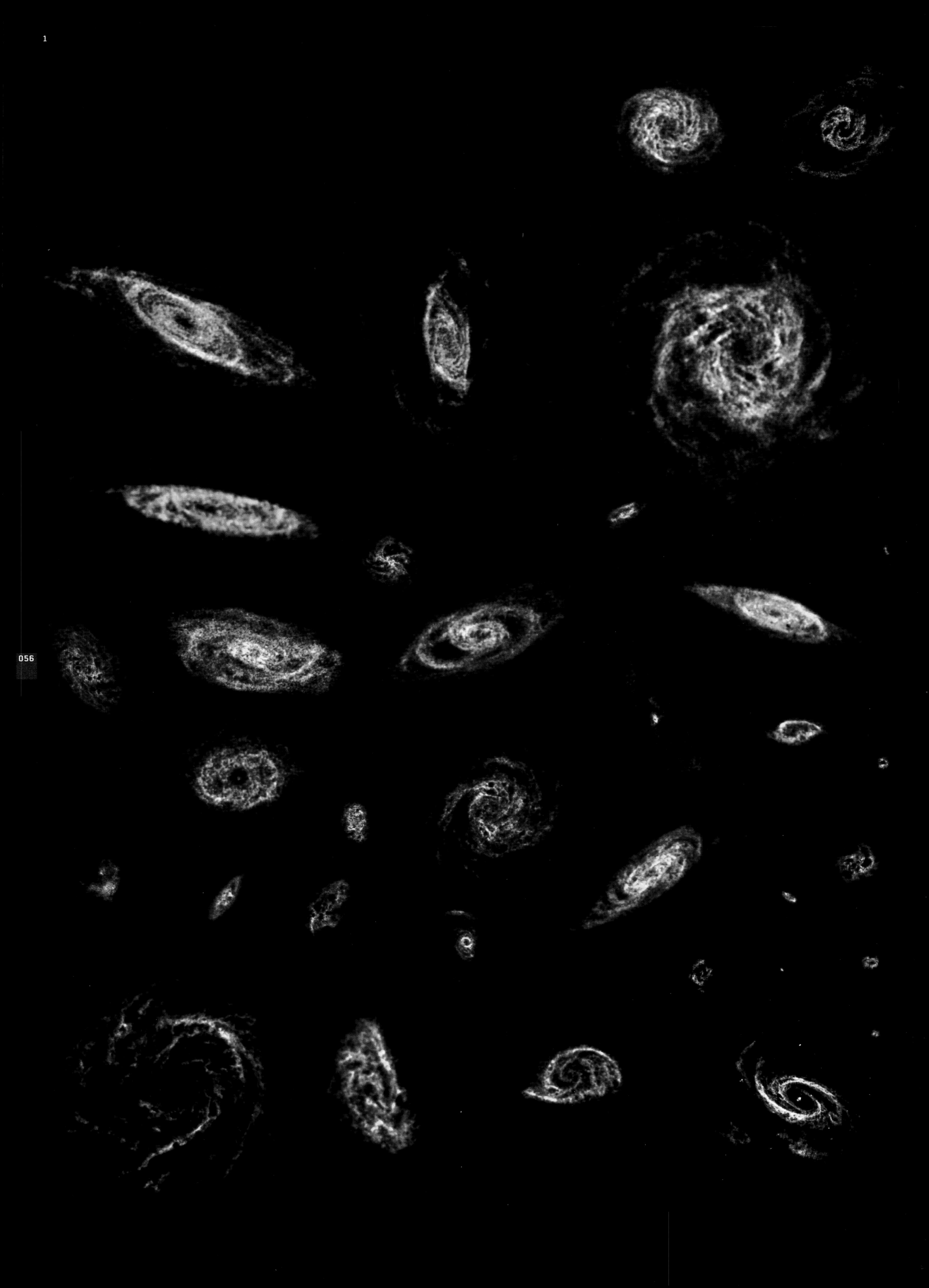
1

Spiral arms

These are the most distinctive features of a spiral galaxy, but we see a huge variety of them. Some spiral galaxies have just two giant arms that encircle the nucleus a number of times. Other spiral galaxies are composed of many short arm segments.

Gaseous arms

[1] Although the spiral arms of a galaxy show up mostly through the hot stars that form within them, observations made at radio wavelengths can show just the hydrogen gas that has yet to be incorporated into stars. These clouds also follow the spiral pattern. This menagerie of galaxies shows how pronounced that pattern can be.

Not all the galaxies shown here are spirals. The smaller ones are dwarf galaxies, containing enough hydrogen to make about 10 million stars like the Sun. The spirals, on the other hand, contain some 10 billion Sun-like stars' worth of hydrogen.

Density waves

A spiral pattern can be formed if stars travel in elliptical orbits [2] that, as well as being nested within one another, progressively vary their orientation with increasing distance from the galactic centre [3]. This arrangement allows the elliptical orbits to draw together, creating a spiral pattern of density enhancements that winds around the centre of the Galaxy [4]. Gas clouds follow similar orbital paths and so too become denser in the same spiral pattern. Where the gas clouds bunch and become denser, so new stars form. These blaze into space, lighting up the gas surrounding them [5].

3
4
5

Dust clouds

It is not just stars that fill spa
account for a large proportion
of normal matter in the Galaxy
important store of material fr
stars can form.

2

3

4

[1] IC2118 REFLECTION NEB
The Witch Head Nebula
Tenuous clouds of dust and ga
in space unless a nearby star
These often appear blue as in
lies next to the bright star Rig

DISTANCE 664 LIGHT YEARS SIZE 34 LIGHT YEARS

[2] IC4592 REFLECTION NEB
IC 4592 surrounds the star Nu
The gas and dust itself is not g
instead it is simply reflecting t
the nearby stars, hence the na
objects: reflection nebulae.

DISTANCE 437 LIGHT YEARS SIZE 25 LIGHT YEARS

[3] NGC 6726, 6727, 6729, IC4
REFLECTION NEBULA
Corona Australis Compl
The Corona Australis cloud is a
example of a dust cloud being i
this time by stars that have for
its dusty confines. There are fo
reflection nebulae in this view.

DISTANCE 420 LIGHT YEARS SIZE 2 LIGHT YEARS

[4] REFLECTION NEBULA
Rho Ophiuchi Complex
The Rho Ophiuchi cloud is a mu
complicated system altogether.
reflection nebulae can be seen
of blue regions, whilst the unill
parts of the cloud are deepest
gigantic red star called Antare
the yellow portions of the clouc
pinkish region is fluorescing hy

DISTANCE 500 LIGHT YEARS SIZE 10 LIGHT YEARS

ed view

e visible light cameras for
rs, astronomers can see much
before. Optically invisible
brightly at infrared
ause of its temperature.
copes can detect the faintest
llar dust. The appearance of
al resembles high-altitude
Earth and so they have been
cirrus clouds [1]. The dust
tremely cold, somewhere
30° Kelvin. It would be even
t for the faint traces of heat it
n the surrounding starlight.

D

Snake

oject is a sinuous column of
e enough to swallow dozens of
is so thick that if Earth were
orted into its bulk, there would
e except black sky around you
would block out all the

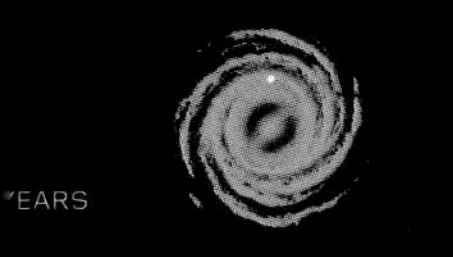

EARS

GC 2238, NGC 2239, NGC

EMISSION NEBULA

Nebula

laxy's ink black regions were
es in the celestial objects,
ne patterns of stars. Now,
w that they are dusty clouds
radually collapsing due to
ing pushed together by some
n the case of the Rosette
lanes are being compressed
of newly formed stars, just
s image.

0

YEARS

2

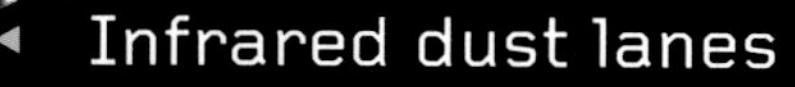

Infrared dust lanes

To ordinary telescopes this view would appear completely black, obscured by intervening dust. At infrared wavelengths, which can penetrate dusty clouds much more easily than normal light, the view shows hundreds of thousands of stars crowded into the swirling core of our Galaxy.

Being infrared, this picture has been colour-coded. Old and cool stars are blue, while dust zones lit up by blazing stars are shown in a reddish hue. The brightest white spot in the middle marks the very centre of the Galaxy.

The region pictured here is immense, spanning 890 light years across and 640 light years high. Both bright and dark cloud filaments can be seen stretching across the Milky Way, with the brighter ones harbouring stellar nurseries.

The vertical dust lobes that stretch away from the plane of the Milky Way are thought to have been blown there by the radiation of massive stars.

The galactic core

Lying at the centre of the spiral arms, the galactic core is a bulbous mass of stars around which everything else rotates. There is little star formation going on here, just a closely packed mass of billions of older, longer-lived stars.

[1] Centred on the galactic core, this panoramic view shows almost the whole sky at short infrared wavelengths. Little dust is seen at these wavelengths but the stars shine brilliantly. Half a billion stars are shown here, representing just half a percent, or even less, of the Galaxy's total population. The faint smudges in the lower right area of the image are the Large [2] and Small [3] Magellanic Clouds, two of the Milky Way's satellite galaxies.

At X-ray wavelengths [4], the galaxy core looks very different. Spanning 400 by 900 light years, this image reveals hundreds of stellar corpses: white dwarf stars, neutron stars and black holes, all bathed in an incandescent fog of multimillion-degree gas.

The colours indicate the energy of the X-rays. Red emission is the lowest energy, green the medium and blue the highest. The very centre of the Galaxy is the bright white patch, indicating radiation of all energies. The image suggests that hot gas is being expelled from the centre of the Galaxy and will enrich the galactic suburbs.

4
065
2
3
4

1

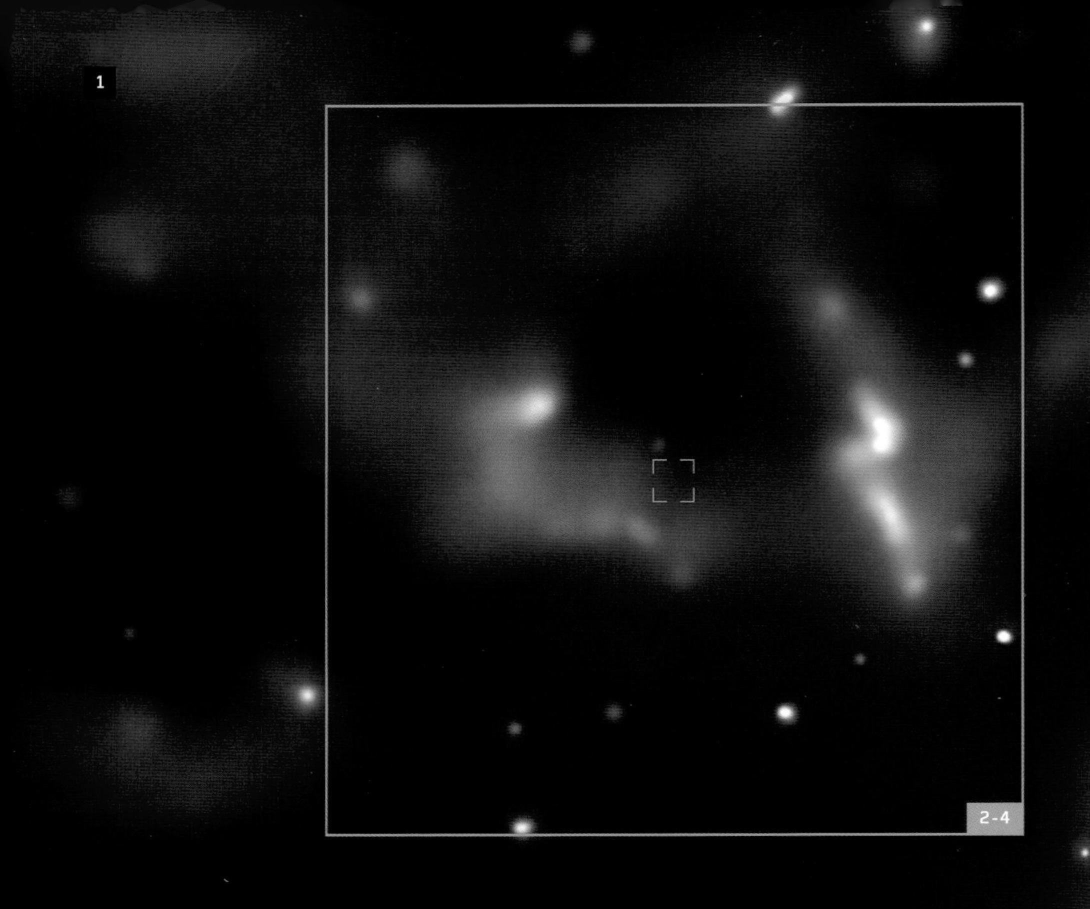

2 3

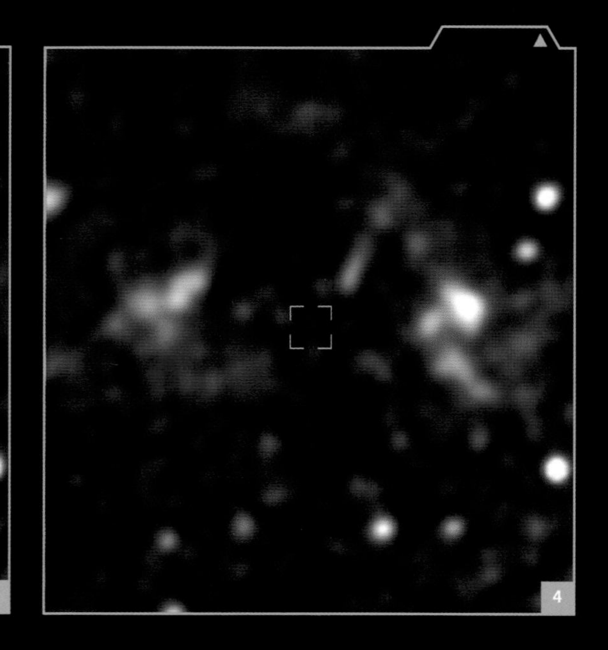

The dark heart of the Galaxy

At the very centre of the Milky Way lurks a colossal celestial object, perhaps as big as our entire Solar System. It creates a fearsome gravitational field and is certainly the dark heart of our Galaxy.

The object is known as Sagittarius A*, pronounced A-star, and is the centrepiece of the Milky Way. It is thought to be a supermassive black hole, containing two and a half million times the mass of the Sun. Anything that falls into its grasp will never escape, not even light. Astronomers have investigated this region of space with many telescopes, working at different wavelengths, in their attempts to understand the environment of the galactic core and the nature of Sagittarius A*.

X-rays offer a good view of the region around the Galaxy's black hole [1]. Here, Sagittarius A* is a bright triangle just to the right of the bright curve in the lower right area of the image. Two clouds of gas above it, in the upper left area, act as mirrors and reflect the X-rays produced by matter falling into the black hole. By monitoring these clouds over time, astronomers can build up a picture of the variable activity at the centre of our galaxy. The sequence of images [2-4] shows the variation in the clouds over the course of three years.

Stars crowd into the same region as shown by this combined optical and infrared view [5], where blue stars are hotter and red stars are the cooler. The black hole cannot be seen but it is located at the very centre of the image. Stars close to it can reach the extraordinary speed of 5000 kilometres per second as they orbit around it.

At radio wavelengths [6] parallel columns of gas seem to line up and then turn sharply inwards towards the black hole, the bright blob at the lower right of the image. These gas streams are perhaps being guided by a magnetic field in the region.

DISTANCE 26 THOUSAND LY

SIZE 6.7 BILLION KM

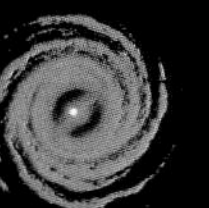

5

6

The Milky Way and dark matter

Astronomers believe that there are more kinds of matter in the Universe than just atoms. The most prolific is said to be dark matter. Although this has yet to be detected, its influence is said to shape our Galaxy.

In common with most galaxies, the Milky Way suffers from a speed problem. The stars in the outer edges of the Galaxy are travelling faster than astronomers expect. This is because the orbital speed of an object is determined by the amount of matter within its orbit. When astronomers calculate the speed of the stars based on the amount of matter they can see in the Galaxy they come up with a figure much smaller than they observe.

Assuming the laws of gravity that work on Earth and throughout the Solar System are valid right to the outer edges of the Galaxy, then the Milky Way should be flying apart. Its stars are simply travelling too fast to be held by the gravity generated by the dust and gas and stars and other celestial objects within.

In order to explain this problem, astronomers speculate that a large cloud of dark matter surrounds the Galaxy. This is left over from the formation of the Galaxy and will increase its mass by an enormous ten times, sufficient to hold it together. According to our understanding of the Big Bang, this matter cannot be simply more dust and gas. Instead it has to be the mysterious dark matter that astronomers have yet to detect.

Computer simulations show the possible distribution that this matter can take [main image]. Like normal matter, the dark matter cloud fragments into individual clumps. If the dark matter is of one particular type, known as neutralinos, these clumps will produce a faint glow of gamma rays. This can also be computed and displayed on simulated maps, which show astronomers what to look for [2].

Other astronomers believe that there is no such thing as dark matter and that the laws of gravity are wrong. A small strengthening of gravity in the rarefied regions of space would hold the Milky Way together.

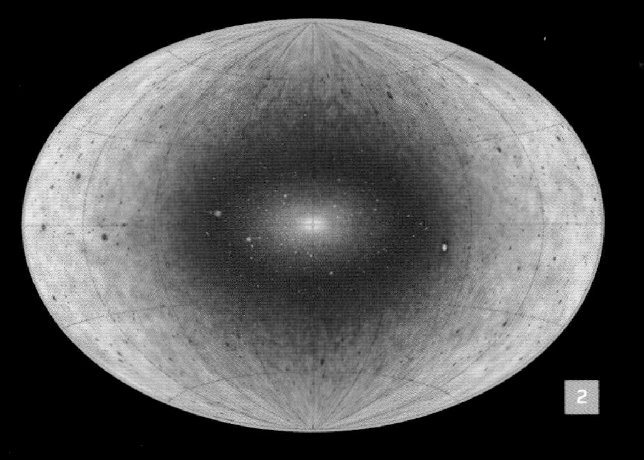

2

03

STARS_

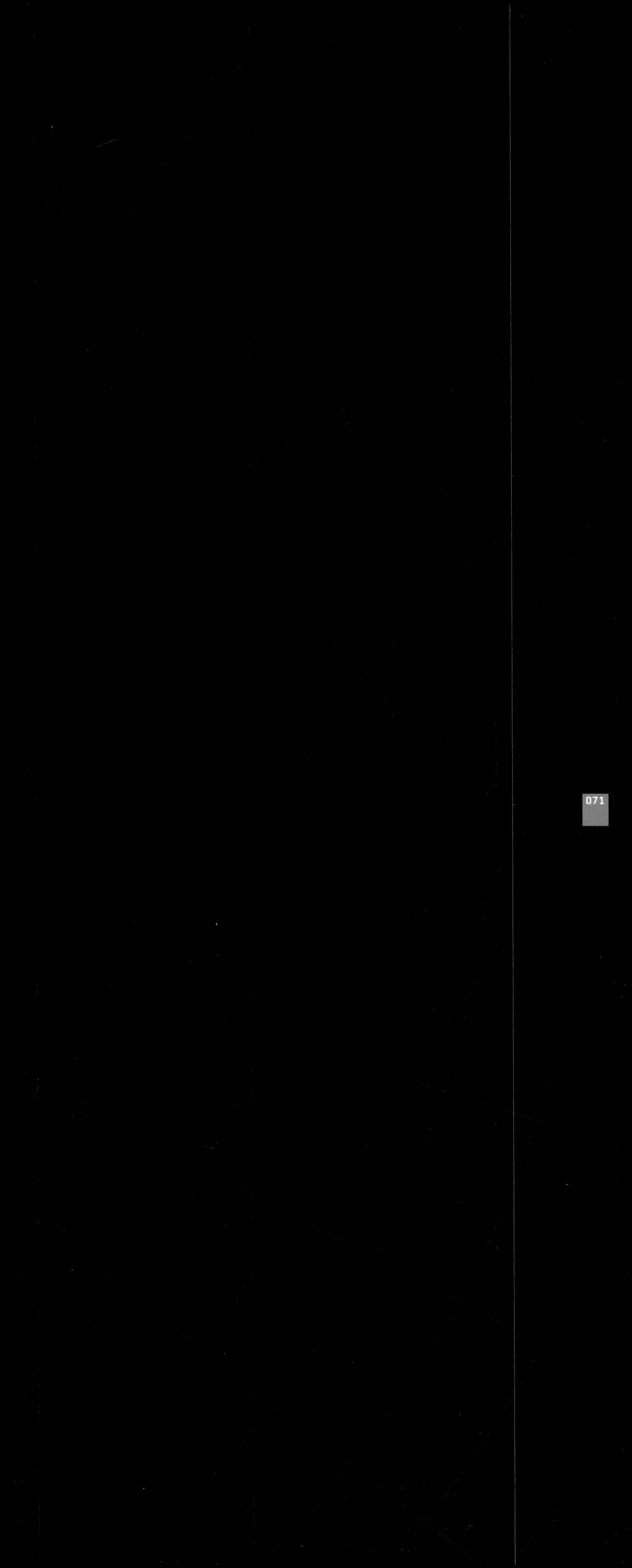

STAR LIFE_

Looking up night after night to the seemingly unchanging night sky, it is easy to think that the stars are eternal beacons of light scattered throughout the Universe. After nearly one hundred and fifty years of study, however, astronomers know now that the stars live dramatic and sometimes violent lives.

The breakthrough came in 1859 with the invention of a technique called spectral analysis made by the chemist Robert Bunsen and the physicist Gustav Kirchhoff in Heidelberg. By passing starlight through a prism, the chemical composition of the star was revealed as a pattern of dark vertical lines. Each atom absorbed a unique set of specific wavelengths of light, creating the dark lines. Bunsen and Kirchhoff's great triumph was to realize how to relate those lines to the chemicals found on Earth. It opened up the field of astrophysics, which allows astronomers to deduce the nature and behaviour of distant celestial objects.

Brief glimpses of the life cycle of stars have been scattered throughout history's night skies. but astronomers were never sure how to interpret them. In 1572, the Danish astronomer Tycho Brahe saw a new star burst into the night sky. At the time, it was accepted wisdom that the heavens were the realm of God and so perfect and unchanging. So, new objects such as Tycho's star, were assumed to be phenomena that took place within the atmosphere of the Earth.

But Tycho watched the bright object night after night and saw no variation in its movement against the stars. He therefore correctly argued that it must be a phenomenon in the distant stellar realms of the cosmos. He coined the term 'nova' but because the idea of a newly created star did not fit with contemporary thinking about the way the cosmos worked, the discovery was thought of as a peculiarity rather than a signpost that there was more waiting to be discovered.

In a more modern recreation of these events, astronomers began to detect bursts of gamma rays exploding from outer space in the mid 1960s. Military satellites designed to police the ban on testing nuclear weapons in space picked up these natural cataclysmic releases of energy too. For decades, astronomers struggled to understand the brief but glorious flashes. They lasted for a few seconds and came from completely unpredictable regions of space two or three times a day.

This time, the astronomers did pursue the topic but it was hard work. They did not even know at what distance the flashes were occurring. So, whilst one school of thought held that they were nearby events, distributed in the halo of the Milky Way, another thought they were coming from distant galaxies. Yet, little progress could be made. So stymied did investigations become that some astronomers began to joke that perhaps the gamma-ray bursts were the exhaust plumes of alien spacecraft jumping to warp speed!

The breakthrough finally came in the 1990s when the Hubble Space Telescope caught the fading optical glow of a gamma-ray burst. It showed that these events are indeed confined to the distant Universe and are the death knells of supergiant stars.

Slow-burn lifetimes

The lifetime of even the most short-lived star is enormous in human terms, spanning tens of millions of years. So, it is impossible to watch a star pass through all phases of its existence. The longest-lived stars, red dwarf stars, live for more than 100 billion years, about ten times the current age of the Universe.

Because of this colossal span of time, even transitory phases can last thousands of years. It is therefore very difficult to see a star pass from one stage of its existence to another – but not impossible. Exploding stars are the

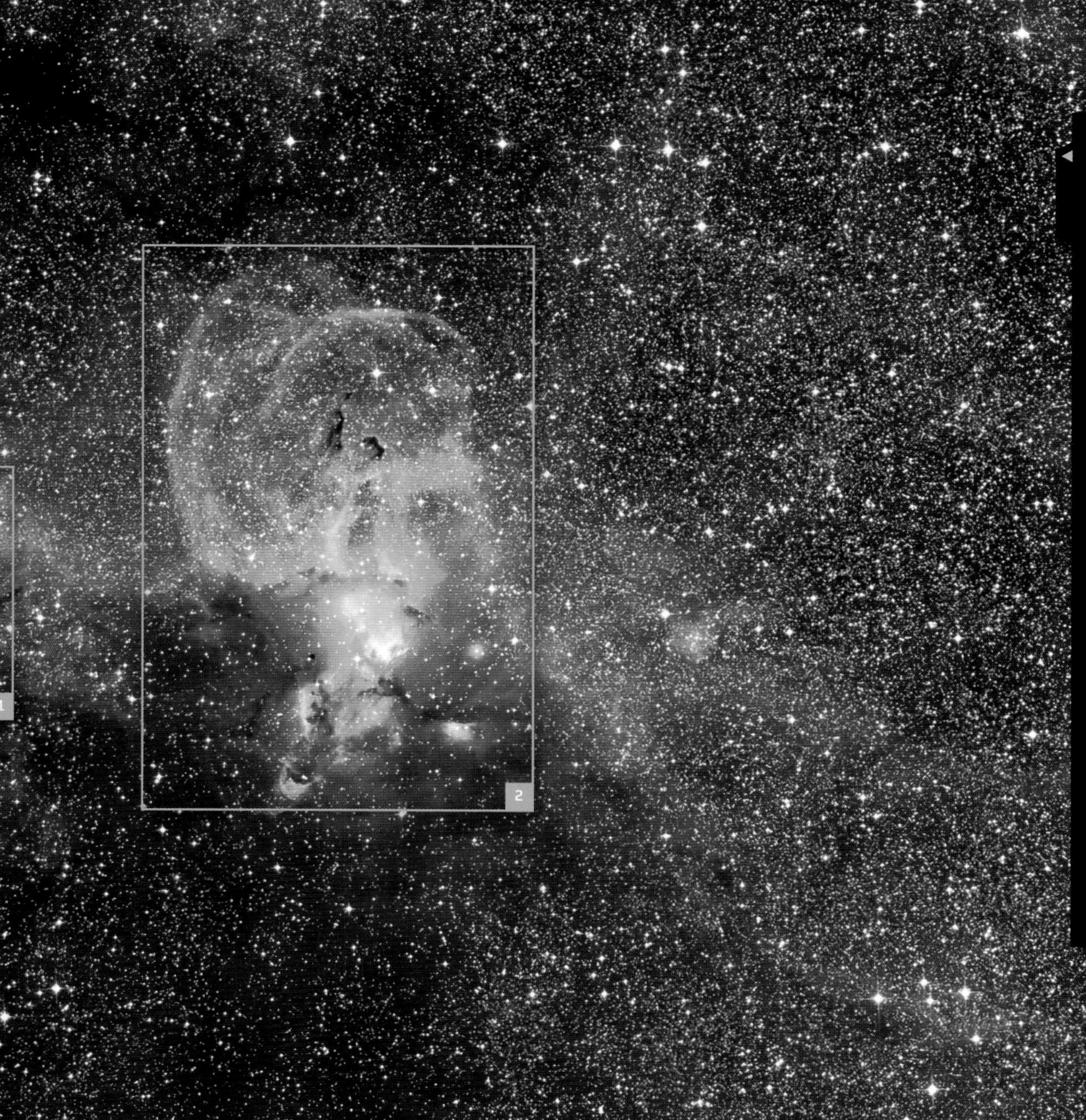

[1] NGC3603 EMISSION NEBULA
Stars of all masses cluster into the centre of this nebula. Too close to be seen as individuals on this wide scale image, their light merges into a bright white glow. Such clusters are useful because they allow astronomers to study different stars that have all been born around the same time, and hence are the same age.

DISTANCE 20 THOUSAND LY — SIZE 17 LIGHT YEARS

[2] NGC3582 EMISSION NEBULA
Hidden in this cloud are a number of older stars as well. They betray their presence by the loops that extend from the top of this nebula. These loops were created when the pressure of radiation in the older stars temporarily overcame the gravitational force holding the star together and blew off the outer layers.

Such eruptions usually signal a star preparing to pass from one phase of its life cycle to another.

DISTANCE 6 THOUSAND LY — SIZE 5 LIGHT YEARS

most dramatic moments of transition and astronomers watch for these constantly.

Thankfully, the process of star formation is a continual one and so there are examples of stars of all ages spread throughout the Galaxy. Astronomers now feel confident that they have organized them into a true sequence of how stars are born, age and die.

The life cycle of a star is governed by the interplay of gravity and pressure. Gravity tries to pull the star into an ever more compact configuration, whilst internal pressure tries to tear it apart. The pressure is usually the result of the star generating energy in its core. As this energy fights its way out of the star, it collides with the surrounding atoms of gas and attempts to push them outwards too.

At the Sun's surface, radiation pressure can sometimes overwhelm gravity, if it has the help of magnetic forces. Magnetic windows can open in the Sun's atmosphere, which results in a constant stream of particles, known as the solar wind, flowing from the surface. In this way the Sun loses around 1.3×10^{31} particles of matter every second. This amounts to some 4×10^{16} kilograms every year. This is expected to be the same for many stars. Indeed, solar wind-blown holes are seen in many gas clouds surrounding newly formed stars.

Throughout the interior of a stable 'middle-aged' star, gravity and pressure are in a state of approximate equilibrium. As the amount of radiation generated at the centre of the star gradually increases with time, so this changes the outward appearance of the star. Towards the end of a star's life it swells up and its surface layers cool. This is known as the red giant stage and soon the star will begin down its path to destruction and death.

Our Sun sits in an area inhabited by some 50 stars younger than 60 million years. These stars are located in a flattened structure called Gould's Belt [3] about 3000 light years in diameter, with the Sun only about 325 light years from the centre. The green tinges are jets of hydrogen gas expelled by the young stars and the red clouds are traces of complex molecules containing carbon. At 4.6 billion years old, the Sun was not born here. Instead, the Sun has circled the Galaxy some 20 times during its existence and just happens to have drifted into this region of space.

No one knows for sure the origin of this belt of stars. It is inclined to the general plane of stars in the Galaxy by some 20 degrees, indicating that more local star-forming processes can sometimes overwhelm large-scale galactic ones.

The stellar life cycle

The grand process of stellar life and death can be visualized as a never-ending cycle of birth, destruction and rebirth. From the moment a cloud of gas begins to draw itself together under gravity, a star can develop in a number of different ways.

The first peril it faces is whether it will accumulate enough mass to ignite nuclear fusion and become a bona-fide star. If it is unsuccessful, its destiny is to be sidelined as a ball of virtually inert gas, known as a brown dwarf. Such failed stars are thought to outnumber the real stars in the Universe.

Assuming that the star does gather enough material to ignite nuclear reactions in its core, then it settles into its main sequence life for millions or billions of years depending upon how much mass it has accumulated. Against expectations, high-mass stars live the shortest lives because although they have more fuel they burn it more quickly.

The next big turning point is when that fuel runs out. If the star contains a lot of mass, then it becomes a red supergiant star and begins down a path towards spectacular destruction. It will explode as a Type 2 supernova, leaving behind a dense remnant that was once its nuclear core. Depending on the remaining mass of the core, this will now be either a dense neutron star or that most mysterious of celestial objects: a black hole. The rest of the star, which has been blown outwards by the supernova, is recycled back into the interstellar medium, ready to make more new stars.

If the star is less massive, it will turn into a red giant that gradually puffs its outer layers into space, leaving a dead core behind known as a white dwarf. If the white dwarf is in orbit around another star, it can enjoy a stellar afterlife by pulling gas from its companion star, in a process call accretion. As layers of gas build up on the white dwarf, they can periodically ignite, creating regular nova explosions.

Such resurrection comes at a price though. If the white dwarf steals too much material from its companion and its mass exceeds the Chandrasekhar limit, then the resulting explosion can be many times more powerful, blowing the white dwarf to pieces in a Type 1 supernova. But again, the shock waves this sends off into space can help trigger a new round of star formation.

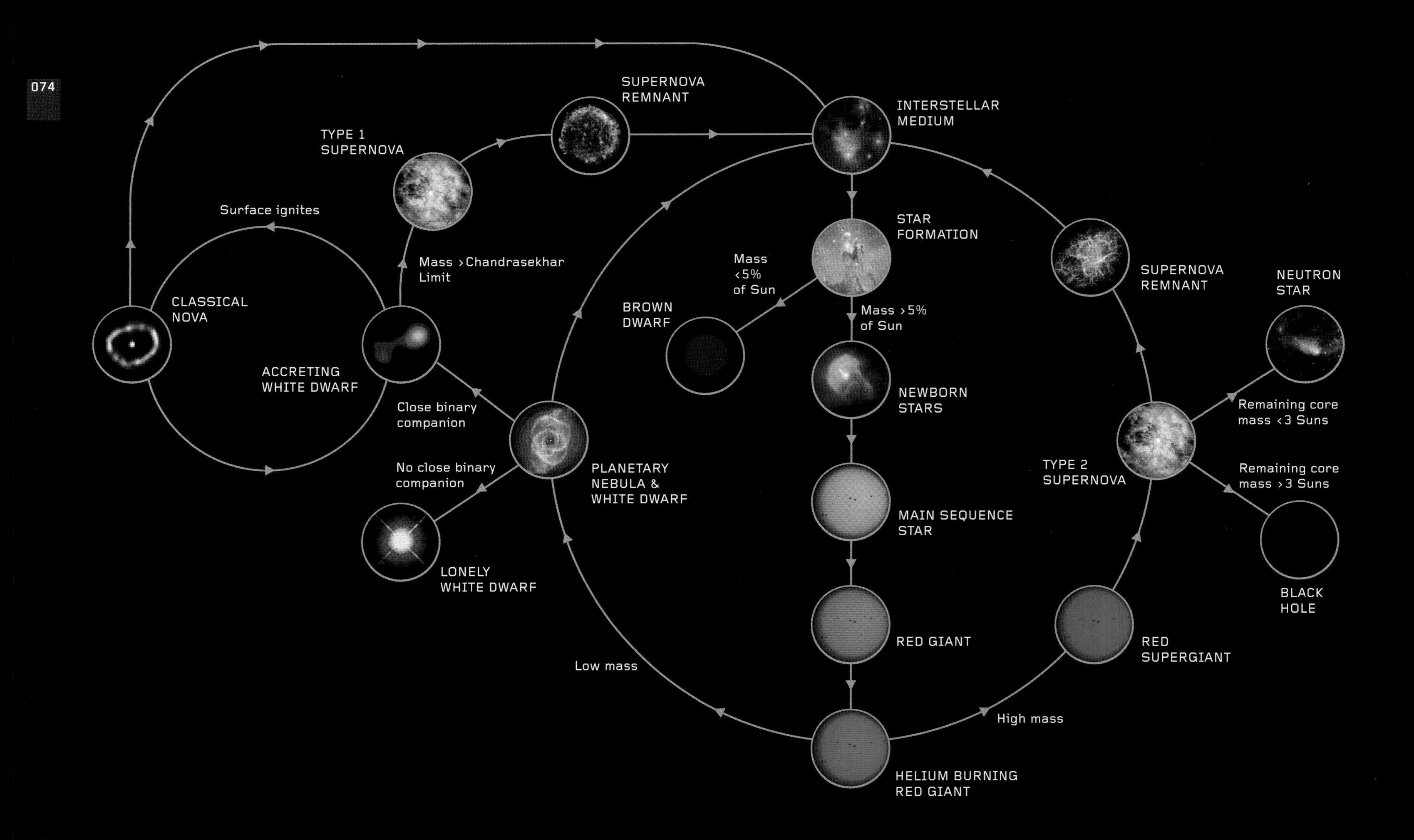

NGC3603 OPEN STAR CLUSTER

The beginning of a star's life cycle is on display here. A cluster of young stars has burst out of a gas cloud and is now illuminating it. Within the remains of the cloud, there are dark areas surrounded by red gas. They indicate denser areas in which new stars are currently forming, ready to become the next generation.

DISTANCE 20 THOUSAND LY

SIZE 17 LIGHT YEARS

BIRTH_

Stars are born in darkness, hidden within dense cocoons of dust and gas from which they burst out to shine into space. It is a continual process that takes place both within the Galaxy and across the Universe. Every year our Galaxy creates an average of seven new stars.

About half the atoms in our Galaxy are drifting through space as either dust or gas. The coldest of these atoms can join together into molecules and accumulate in giant clouds that stretch for hundreds of light years across space. It is thought that star formation takes place in molecular clouds because they are the only places in the Galaxy that contain enough cold gas capable of falling together to form a star. Each molecular cloud contains between 10,000 and a million times the quantity of gas inside the Sun. Dust in the outer layers prevents external starlight and heat entering a giant molecular cloud, and so its interior cools further. The molecules become even more sluggish and create dense molecular cores within the cloud. In these, the process of star formation can truly begin.

With exquisite slowness, the dust in the dense molecular cores separates into distinct conglomerations. Because this is literally driven by the feeble gravitational fields of individual dust grains the initial stages of this process take millions of years. These conglomerations are what will become stars. If they continue to fragment they do not produce single stars but double or multiple stars that will spend their lives orbiting each other in a gravitational embrace.

Central condensation

In the centre of the condensation, the gas becomes denser and denser as gravity pulls everything together. Eventually this reaches a sufficient mass to generate an appreciable gravitational field and suddenly the gassy conglomeration accelerates down the road to stardom. It does this by vigorously extracting gas and dust from the surrounding dense cloud.

The more mass the protostar attracts, the more strongly it pulls on its surroundings and itself. This has the effect of making it more compact and as it packs more matter inside itself, so it heats up. Initially this heat is radiated away at infrared wavelengths but soon something magical happens inside the protostar. A rare form of hydrogen gas, known as deuterium, begins to fuse together. This starts to release energy, increasing the protostar's temperature. Now it begins to shine faintly at the red end of the visible spectrum but astronomers still find it hard to see these objects. The reason is that protostars are still so deeply embedded in their dense cocoons deep within the molecular clouds.

Infrared telescopes can see into these cocoons revealing another remarkable sight: dusty discs of matter surrounding the protostars. As the dense molecular core collapses to become the protostar, it spins ever faster – like an ice skater drawing in their outstretched arms – forcing the infalling particles to flare outwards into a disc that then 'drains' inwards onto the star. Within this disc gravity is also at work, creating the seeds of what will one day be planets.

There are still uncertainties about the details of star formation, mostly brought about by the difficulty astronomers experience when trying to peer inside the dense molecular cores. Overall, however, the picture generally fits the available facts.

Once a giant molecular cloud forms high-mass stars, its fate is sealed – where one occurs, others will follow. The intense radiation given out by these stars compresses nearby cloud regions, spawning new stars. These stars will then repeat the process and so, over the course of many millions of years, the whole

M78
Light from newborn stars spills out from the depths of these dense clouds' cores. The light reflects off other gas and dust, creating the fog of light seen around the denser, darker regions. Eventually these stars will blow away their surrounding shells of gas and shine into the Universe.

DISTANCE 1.6 THOUSAND LY
SIZE 4 LIGHT YEARS

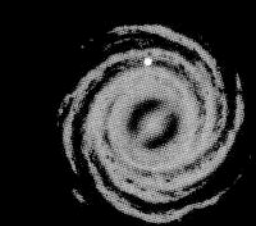

cloud will be transformed into stars. Such areas of young high-mass stars surrounded by protostars are called OB associations. This is because the technical classification for a high-mass star is either an O or a B, depending upon its surface temperature.

By charting the different rates of star formation in galaxies at different distances (and therefore ages), astronomers can build up a picture of how the overall rate of star formation has changed throughout the history of the Universe. By doing this, they are now confident that when the Universe was half its present age, the star formation rate was roughly ten times higher than it is now.

Although the present rate of star formation in the Galaxy is likely to diminish steadily with time, it will be given a final rejuvenating burst in about three billion years, when the Andromeda Galaxy smashes into us. As it does so, gas clouds and molecular clouds will be squeezed together, triggering a massive conflagration of star formation. It is likely to use up all of the Milky Ways's, and Andromeda's, remaining star-forming fuel in one fell swoop.

Such furious rates of star formation were common in the Universe's early history, allowing a good stock of elements heavier than hydrogen and helium to be quickly synthesized. Such heavy elements are the essential building blocks of planets and life. The fact that the Universe experienced an early burst of star formation means there is a possibility that planets and life emerged early in the history of the Universe, perhaps becoming viable when the Universe was 4.5 billion years old and just one-third of its present age.

Although astronomers are now beginning to understand the process of planet formation, the biologists are still struggling to put together all the steps in the origin of life on Earth. So, whilst we can be certain that forming stars have also made planets for billions of years now, we still cannot be certain whether it is likely that any of those planets generated life.

Starbursts

Such amazing bursts of star formation activity are known, perhaps unsurprisingly, as starbursts. They create an extraordinary upset in a galaxy when they occur. Suddenly, new stars begin pouring out radiation into their environments and energizing the surrounding stocks of gas. The galaxy literally lights up, burning many times brighter than normal.

When the high-mass stars created in the starburst approach the end of their lives and explode, their titanic detonations also have a profound effect on their surroundings. As the star formation rates soar, so do the rates of supernovae and these blasts compress nearby clouds, spurring yet more star formation and so sustaining the starburst.

Whatever the rate of star birth, the act itself rejuvenates the host galaxy, adding a population of younger stars to its contents. With every population of stars that lives and dies, the chemicals found in the galaxy are enriched. Thus as a galaxy ages, so it changes its chemical composition with the proportion of hydrogen and helium decreasing as the quantity of heavier elements rises.

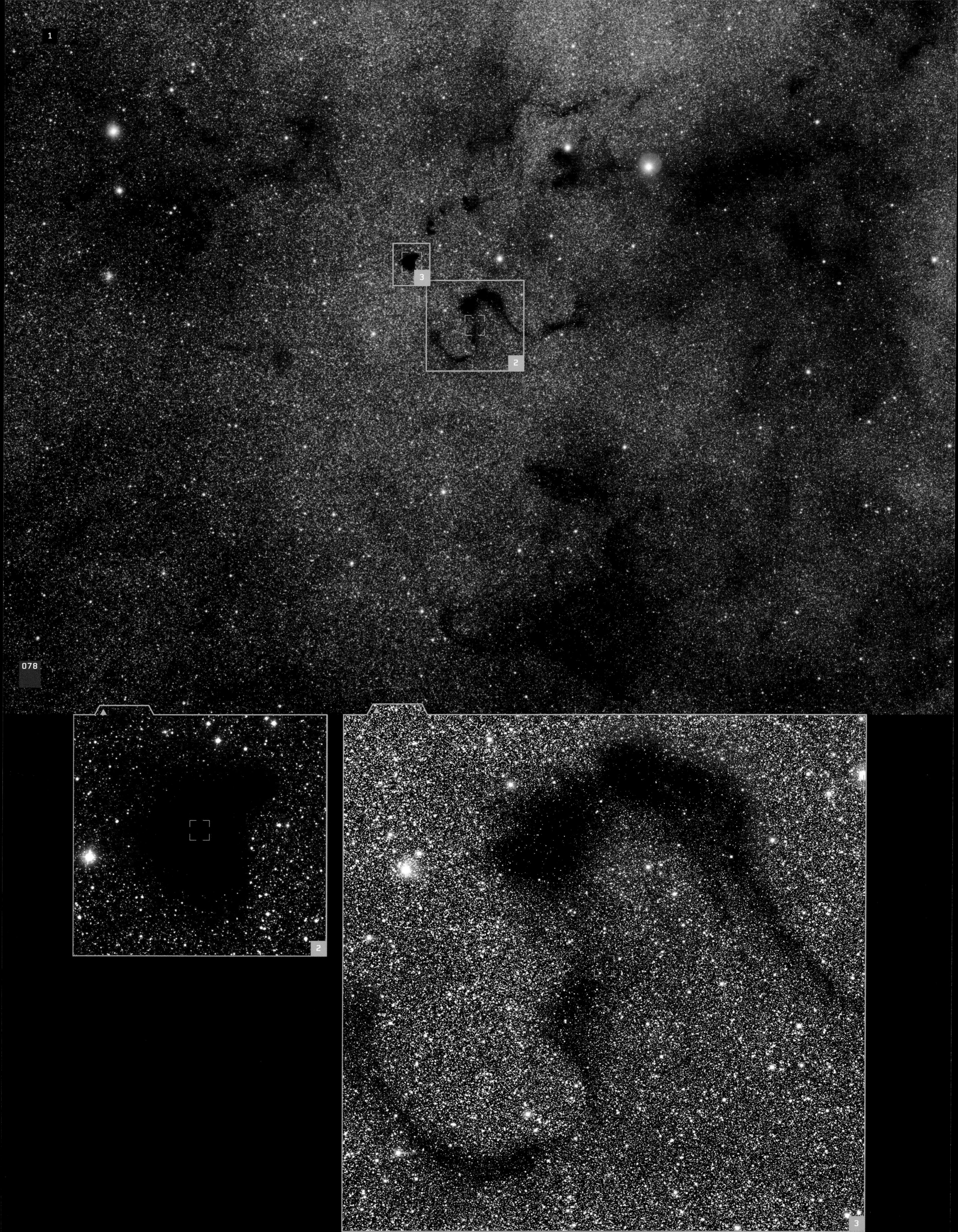
1
3
2
2
3

4

Dark clouds and emission nebulae

The large clouds of gas that fill space between the stars show themselves in a variety of ways. Those that become dense enough can block out the light from objects behind them and so they appear as jet-black silhouettes known as absorption nebulae or simply dark nebulae. On the other hand, clouds of gas with embedded hot stars are driven to glow. Usually this colour is red, the sign of hydrogen gas. These are called emission nebulae.

[1] BARNARD 72 ABSORPTION NEBULA
The Snake Nebula
Looking towards the star clouds at the centre of the Galaxy provides an excellent backdrop against which to see the dark clouds in which stars are forming. The Snake Nebula is a good example [3]. Its curving S-shaped band of dust and gas meanders across a couple of light years. Inside, the secret process of star formation is taking place.

DISTANCE 650 | SIZE 3

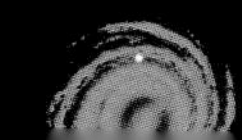

[2] BARNARD 68 ABSORPTION NEBULA
Barnard 68 is a small molecular cloud that is sufficiently dense to blot out the light from the background stars. At the edges, where the cloud thins outs, a few red stars can be seen. These are background stars that have had the colour of their starlight altered by its passage through the gas.

DISTANCE 500 LIGHT YEARS | SIZE 0.2 LIGHT YEARS

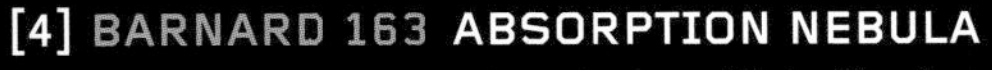

[4] BARNARD 163 ABSORPTION NEBULA
Barnard 163 is a dark nebula within the large emission nebula IC1396. Many dark nebulae belong to the catalogue compiled by Edward Emerson (E.E.) Barnard (1857–1923), an American astronomer, who discovered many of them during his pioneering use of photography to record the night sky. He published his list of 366 dark nebulae in 1919.

DISTANCE 3 THOUSAND LY | SIZE 3.4 LIGHT YEARS

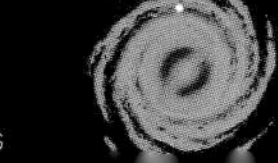

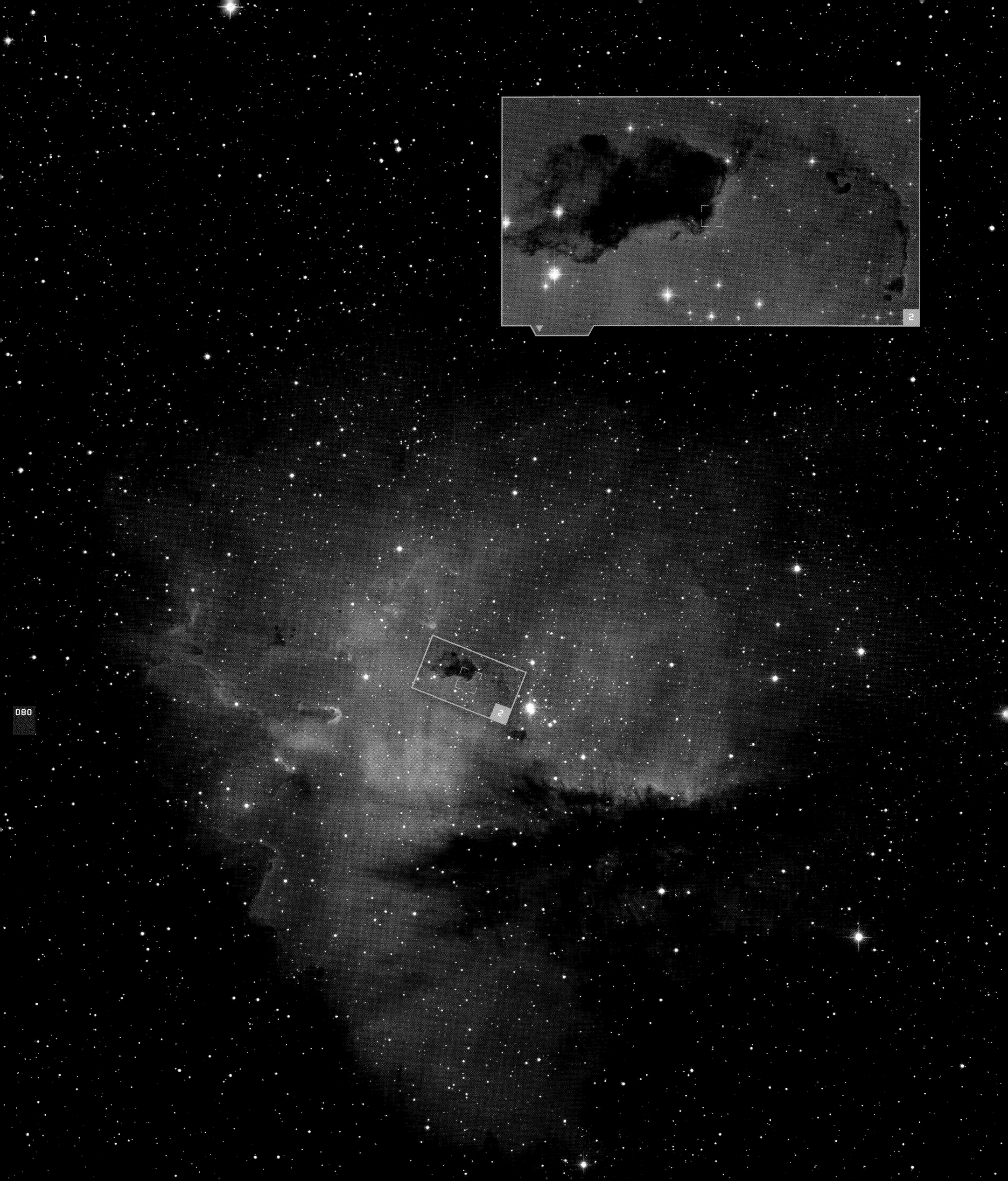
1
2
2

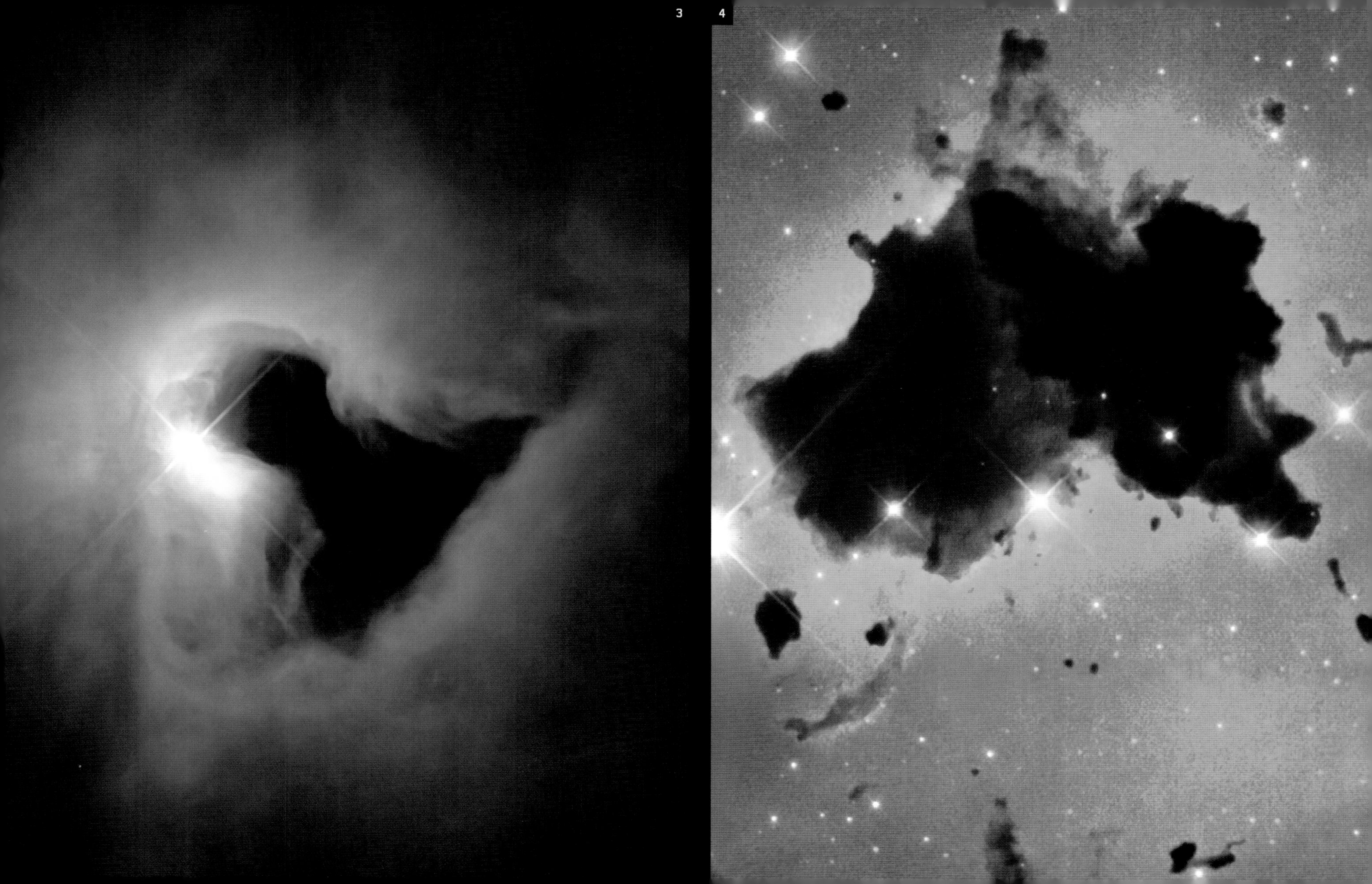
3
4

NGC 2264 **ABSORPTION NEBULA**

Cone Nebula

The fierce ultraviolet light from a giant star (which is not seen in this image) is slowly eroding this enormous pillar of dust and gas. Firstly, the gas is given enough energy to escape the gravitational clutches of the dust cloud and then it is provided with even more energy to start glowing. When the process is complete, only the densest clumps will survive. These will eventually become new stars and planets.

DISTANCE
2.5
THOUSAND LY

SIZE
2.5
LIGHT YEARS

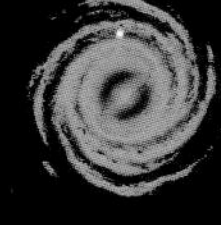
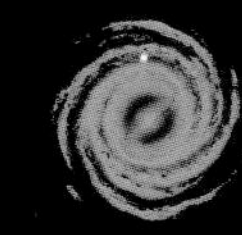

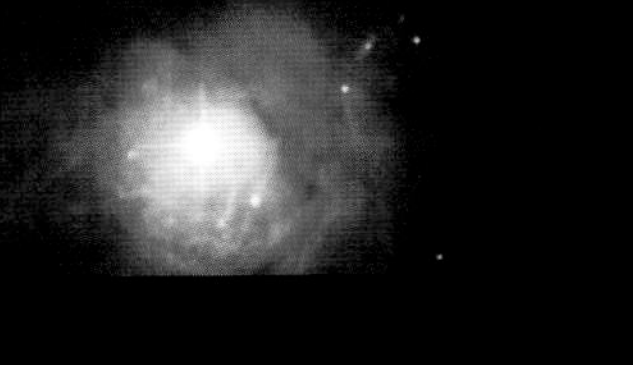

BARNARD 33 **ABSORPTION NEBULA**

Horsehead Nebula

This dark tower of dust has a hooked end that resembles the silhouette of a horse's head. Part of the Orion molecular cloud complex, it extends from the bulk of the dust and gas

1

[1, 2] W5 EMISSION NEBULA
Mountains of Creation

Infrared light is better able to penetrate dusty regions than visible light, which is blocked by interactions with atoms and dust. At visible wavelengths [1] the true extent of this molecular cloud is lost. Switch to the infrared [2], however, and suddenly the dust itself becomes radiant. These dusty mountains of creation contain thousands of forming stars.

DISTANCE 7 THOUSAND LY

SIZE 50 LIGHT YEARS

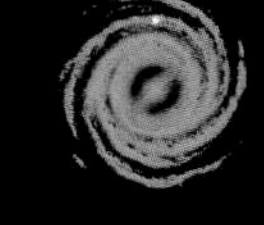

2

IC1396 ABSORPTION NEBULA

Elephant Trunk Nebula

The Elephant Trunk nebula is a dense, elongated cloud of gas inside a bright cluster of stars known as IC 1396. The trunk conceals many young protostars that are in the process of forming. To see inside the trunk, astronomers switch to infrared where the gases become bright and the young stars pop into view. The infrared view [3] shows that a couple of stars, probably a million or two years old, have blown a hole in the head. These will now continue to blow away the gas from the inside out.

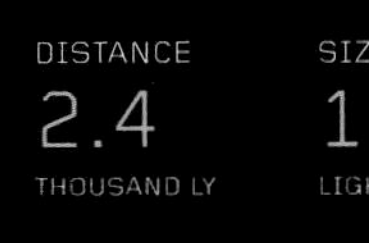

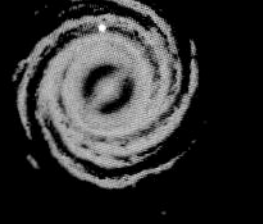

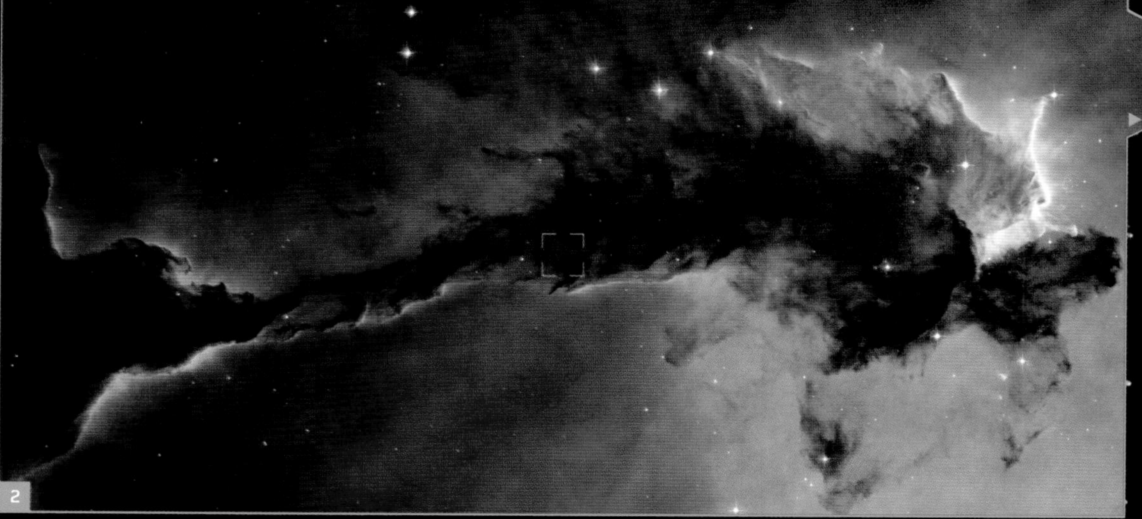

M16 **EMISSION NEBULA**
The Eagle Nebula

A cluster of bright stars sits in the upper left reaches of the Eagle Nebula, [main image] shining light across the gas cloud. As this ultraviolet onslaught erodes the nebula, young stars in the darker, denser stretches find themselves in a race against time to accumulate enough material before their surrounding reservoir is blown away.

Three iconic pillars [1] form the Eagle's talons. They protrude from the wall of the original molecular cloud like stalagmites from the floor of a cavern.

Another spire stretches for almost 9.5 light years protecting a brood of stellar youngsters within [2]. Computer processing has changed the colours to show blue for oxygen and red for hydrogen.

DISTANCE
7
THOUSAND LY

SIZE
40
LIGHT YEARS

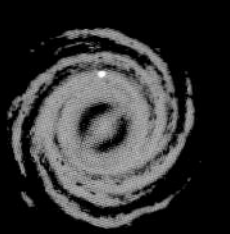

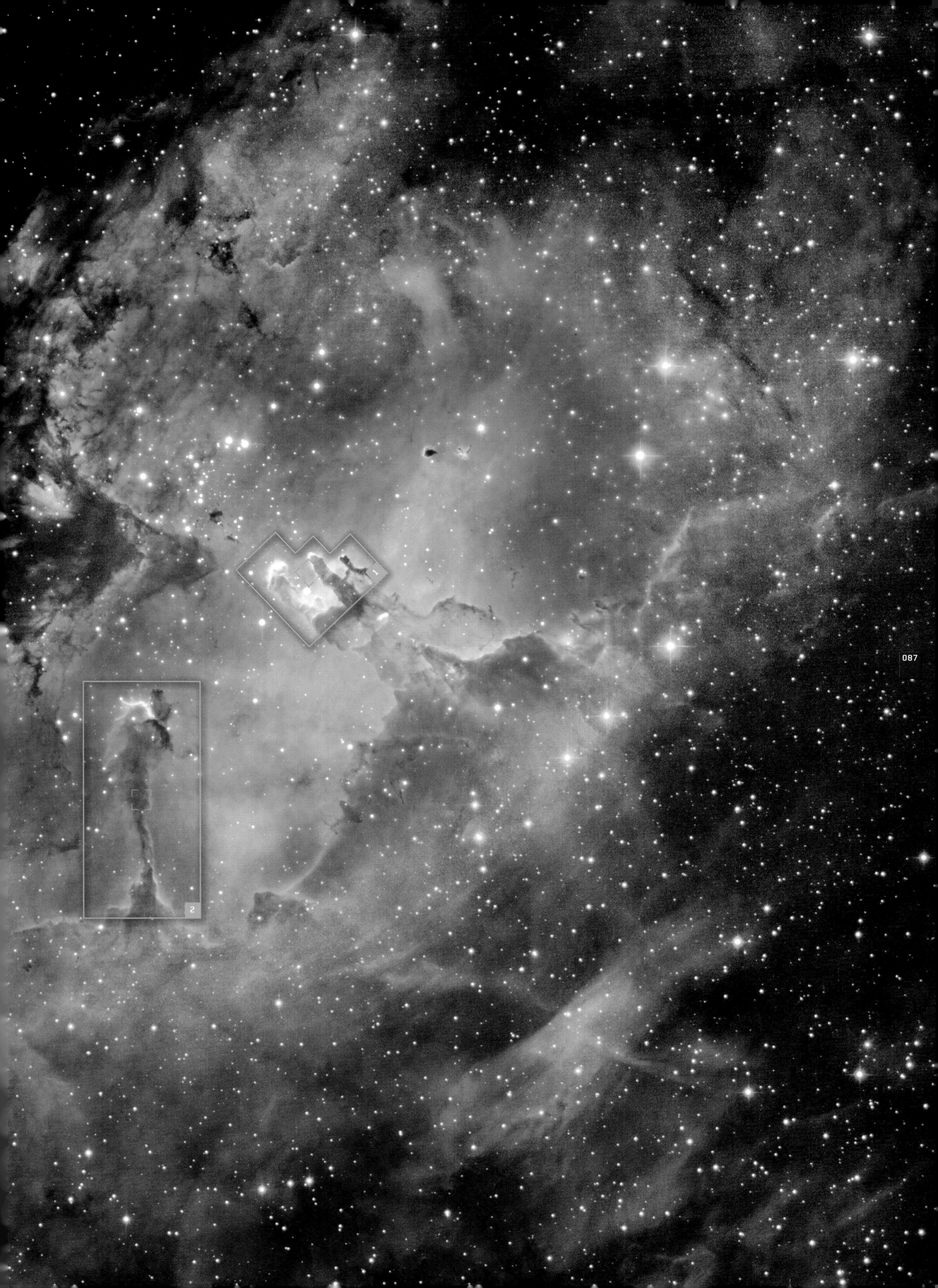
1
2

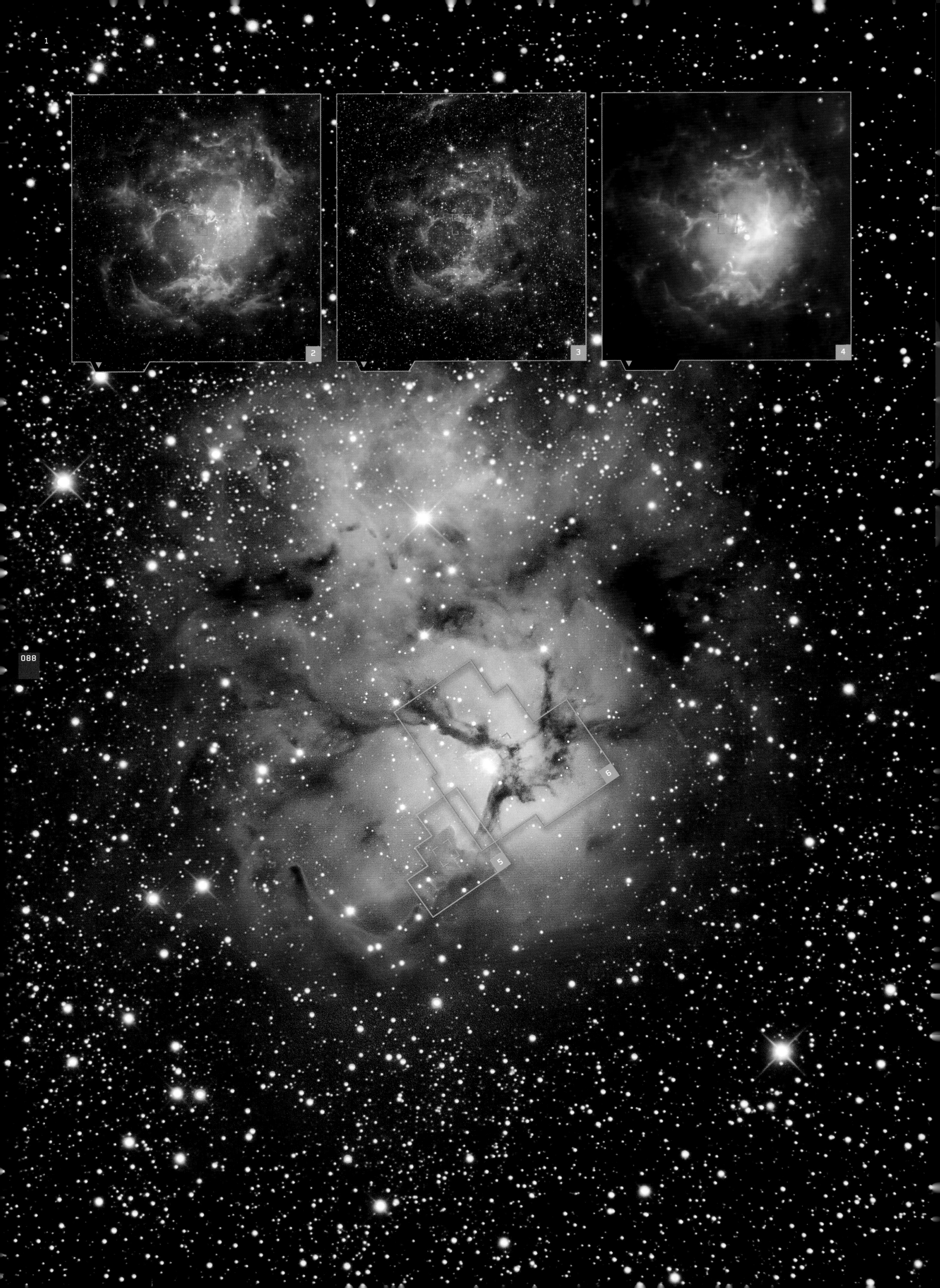
1
2
3
4
5
6

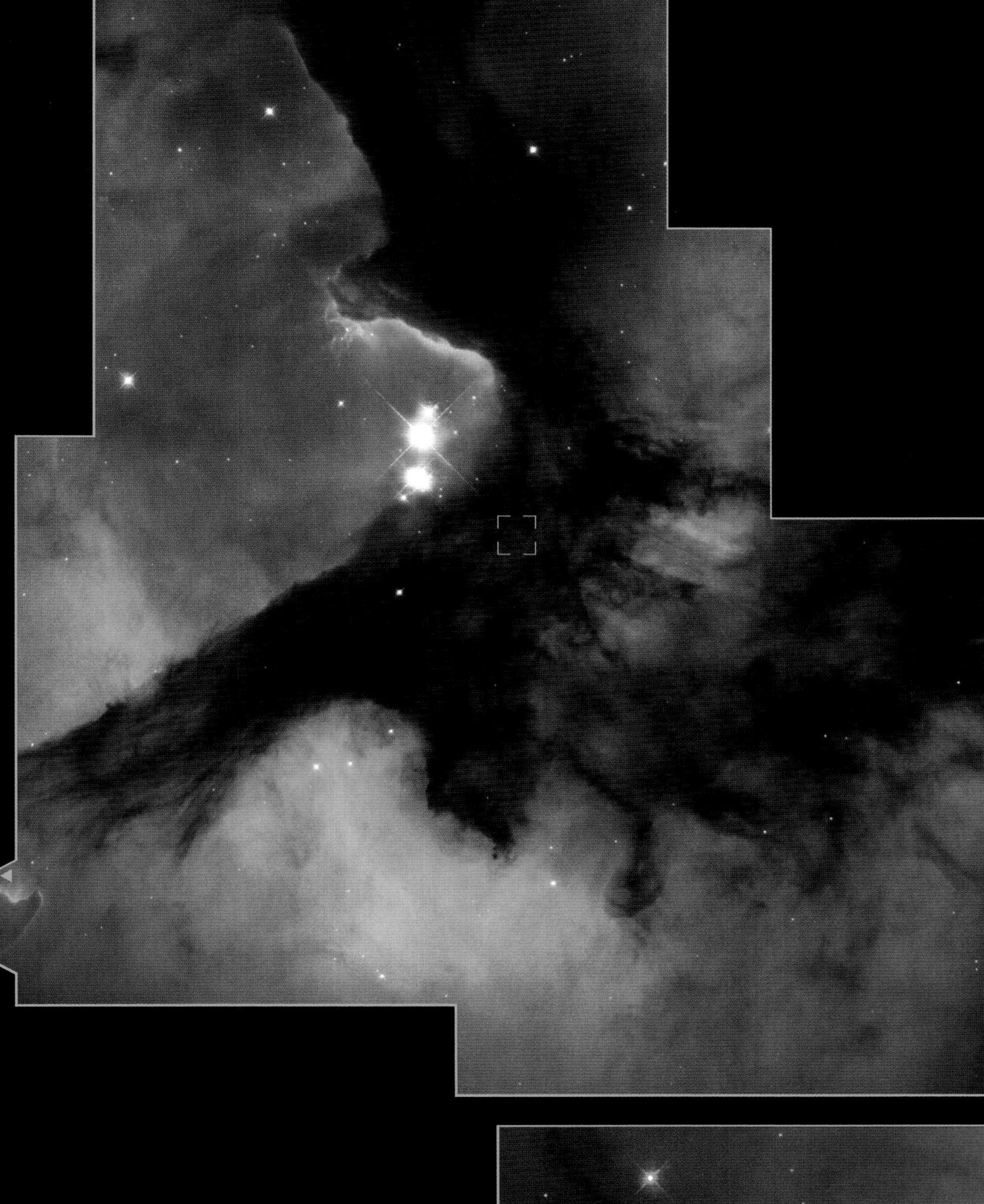

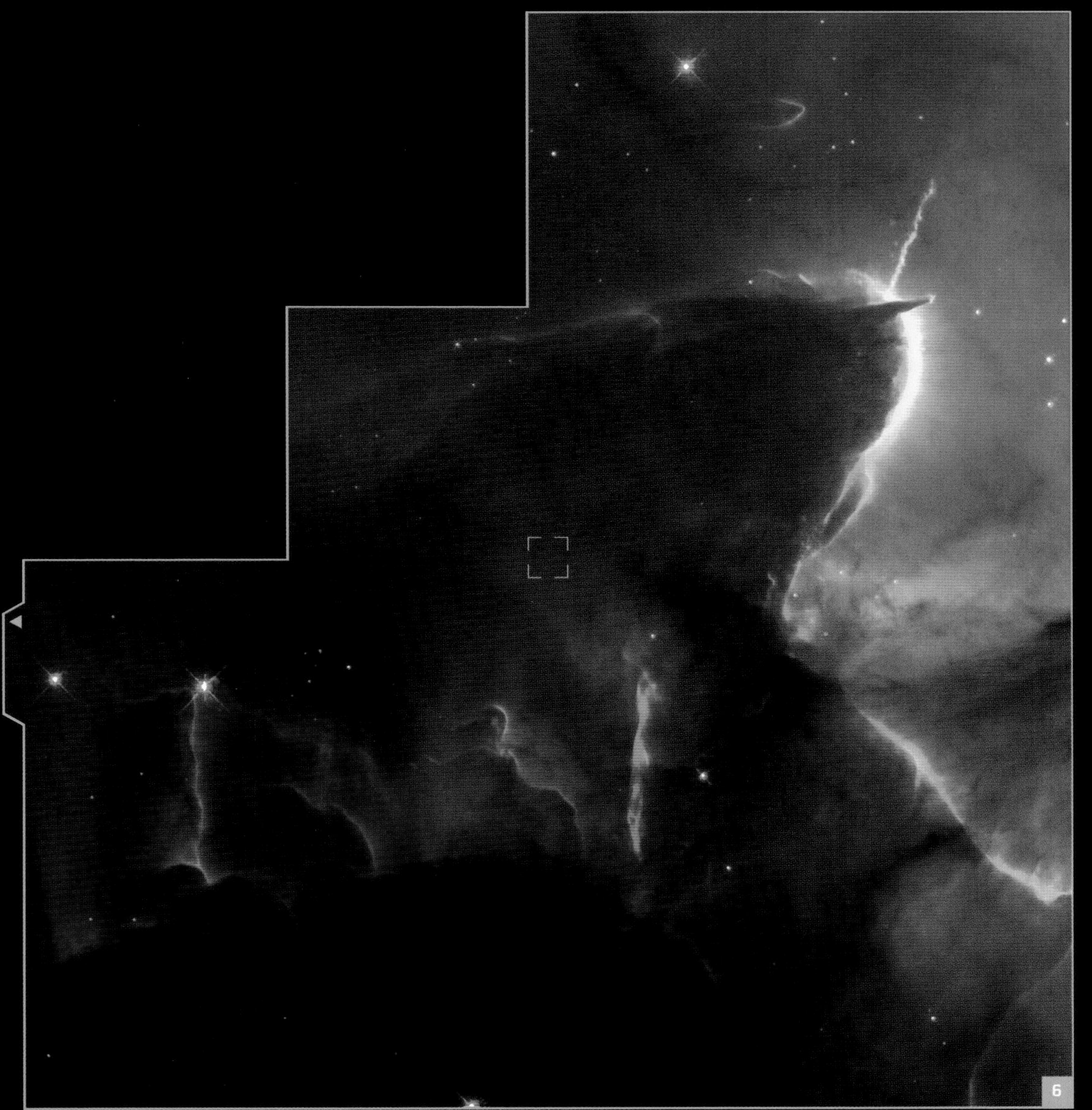

[1] M20 EMISSION & REFLECTION NEBULA
The Triffid Nebula

The red emission in the Triffid Nebula comes about because the ultraviolet light from the bright blue star cluster near its centre breaks up the surrounding hydrogen gas. Further out, where the radiation from these stars becomes too weak to have much effect, the starlight scatters off the gas and dust, appearing blue in the process.

The combined infrared view [2] changes the picture, revealing the interior of the nebula. In the shorter infrared wavelength view, [3] 30 massive embryonic stars and 120 smaller newborn stars shine through. They can be seen throughout the nebula, in both its dark lanes and luminous clouds. Longer infrared waves reveals the nebula's dust content [4].

A close-up of the central region of the Triffid [5] shows the cluster of giant stars that light the entire nebula. Their fearsome radiation has sterlized their immediate vicinity, halting local star formation, but at greater distances it only encourages futher star birth as it collapses gas and dust clouds.

The dense pillar of dust [6] plays host to at least one protostar. The bright spike is a jet of sub-atomic particles being released by the star as it starts to break out of its dusty incubator and take its place in the cosmos.

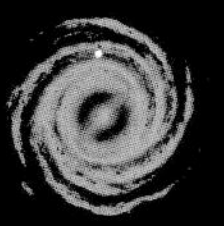

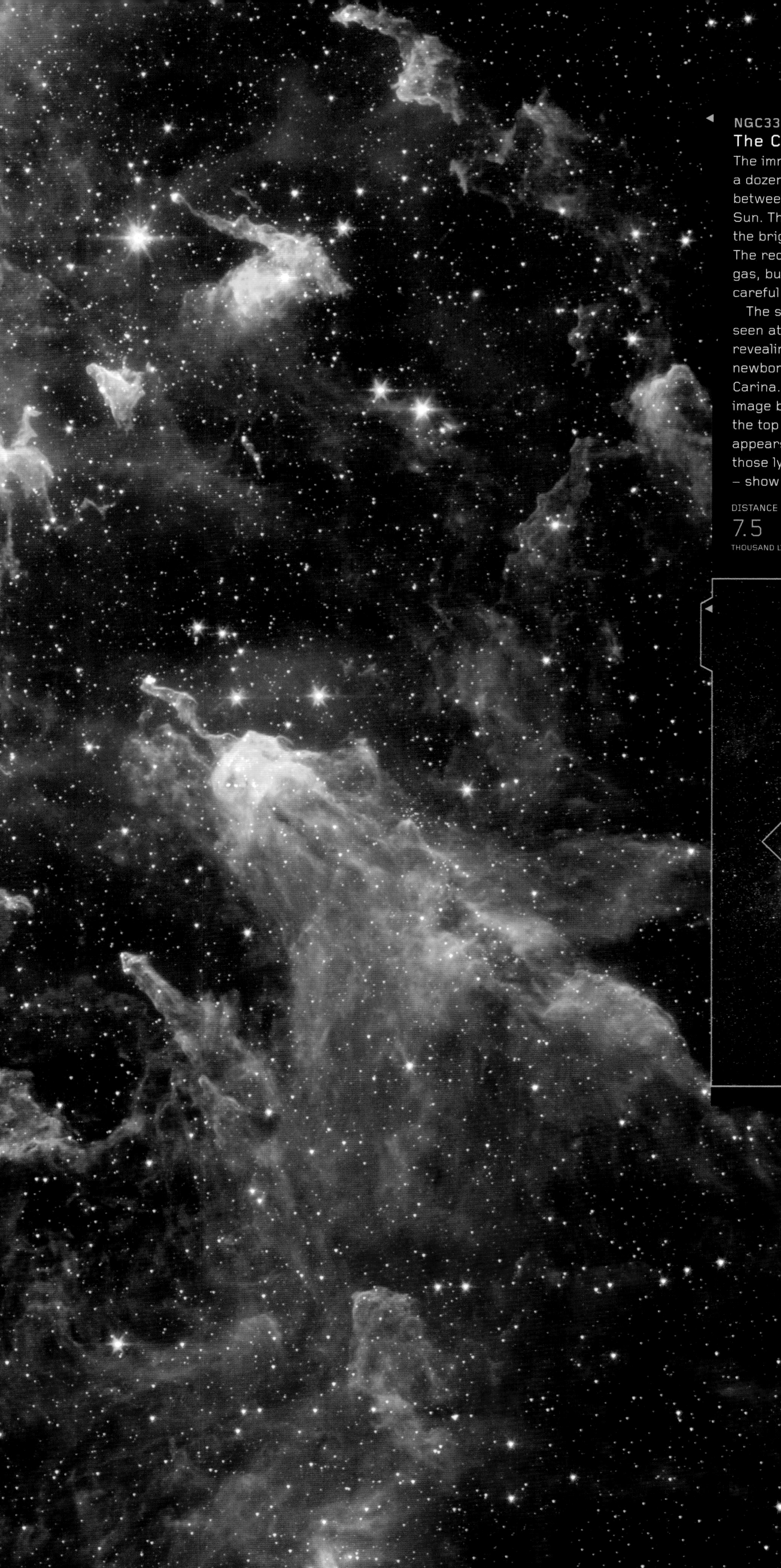

NGC3372 **EMISSION NEBULA**

The Carina Nebula

The immense Carina Nebula is lit up by at least a dozen brilliant stars, each estimated to be between 50 and 100 times the mass of our Sun. The king of these is Eta Carina, which in the bright centre of the wide-field image [1]. The red colour of this image shows hydrogen gas, but other gases can be picked out by careful imaging techniques.

The substructure of the nebula can be seen at infrared wavelengths [main image] revealing pillars of dust and gas protecting the newborn stars inside from the fiery light of Eta Carina. The giant star is just off stage in this image but its light shines as yellow beams into the top of the image. Hot gas in this image appears green, and any foreground stars – those lying in our line of vision to the nebula – show up as blue.

DISTANCE 7.5 THOUSAND LY

SIZE 200 LIGHT YEARS

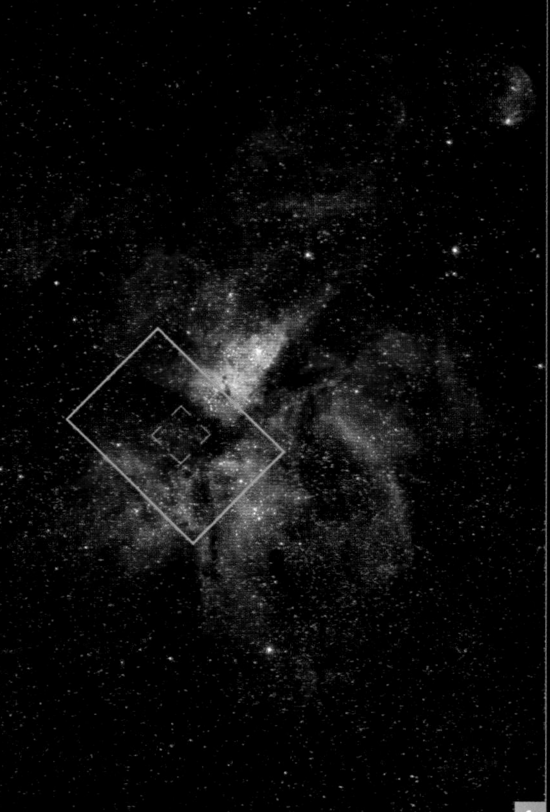

1

NGC3372 **EMISSION NEBULA**

The Carina Nebula

This 50 light-year portion of the Carina Nebula shows the utter confusion created by Eta Carinae. This giant star can be seen as the bright double spot [1]. It is producing so much radiation that the star itself is having trouble staying together. The dumbbell shape is the product of former eruptions from the star. Astronomers believe that it is the star in our Galaxy most likely to explode – perhaps even within our lifetimes, giving astronomers an unprecedented opportunity to study such a stellar cataclysm.

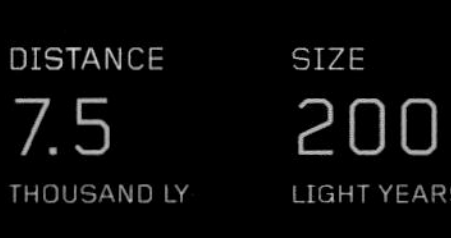

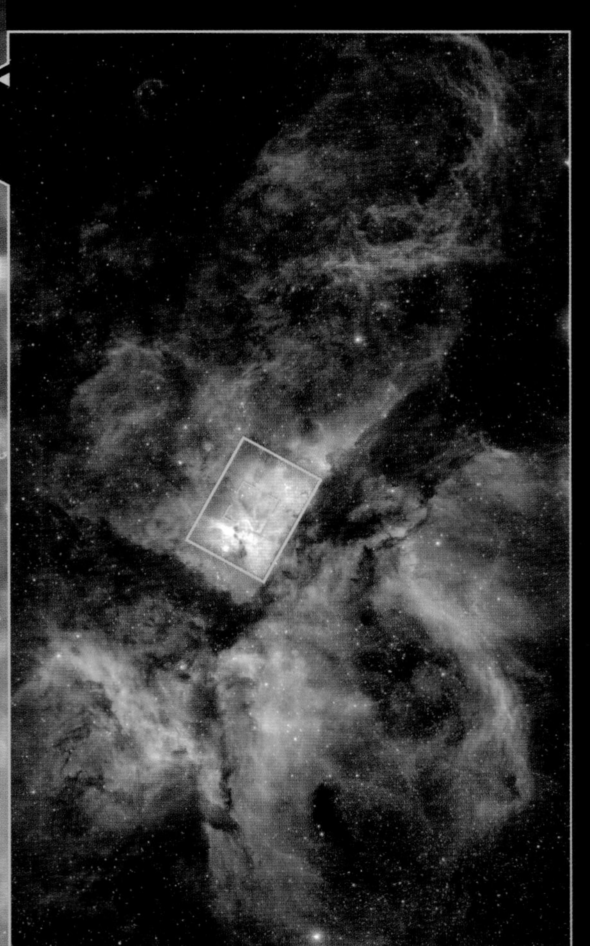

M42 **EMISSION NEBULA**
The Orion Nebula

The Orion Nebula is the nearest star forming complex to the Earth that is giving birth to high-mass stars – the giant stars responsible for the ultraviolet radiation that makes emission nebulae glow. In total, astronomers believe the Orion Nebula contains more than 1000 young stars. Not all are massive. The vast majority are smaller stars like the Sun. This is representative of the way the Universe behaves now: it makes a few large stars and a lot of small ones. Astronomers use this as a clue when working out the process of star formation.

The Orion Nebula, despite its vast size on a human scale, is only a tiny part of the larger Orion molecular cloud complex. Only in the infrared is the hidden bulk of this celestial giant revealed [1]. The entire cloud lights up as the dust radiates its feeble heat as infrared waves. The dust maps out the concentration of gas in the cloud and eventually it will all be transformed into millions of stars.

At optical wavelengths [2], the central section of the cloud is rich in visible nebulae: the flame nebula, the horsehead nebula, and the Great Orion Nebula [main image].

DISTANCE 1.5 THOUSAND LY

SIZE 25 LIGHT YEARS

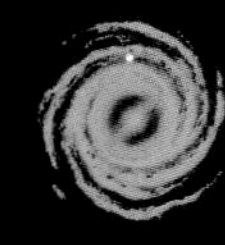

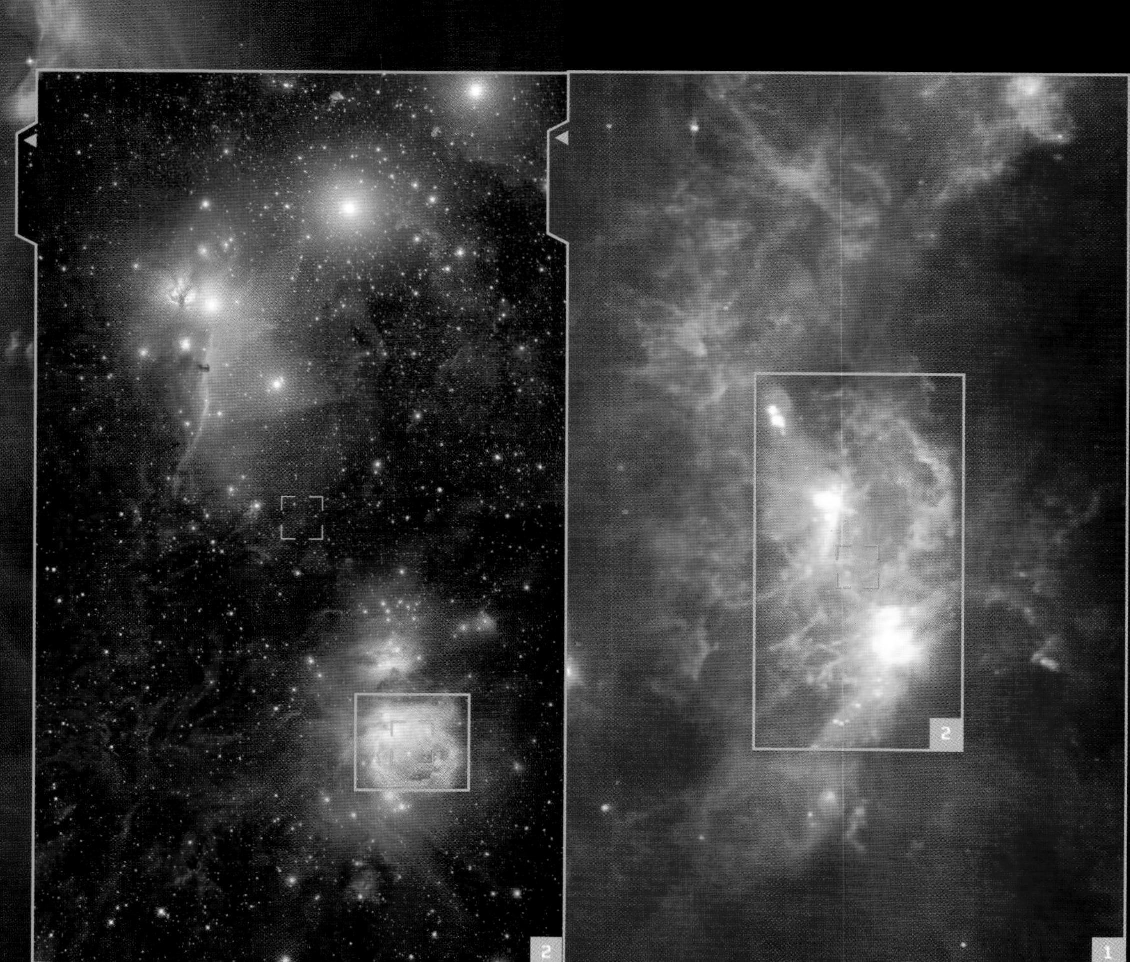

1

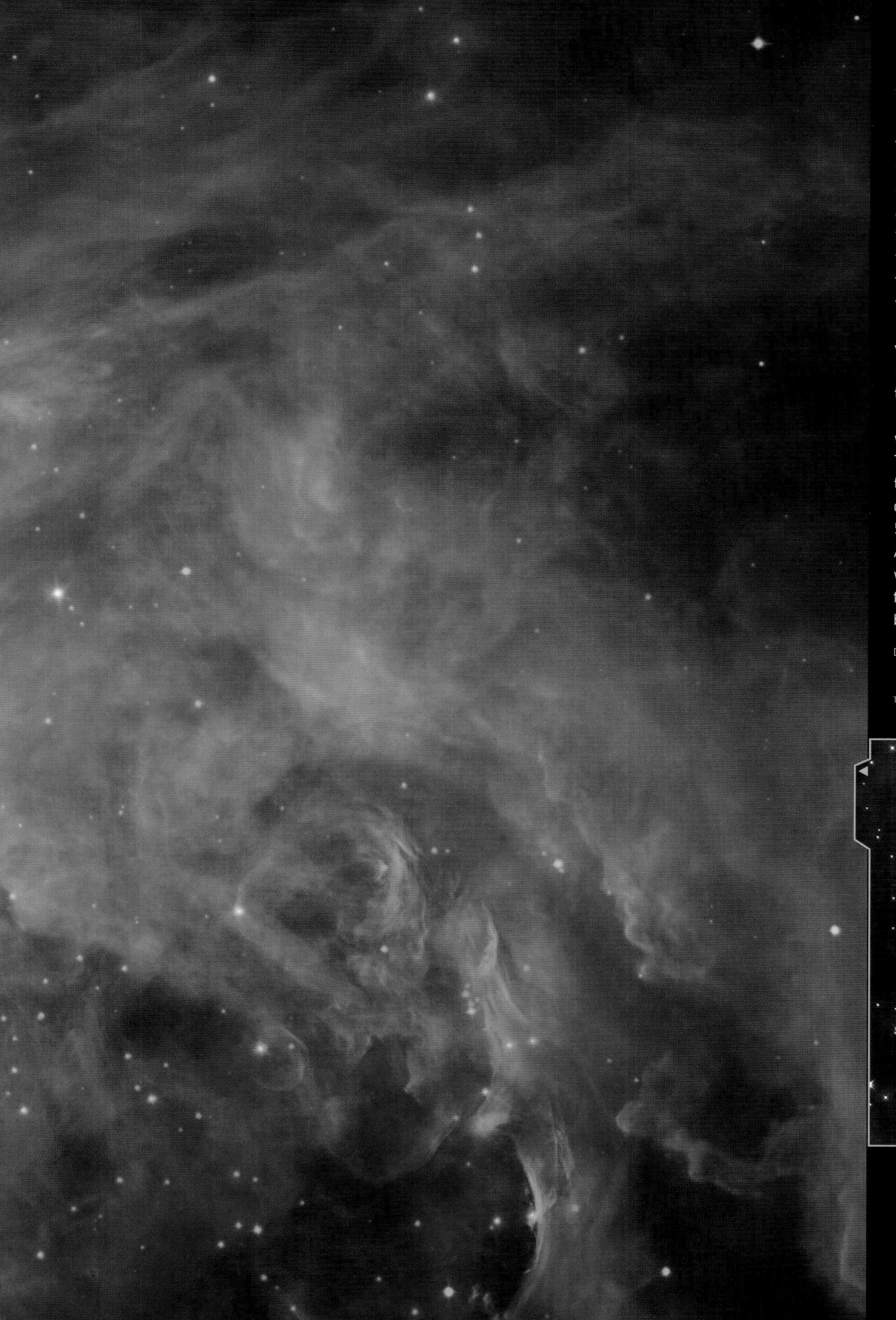

Orion across the spectrum

This multi-wavelength view of the Orion Nebula combines visible, infrared and ultraviolet [main image]. Swirls of green reveal hydrogen and sulphur gas. Meanwhile, reds and oranges expose carbon-rich molecules called polycyclic aromatic hydrocarbons in the cloud. On Earth, these organic molecules are found on burnt toast and in automobile exhaust. In space they form naturally in the cooling gas flows found within star-forming regions.

Stars show up as dots and the orange-yellow ones are deeply embedded infant stars. Less embedded stars are specks of green and the blue spots are foreground stars.

The stars responsible for illuminating the whole nebula are four stars known as the Trapezium. They sit in the yellow smudge near the centre of the main image but can be seen clearly in the infrared zoom surrounded by 50 failed stars known as brown dwarfs [1]. Although they shine brightly at infrared wavelengths, these celestial stillborn have failed to accumulate enough gas to become bona-fide stars.

DISTANCE 1.5 THOUSAND LY

SIZE 25 LIGHT YEARS

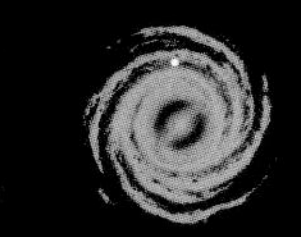

NGC 2237, NGC 2238, NGC 2239, NGC 2244, NGC 2246 **EMISSION NEBULA**

The Rosette Nebula

Originally classified during the 19th century as five separate regions of nebulosity and a star cluster, better telescopes have now shown that it is all part of the same object. The Rosette Nebula is a cloud of gas containing 10,000 times the mass of the Sun.

About three million years ago, the first stars formed. Over the intervening years, they have blown a giant cavity in the surrounding cloud of gas. This has triggered a new wave of star formation in the ring of compressed gas that remains.

DISTANCE 5.2 THOUSAND LY

SIZE 130 LIGHT YEARS

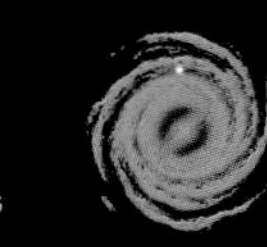

NGC 2467 **STAR CLUSTER**

The Skull and Crossbones

Star clusters are often found at the centres of nebulae. They represent the first stars to break free and light up their surroundings and are usually just a few million years old. This one is sometimes referred to as the skull and crossbones but for rather obscure reasons; probably because of the way it appears in small telescopes.

DISTANCE 27.5 THOUSAND LY

SIZE 60 LIGHT YEARS

NGC 6334 EMISSION NEBULA

The Cat's Paw Nebula

The Cat's Paw Nebula is a region of on-going star formation in which a number of young stars have managed to reach ten times the mass of the Sun. Many others contain more moderate masses.

The colours in this image are natural. They are unusually red because dust banks between Earth and the nebula have preferentially deflected bluer wavelengths of light away from Earth, leaving only the red light. The similar effect happens in Earth's skies and explains why the setting sun appears progressively red as its light passes through successively deeper layers of our atmosphere.

DISTANCE
5.5
THOUSAND LY

SIZE
60
LIGHT YEARS

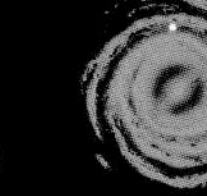

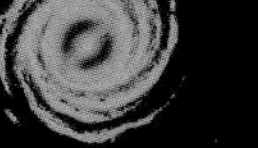

NGC 3582 EMISSION NEBULA

At least 33 massive stars are nearing the final stages of their formation in this portion of complex RCW57. They are not the first to exist here; a previous generation of stars has already blown bubbles in the surrounding gas, as seen in the giant loops at the top of the image.

As in the Orion Nebula, astronomers have discovered the complex carbon molecules known as polycyclic aromatic hydrocarbons. Their development in the Sun's formation nebula five billion years ago may have been a step towards the origin of life on Earth.

DISTANCE
6
THOUSAND LY

SIZE
5
LIGHT YEARS

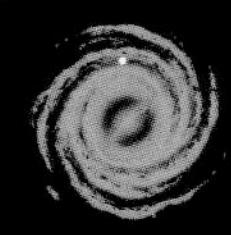

1

[1] IC5070 **EMISSION NEBULA**

The Pelican Nebula

So called because in wide-angle shots it resembles the silhouette of a pelican, this nebula is a particularly active mix of star formation and evolving gas clouds. The light from young stars is slowly heating up the cold gas in the cloud and 'boiling' it off into space. This is obvious in the blue colours at the top of the dense pillar of dust and gas.

All star formation faces this struggle once the first stars have formed and it becomes a race to see how fast other stars can be built before the surrounding gas is blown into space.

[2] M8 **EMISSION NEBULA**

The Lagoon Nebula

Inside the Lagoon Nebula stars do battle with dust and gas. The stars try to blast the tiny stuff away, whilst the dust and gas do their best to hold on to each other using gravity.

In the deepest centre of the nebula, the massive star Herschel 36 is whipping up a storm [3]. It is heating the outer edges of large dust columns. On Earth, when air pockets are warmer outside than inside, they begin to twist and form tornadoes. Could the same be happening on a much longer, grander scale here in the Lagoon Nebula? Astronomers must watch and wait to find out.

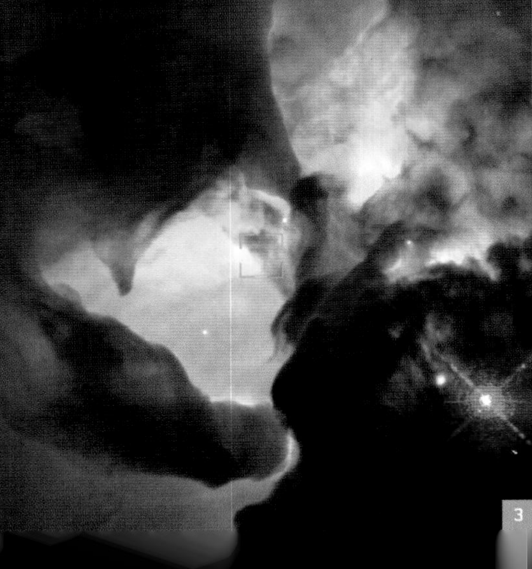

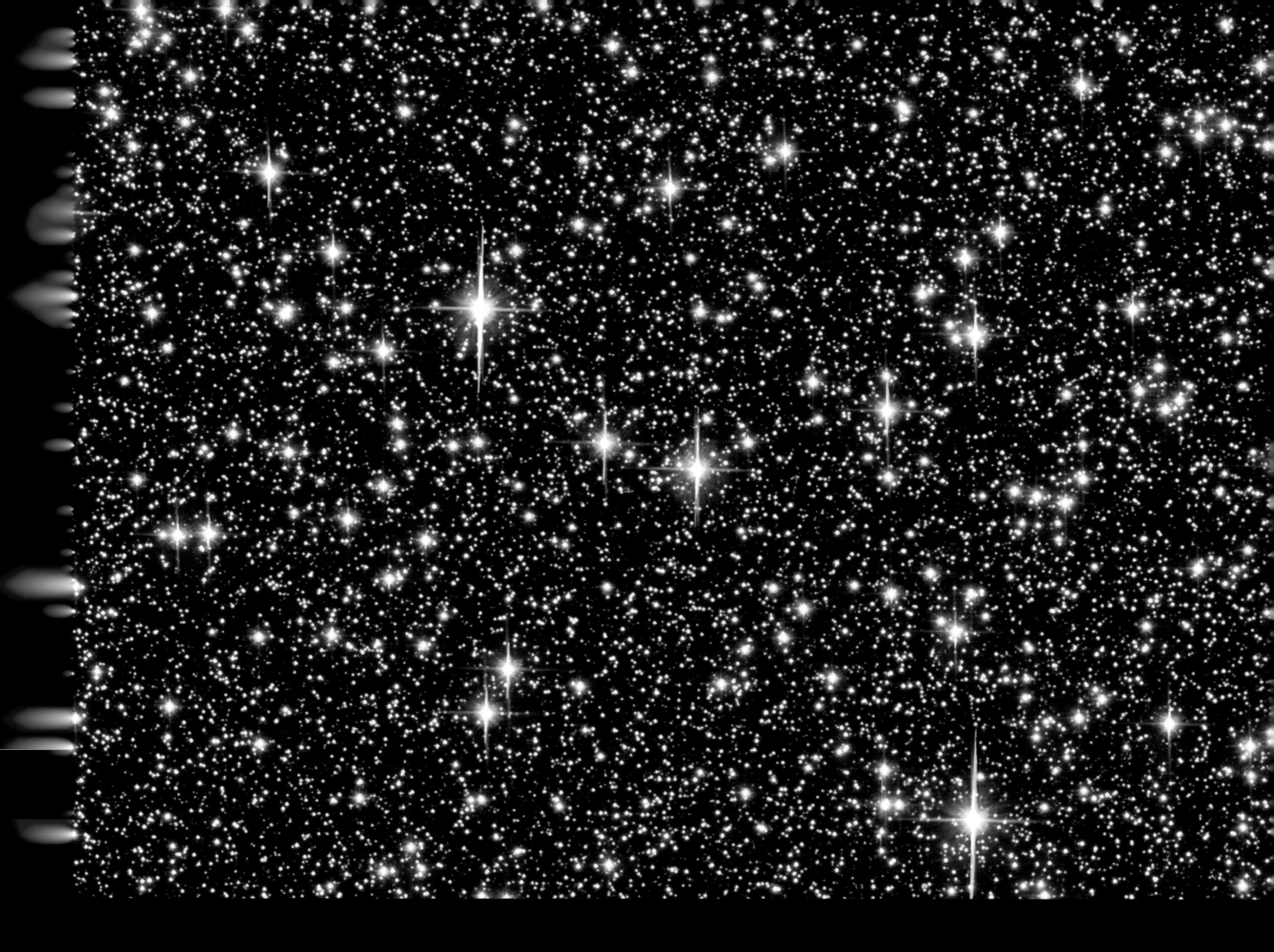

MATURITY_

A star reaches maturity when it gathers together enough matter for the density and temperature in its core to allow nuclear fusion to take place.

As a protostar pulls itself together under the force of its own gravity, so it becomes denser. Nowhere is this density greater than at the centre of the star, which is being compressed by the weight of the overlying gas layers. In a star like the Sun, the core comprises just 10 percent of the total volume, yet holds 40 percent of the Sun's total mass. Each cubic metre of highly compressed gas weighs 150 tonnes and is 150 times the density of water.

Temperatures soar and, when they reach millions of degrees Kelvin, the nuclear fusion of hydrogen can begin. The conversion of hydrogen into helium is the principal source of energy for most stars in the Galaxy; indeed this is thought to be true for most stars throughout the Universe. The smallest stars, known as red dwarfs, have less than half the mass of the Sun and core temperatures of about 4 million Kelvin. At these temperatures, hydrogen fusion is a relatively sedate affair. The stars exist in a state of slow burn and will eek out a luminous existence for more

The rate of nuclear fusion is highly temperature sensitive, so even a moderate rise in core temperature is accompanied by a leap in the energy being released. Higher core temperatures are reached by adding more mass to a star. The Sun's core is approximately 10 million Kelvin and will exhaust its hydrogen in about 10 billion years.

At the high end of the mass scale, stars live fast, burn brightly and die young. Although the core temperature may only be four times higher than the Sun's, the rate of fusion rockets upwards. High-mass stars contain 20 times or more mass than the Sun, and still manage to work through it all in, typically, a few tens of millions of years.

The ignition of nuclear fusion within a star of any size can herald a phase of unpredictable behaviour. Like human adolescents, it often takes a star a while to settle down to its new internal conditions.

Jets and outflows

As the star bursts into life, the relatively gentle release of energy is usurped by the sudden ignition of a nuclear furnace. Until now, gravity has been steadily exerting its influence and pulling the star into a tighter and tighter ball

ignition begins to fuse hydrogen into helium and this releases a torrent of radiation that tries to tear the star apart. As the star expands the temperature in the core drops and nuclear fusion slows down. This removes some of the outward pressure and so the star begins to contract, starting the cycle over again.

As the star settles into a state of mature equilibrium between these two opposing forces, it is still enshrouded in dust and gas. Much of this has settled into a thick disc around the equator of the star. It is here that planets are probably forming.

Near the rotation poles of the star, matter stops falling inwards and is, instead, expelled. These are most often in the form of jets of electrified particles that head off from the star's north and south poles, apparently forming a skewer of matter with the star at its centre. Along with each narrow jet, there is usually an outflow of gas, although it is much more difficult to see. Together they push away the surrounding cloud, exposing the star to view.

The exact mechanism that produces these jets and outflows is as yet unknown but it is thought to involve magnetic fields both created

Milky Way star field

There are 180,000 stars crowded into this view of the Milky Way, most of them several tens of thousands of light years away. The vast majority of them are mature stars living stable lives that last for billions of years. In contrast, many of the red stars have already reached their old age.

forming disc. Outflows of material are observed around many young stars and mark their burgeoning maturity. When these jets slam into denser gas around the star they create small knots of glowing nebulosity called Herbig-Haro objects.

Some stars do not make it to maturity. These stellar stillborns are called brown dwarfs. They are thought to be a similar to gas giant planets, only larger. Their increased mass means that their interiors are hot enough to keep them constantly churning over and over whereas, inside a gas giant planet, matter settles into layers of proportionally greater density. The mass range for a brown dwarf runs from 13–80 times the mass of Jupiter, the largest planet in our Solar System.

Mature stars often come in pairs or more. Fully half the stars in the Galaxy are thought to have other stars gravitationally bound to them. This means that they orbit each other around a point in space known as the centre of mass. Many stars that appear to be single stars to the unaided eye were resolved into pairs by the invention of the telescope. As telescopes become ever more powerful, so this trend continues.

On the other hand, some stars appear close to one another because of chance alignments rather than because they are gravitationally bound to each other. To differentiate these from true pairs, astronomers call them double stars, reserving the term binary stars for the gravitationally bound couples.

Binary stars exist in a dizzying variety. Some are so close to one another that they pull each other around in a complete orbit in just a few hours. Most, however, orbit in a matter of days, weeks, years or even decades. Binary stars are particularly valuable to astronomers because, by analysing the orbital motion of the two components, they can determine accurate masses for the stars.

If the stars are orientated in such a way that they eclipse one another as seen from Earth, then the binary star can change its collective brightness. These are classified as a type of variable star. Other types of variable star include solitary objects that do vary their intrinsic brightness, usually by pulsing in and out.

Stars of different masses combine to become binary stars and this means that they age at different rates. The higher-mass component will complete its life cycle faster than the lower-mass one. If the binary stars are close enough, they can have a profound influence over each other as they age.

When the more massive companion expands to become a red giant star, it can swell so much that gas will flow from its outer layers over onto the smaller member. This robs mass from the larger star but boosts that of the smaller star. As the secondary star accumulates more matter, so it gets hotter and nuclear fusion speeds up inside, accelerating it down its own evolutionary path.

If both stars reach the red giant phase simultaneously, then they can merge into a single elongated stellar object, called a common envelope. Inside, the two stellar cores continue to orbit one another but from the outside, the star looks like a single, peanut shape entity.

Regardless of its age or mass, each star is a nuclear factory fusing hydrogen into helium to produce the light that it then shines into space. Each parcel of light or photon that has struck the detector to make the above image has been travelling through space for tens of thousands of years but that is nothing to how long it has taken them to wrestle their way out of the centre of their parent star. From the point of creation to its eventual escape at the surface of the star, each photon will take hundreds of thousands of years to push through the dense gas inside the star.

Young stars

As a young star bursts out onto the cosmic scene, it announces its arrival with an outpouring of energy. This lights up the surrounding gas clouds, creating beautiful, if fleeting, sculptures of light.

[1] HH-34 HERBIG-HARO OBJECT

An orange jet points downwards to an arc-shaped Herbig-Haro object. An invisible jet points upwards to another, fainter arc of nebulosity. Analysis shows that matter in the jet is moving at 250 kilometres per second. The overwhelming 'waterfall' in the upper left of the image is an enigmatic feature that remains unexplained.

DISTANCE 1.5 THOUSAND LY — SIZE 3 LIGHT YEARS

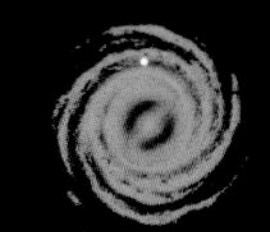

[2] HH-32 HERBIG-HARO OBJECT

The jets cannot be seen from this star, the bright left one, but the Herbig-Haro objects they excite are easily visible as the blue and green knots of emission above and below the star. The jets are tilted to our line of sight with the lower one further away, and the upper one closer.

DISTANCE 1 THOUSAND LY — SIZE 0.5 LIGHT YEARS

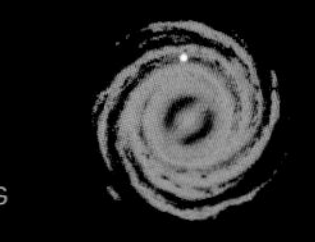

[3] HH-47 HERBIG-HARO OBJECT

The twists in the jet of matter represent the star wobbling on its rotation axis. This is probably the result of the star swallowing its final layers of matter, which temporarily destabilizes the rotation of the newborn star.

DISTANCE 15 THOUSAND LY — SIZE 0.5 LIGHT YEARS

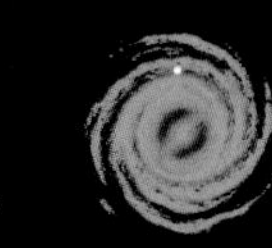

[4] LL ORI STELLAR BOW SHOCK

As this young star finds its feet, it begins to emit a 'wind' of particles into space. This collides with its surroundings, creating a bow shock. This is similar to the build up of water at the front of a fast-moving ship. The wind of particles clears away the last of the star's birth cocoon.

DISTANCE 1.5 THOUSAND LY — SIZE 0.5 LIGHT YEARS

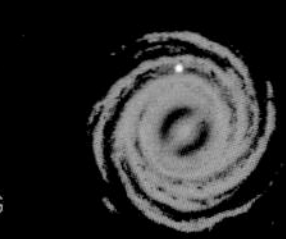

[5] NGC 2261 REFLECTION NEBULA
Hubble's Variable Nebula

This delicate fan of dust belongs to the newly born star R Monocerotis. The star is approximately the size of the Sun and is located at the bright apex of the fan, which denotes the walls of a conical cavity it is carving within its birth cloud. This fan will grow bigger with time and eventually the star will emerge.

DISTANCE 2.5 THOUSAND LY — SIZE 1 LIGHT YEAR

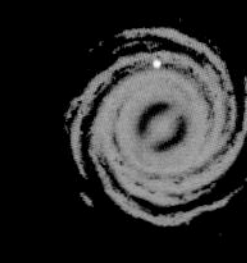

1

2

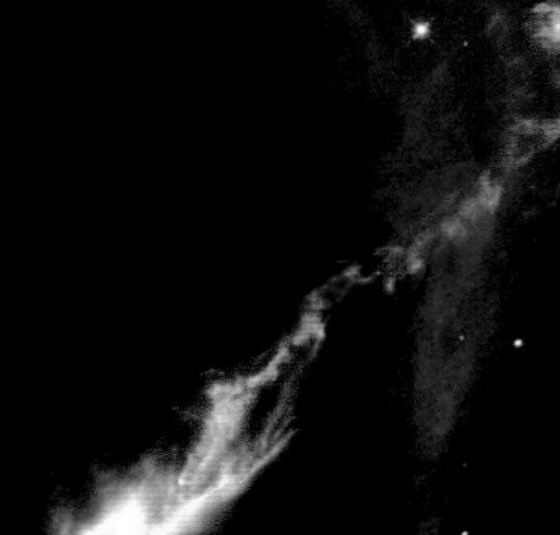

3

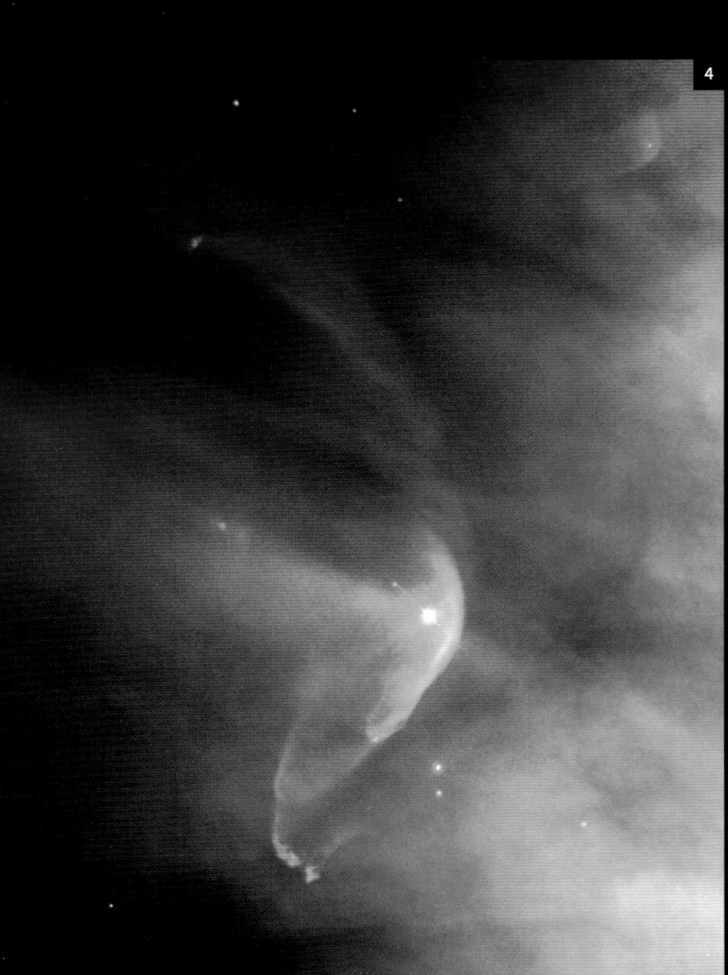

4

5

IC405 **EMISSION NEBULA**

The Flaming Star

AE Aurigae is another stellar youngster but much more massive than the Sun so it is having a more profound impact on its surroundings. The incredible energy from this hot, massive star is energizing the surrounding gas, causing it to glow in this dramatic view captured by the Canada-France-Hawaii Telescope. About 2.7 million years ago, something happened in the Orion Nebula and expelled this star. It now travels through space at high speed.

DISTANCE 1.5 THOUSAND LY

SIZE 5 LIGHT YEARS

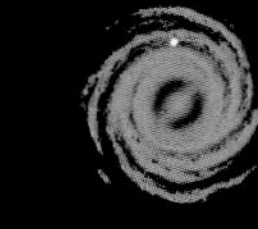

NGC 6357 **EMISSION NEBULA**

The War and Peace Nebula

The bright stars at the top of this image are newly minted celestial objects. The brightest of them, known as Pismis 24-1, had previously puzzled astronomers because it appeared to be at least 200 times the mass of our own Sun. This is far above the mass at which a star's radiation is supposed to tear it apart. The mystery was solved in 2006 when sharper images revealed that Pismis 24-1 is a binary star. Both stars are therefore around 100 solar masses – right at the upper limit of a star's theoretical mass. Such stars are incredibly rare for two reasons. Firstly not many of them form and, secondly, when they do they live for just a few million years. To catch two of them together is astonishing.

DISTANCE 8 THOUSAND LY

SIZE 4 LIGHT YEARS

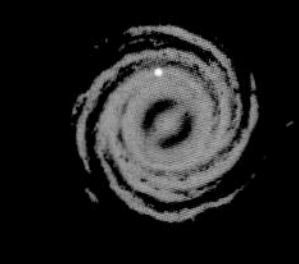

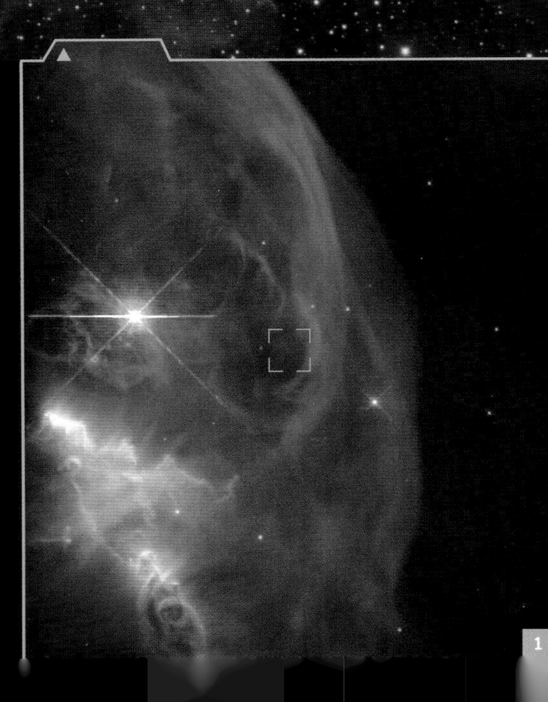

NGC 7635 **EMISSION NEBULA**

The Bubble Nebula

The particles given off by this star have blown a bubble in its surroundings. This bubble is then forced to glow by the bombardment of ultraviolet light given off by the same star. The bubble is lopsided because it is ploughing its way through material of different densities around the central star.

The star itself is known as BD+602522 and contains around 20 times the mass of the Sun.

DISTANCE 11.3 THOUSAND LY

SIZE 6 LIGHT YEARS

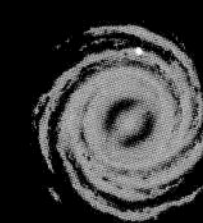

1

Open clusters

It is unusual for stars to be born alone. They are almost always associated with a number of siblings. Together they make their celestial debut in a cluster of stars. Called an open cluster, each family member grows steadily apart until, billions of years after its formation, the individual members are scattered across the Galaxy.

[1] NGC 2264
OPEN CLUSTER AND EMISSION NEBULA
Christmas Tree Cluster

In contrast to the Seven Sisters, this cluster of stars is embedded within the remains of its birth cloud. The nebula stretches over such a large area that astronomers refer to its different regions by different names. At the bottom of the cloud is the dark Cone Nebula; whilst at the upper left is the Fox Fur Nebula.

The gentle curves in orange and blue near the centre of the image are Herbig-Haro objects, a sure sign that a new generation of stellar life is gestating within the nebula.

[2] M45 STAR CLUSTER
The Seven Sisters

Although known as the Seven Sisters, because of the brightest members visible from Earth with the unaided eye, about 1000 stars inhabit this star cluster. As tempting as it might seem, the clouds surrounding them are not the remains of their birth swaddling. Instead, studies of the Seven Sisters' motion expose the clouds as being unrelated; the star cluster just happens to be passing through them.

The clouds are truly revealed at infrared wavelengths [3]. The densest portions appear yellow and red, whilst the more diffuse outskirts show up as green.

The bright light of the Pleiades dramatically illuminates a ghostly scene of gaseous tendrils, including this eerie remnant [4].

DISTANCE
440
LIGHT YEARS

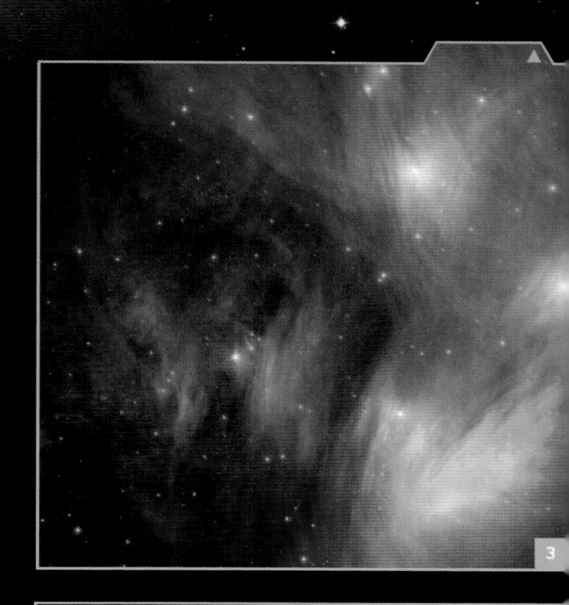
3

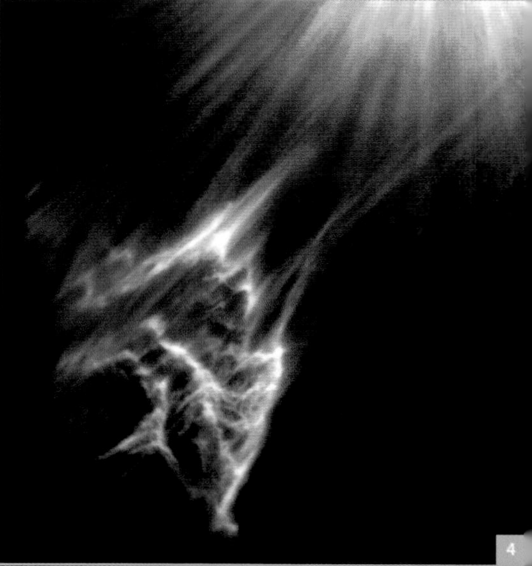
4

Globular clusters

sually found far from the central disc of tars, globular clusters orbit the nucleus f our Galaxy at highly inclined angles. stronomers have discovered around 200 nd found that they contain almost exclusively ncient stars. Deep space observations have ow found globular clusters around many ther galaxies as well, indicating that they re probably a standard feature.

1] M4 GLOBULAR CLUSTER

14 is one of the closest globular clusters o the Sun. Stellar corpses, known as white warfs, have been observed in this cluster nd reveal it to be around 13 billion years old. t that age it must have been one of the first ollections of stars to form in the Universe.

ISTANCE .5 HOUSAND LY

SIZE 75 LIGHT YEARS

2] M80 GLOBULAR CLUSTER

180 is one of the densest globular clusters, queezing several hundreds of thousands of tars into its confines. Some of these stars ave collided to form what astronomers call lue straggler stars. The act of collision gives he conjoined stars a new, if brief, lease of fe. The red stars in this image are about the ame mass as the Sun but more than twice s age. As such, they have swollen up into red iant stars and are approaching the ends of heir lives.

ISTANCE 28 HOUSAND LY

SIZE 90 LIGHT YEARS

1

2

NGC 5139 GLOBULAR CLUSTER

Omega Centauri

The biggest of all the globular clusters to orbit the Milky Way, Omega Centauri is a giant. It contains around 10 million stars, of which 2 million are shown here, packed into the cluster's central regions. It is so big that some astronomers have even suggested it be reclassified as a dwarf elliptical galaxy. At the centre of this cluster lies an intermediate-size black hole of around 40,000 solar masses. This estimate is based on the higher than expected velocities of several stars observed near the centre of the cluster. Only the extra gravitational boost that a black hole can bring seems sufficient to accelerate the stars.

DISTANCE
18.3
THOUSAND LY

SIZE
190
LIGHT YEARS

Stellar mergers

In the rarefied reaches of deep space it is rare indeed for two stars to collide. It can happen however, especially if the stars are linked by gravity in the first place. When stars do collide, the apocalyptic event does not go unnoticed.

[1] V838 MONOCEROTIS STAR

Before January 2002, this celestial bloom [main image] was an unknown star. It brightened precipitously at this time and then began to fade. Then it brightened again and a third time. Astronomers have now abandoned their first inclination that it was an exploding star and decided that it was probably an incredibly rare event: two stars colliding. The first two outbursts were the stars smashing through each other's outer layers. The third flare-up happened when they actually merged.

This sequence [2] covers the evolution of the system over a two-year period following the merger. The expanding nature of the object is actually an illusion created as light from the collision speeds off into space and is then reflected into our line of sight by successively further and further dust clouds. Such phenomena are called light echoes.

DISTANCE 20 THOUSAND LY

SIZE 6 LIGHT YEARS

[3] NGC 6397 GLOBULAR CLUSTER

Colliding stars are thought to be responsible for some mysterious stellar objects found in globular clusters. They are known as blue stragglers and stand out from the majority of other globular cluster stars because they are too blue and too massive. Astronomers believe that they are the result of two stars merging.

Although the chances of two stars merging in the Milky Way is small, in the dense conditions of a globular cluster, the chances probably go up to one merger every few million years. So, in the cluster's 10 billion year lifetime, it will have happened thousands of times at least, hence the smattering of blue stragglers that astronomers now see.

DISTANCE 8.2 THOUSAND LY

SIZE 54 LIGHT YEARS

3

2

M35 OPEN CLUSTER

Several hundred new stars clump together to form this open cluster. It extends across an area of sky equivalent to that covered by a full Moon. Few of these stars are bound to each other by gravity and they are already beginning to drift apart. The cluster is about 100 million years in age.

DISTANCE 2.8 THOUSAND LY

SIZE 24 LIGHT YEARS

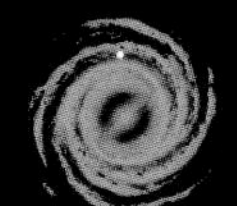

[1] NGC 2158 OPEN CLUSTER

Near to each other in the sky, although widely separated in space, is this older, more compact cluster of stars. Once mistaken for a globular cluster, NGC 2158 is an open cluster. Ten times older that M35, making it about 1 billion years old, this cluster is dominated by the light of longer-lived yellow stars.

DISTANCE 16 THOUSAND LY

SIZE 23 LIGHT YEARS

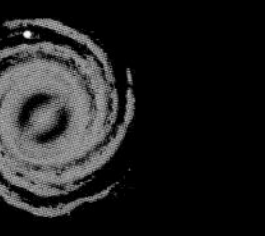

Stellar classification

Stars come in a bewildering array of sizes, colours, masses and temperatures. Most of these properties are then liable to vary throughout a star's lifetime as its internal conditions change. Since the 19th century, astronomers have become increasingly concerned with understanding how stars are different from each other and why they change. The first step in this journey is to classify the stars according to their observed properties.

The Hertzsprung-Russell diagram

Every star in existence can be plotted on the Hertzsprung-Russell diagram. Created in 1910 by Danish astronomer Ejnar Hertzsprung, the diagram was independently proposed by American astrophysicist Henry Norris Russell. It plots a star's surface temperature against its luminosity and, because these two quantities are related to each other by the mass of the star, it allows every star to be compared to every other star.

Most stars fall in a curving band that runs across the diagram. This is known as the main sequence and is the home of mature stars. Originally astronomers wondered whether it marked an evolutionary sequence as well, with stars beginning hot and bright at the top left and sliding down to the lower right as they age, becoming redder and cooler. Now they know that the main sequence position of a star is determined uniquely by its mass. The short-lived, high-mass stars sit at the top left whereas the long-lived, low mass stars occupy the bottom right.

Once a star forms, it can be plotted on the main sequence and pretty much stays at that location on the diagram for almost all of its life. Only at the end of the star's existence does it change its appearance and move upwards to the top right of the diagram, the red giant area. After the death of the star, the stellar corpse changes its luminosity and surface temperature rapidly, so plummets to the bottom of the diagram, ending up in the white dwarf zone.

Stars in globular clusters can be plotted on their own Hertzsprung-Russell diagram to indicate the cluster's age. The top left of the main sequence will be missing because the high-mass stars have died. With no further star formation to replenish this lost population, the main sequence becomes truncated. Where it runs out tells astronomers the age of the globular cluster.

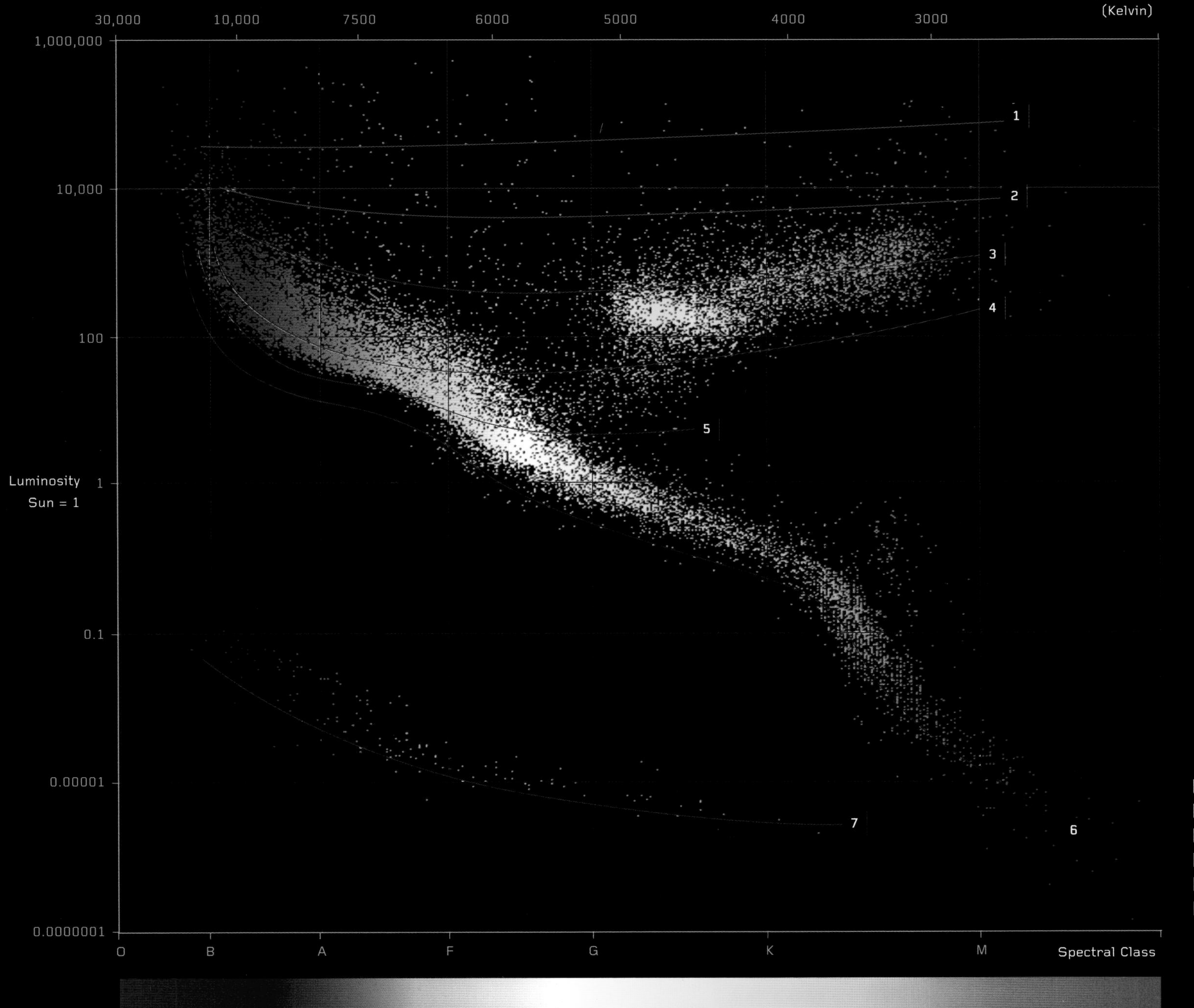

[1-2] Supergiants
[3] Bright giants
[4] Giants
[5] Subgiants
[6] Main sequence
[7] White dwarfs

OLD AGE AND DEATH_

As with so many other things during a star's life, its demise depends largely on how much mass it contains. In the broadest sense, stars can be thought of as falling into two simple categories: high-mass stars and low-mass stars.

Stars are considered to be low-mass if they contain anything less than about eight times the mass of the Sun. Such stars are the longest lived of them all with lifetimes that stretch from between 80 million years for the more massive, to 10 billion years for stars like the Sun, and hundreds of billions – maybe even trillions – of years for the lowest mass red dwarf stars.

Most low-mass stars develop a layered structure with hardly any mixing taking place between the layers. Energy is generated only in the core of the star by the process of nuclear fusion. For the vast majority of a star's life, this fusion process converts hydrogen to helium, releasing energy. For example, a star like the Sun transforms 4 million tonnes of matter into energy every second. As more and more of the hydrogen is used, so the raw fuel needed for the fusion process dwindles.

Although the star's surrounding layers contain more than half the mass of the star, this matter cannot penetrate the core region and replenish the waning stocks. So fusion begins to falter. Without the support of the out-rushing energy, the star begins to contract. This drives up the temperature of the star's interior and ignites hydrogen fusion in a shell around the now largely inert core.

The new outpouring of energy lifts the outer layers of the star, rarefying them to a density much less than that of water. It puffs them outwards, where they begin to cool and the star settles into a new phase of equilibrium. This is known as the red giant stage because the star has swollen from a diameter of approximately a million kilometres to reach hundreds of millions of kilometres. When this eventually happens to the Sun, it could well engulf the three inner rocky planets of the inner solar system and that includes Earth.

Inside the star, changes continue to occur. The core shrinks and as it does, it heats up. If its temperature reaches 100 million Kelvin, it can begin to fuse helium into carbon, or even oxygen if the temperature is high enough. This phase will typically extend the star's lifetime by about 250 million years. All too soon, however, the helium runs out and the star begins to contract again.

Shells of hydrogen continue to burn around the now inert core, not only inflating the star's outer layers, but also blowing them off into space to create a nebula of glowing gases. When the 18th century astronomer William Herschel began seeing these nebulae as pale blobs in his large telescopes, he remarked – not wholly modestly – that they reminded him of the appearance of the planet Uranus, which he had recently discovered. He therefore suggested the name planetary nebulae and, although inaccurate, it has stuck.

At the heart of a planetary nebula lies the dying core of the star. As the surrounding layers lift off into space, it is revealed as a scalding sphere of compressed gas about the size of the Earth and burning at as much as 500,000 Kelvin. Astronomers call these objects white dwarfs. They quickly drop in temperature to around 40,000 Kelvin. An isolated white dwarf does very little except radiate its remaining heat into space over the course of billions of years.

If it is in orbit around another star, however, it can temporarily burst back into life. It does this by robbing gas from its companion's outer layers. The stolen gas spirals onto the white dwarf and builds up. When it reaches a critical mass, a runaway fusion reaction bursts into life, temporarily resuscitating the star and

NGC 7293 PLANETARY NEBULA

The Helix Nebula

Once these bright shells were the outer layers of a star much like the Sun. Now, they have been blown off into space as the star splutters to the end of its energy-generating life.

DISTANCE
650
LIGHT YEARS

SIZE
5.75
LIGHT YEARS

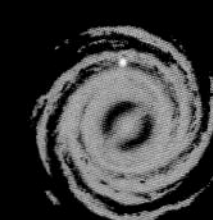

making it shine brightly, albeit briefly, across the Universe. Such a resurrection is called a nova.

High-mass stars suffer a much more spectacular fate. They follow the same pattern as a low-mass star up to the point of helium hierarchy of fusion that runs roughly: hydrogen to helium, helium to carbon and oxygen, carbon and oxygen to neon and magnesium, neon and magnesium to silicon and sulphur. Yet this process cannot go on forever. At the very centre of a mature red initiating a tremendous explosion that blows the surrounding layers into space. This event is known as a Type II supernova.

A more exotic possibility is that the nuclear fusion at the centre of the star is so intense that it zips past the 1.4 solar masses phase

1

2

Planetary Nebulae

Famously misnamed, nothing can take away
he beauty of planetary nebulae. They are
he final butterfly-like stage that heralds
he end of a star's energy-generating
fe. Lasting no more than a few tens of
housands of years, planetary nebulae help
eed space with heavier chemical elements
hat can be incorporated into the next

[1] MENZEL 3 **PLANETARY NEBULA**

The Ant Nebula

Maybe one of the most bizarre planetary nebulae, the Ant Nebula is composed of bubbles and streamers of gas.

DISTANCE 3 THOUSAND LY

SIZE 1.6 LIGHT YEARS

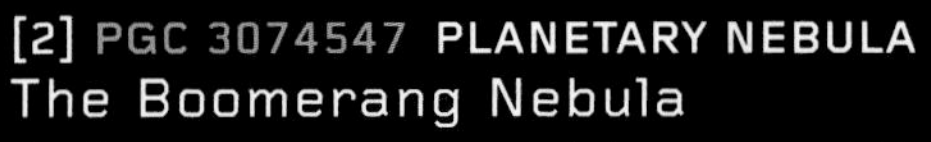

[2] PGC 3074547 **PLANETARY NEBULA**

The Boomerang Nebula

Perhaps more appropriately renamed the Bow-tie Nebula, this young planetary nebula that has yet to achieve its mature shape.

DISTANCE 5 THOUSAND LY

SIZE 2.1 LIGHT YEARS

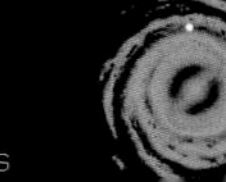

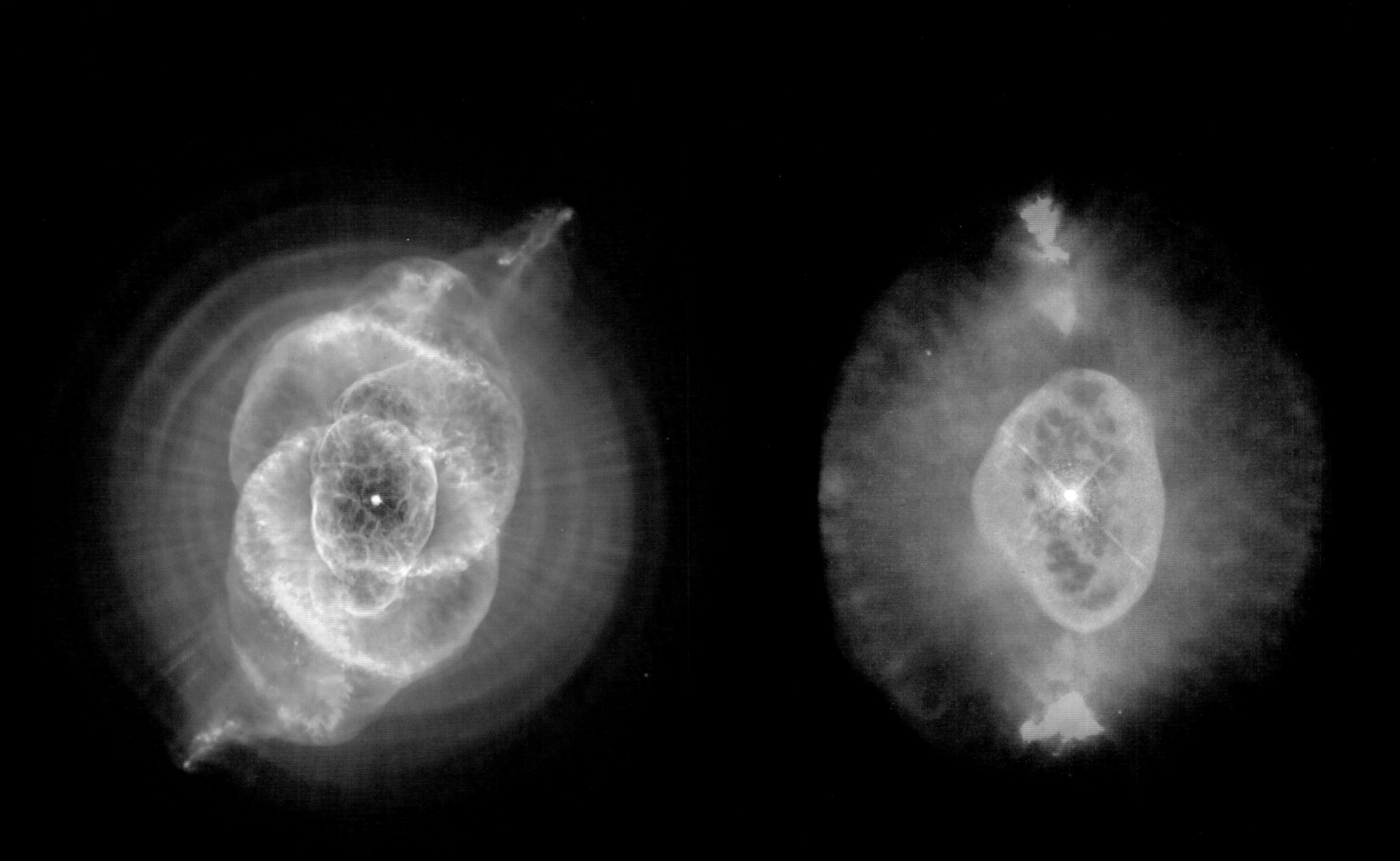

3

4

[3] NGC 6543 PLANETARY NEBULA
Cat's Eye Nebula

Astronomers still do not understand the way that the intricate swirls and concentric shells in this nebula were formed.

DISTANCE	SIZE
3	1.2
THOUSAND LY	LIGHT YEARS

[4] NGC 6826 PLANETARY NEBULA
The Blinking Nebula

This nebula is so faint in small telescopes that it appears to blink in and out of visibility. No one knows what has caused the red 'fliers' on either side of the nebula.

DISTANCE	SIZE
2.2	1.5
THOUSAND LY	LIGHT YEARS

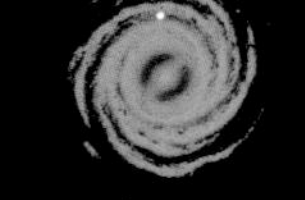

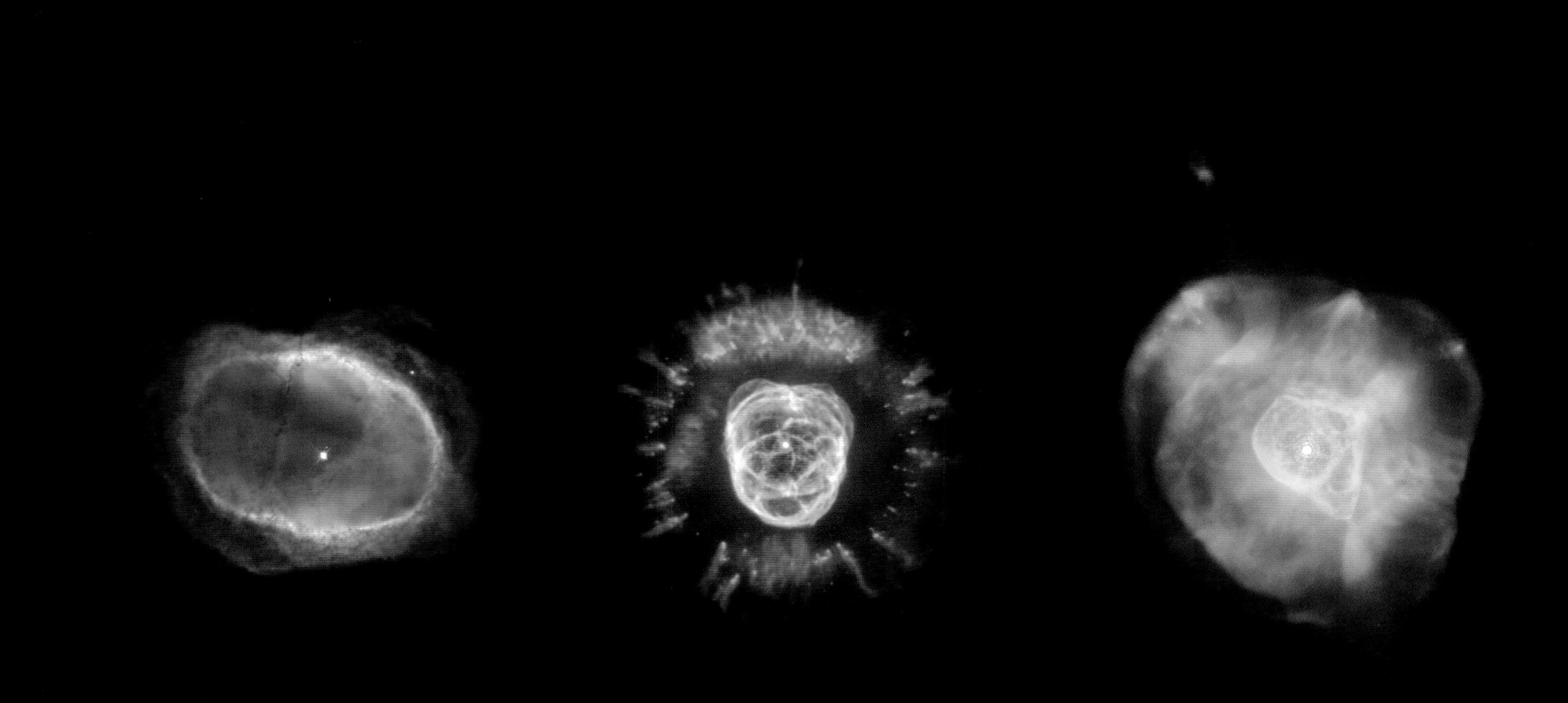

1

2

3

[1] NGC 3132 **PLANETARY NEBULA**
Southern Ring Nebula
Two stars lie at the centre of this planetary nebula; the fainter one is considered responsible for the nebula.

DISTANCE 2 THOUSAND LY | SIZE 0.5 LIGHT YEARS

[2] NGC 2392 **PLANETARY NEBULA**
The Eskimo Nebula
A ring of gaseous 'spokes' surrounds two elliptical bubbles of gas, one rising towards us, the other obscured behind, in this planetary nebula.

DISTANCE 5 THOUSAND LY | SIZE 2 LIGHT YEARS

[3] IC 4593 **PLANETARY NEBULA**
The complex history of this planetary nebula is in evidence; highlighted by the nested bubbles of gas that surround the central star.

DISTANCE 7 THOUSAND LY | SIZE 0.4 LIGHT YEARS

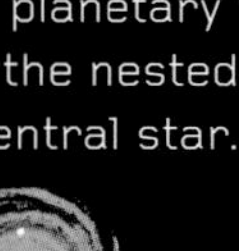

4

5

6

[4] NGC 6369 PLANETARY NEBULA
Little Ghost Nebula
This planetary nebula gets its name because, in smaller telescopes, the ring of gas resembles a ghost surrounding the faint inner star.

DISTANCE 3.5 THOUSAND LY
SIZE 0.9 LIGHT YEARS

[5] NGC 6751 PLANETARY NEBULA
Having formed several thousand years ago, this nebula continues to expand at 40 kilometres per second, even today.

DISTANCE 6.5 THOUSAND LY
SIZE 0.8 LIGHT YEARS

[6] IRAS 18059-3211
PROTO-PLANETARY NEBULA
Gomez's Hamburger
The star is just beginning the transition from red giant to planetary nebula. The dark band represents dust circling the star.

DISTANCE 6.5 THOUSAND LY
SIZE 0.25 LIGHT YEARS

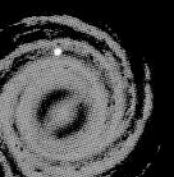

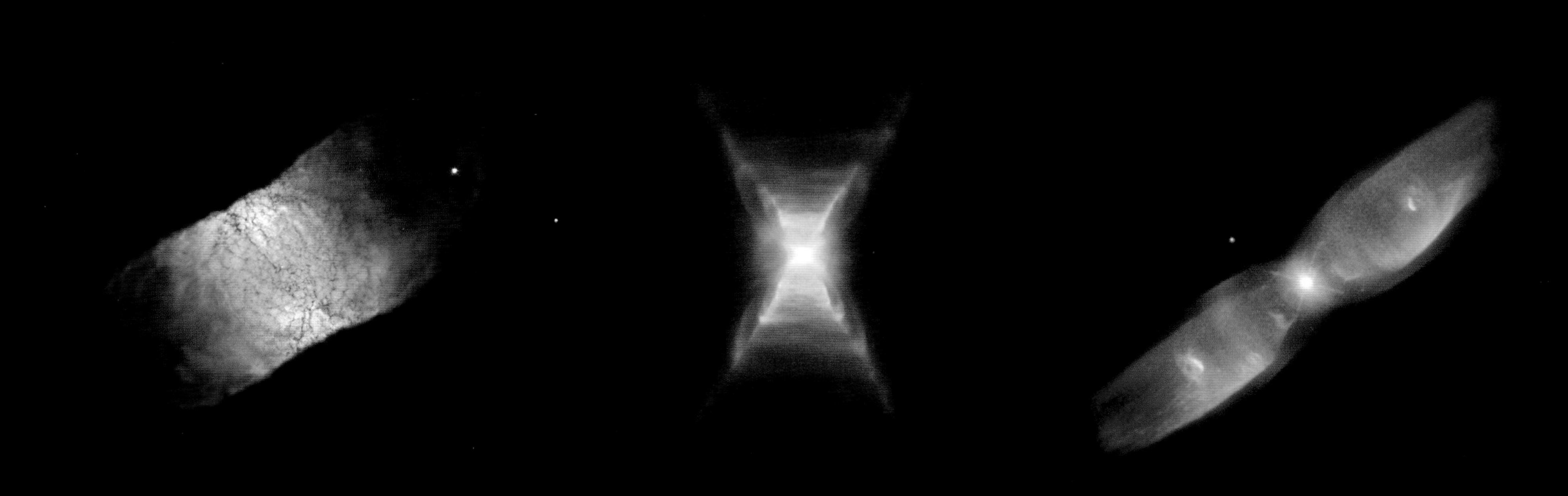

1

2

3

[1] IC 4406 **PLANETARY NEBULA**
The Retina Nebula
Vast clouds of dust, each one wider than our entire Solar System, criss-cross this planetary nebula.

DISTANCE
1.9
THOUSAND LY

SIZE
0.9
LIGHT YEARS

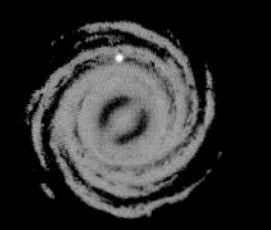

[2] HD 44179 **PROTO-PLANETARY NEBULA**
The Red Rectangle
The 'rungs' in the red rectangle may indicate that the star has undergone several episodes of heightened mass loss, separated by hundreds of years.

DISTANCE
2.3
THOUSAND LY

SIZE
0.4
LIGHT YEARS

[3] M2-9 **PLANETARY NEBULA**
Butterfly Nebula
It has taken this dying star just 1200 years to sculpt this fragile-looking structure from the gases of its outer layers.

DISTANCE
2.1
THOUSAND LY

SIZE
0.7
LIGHT YEARS

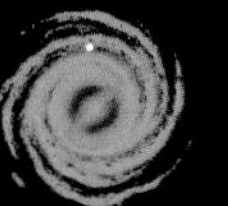

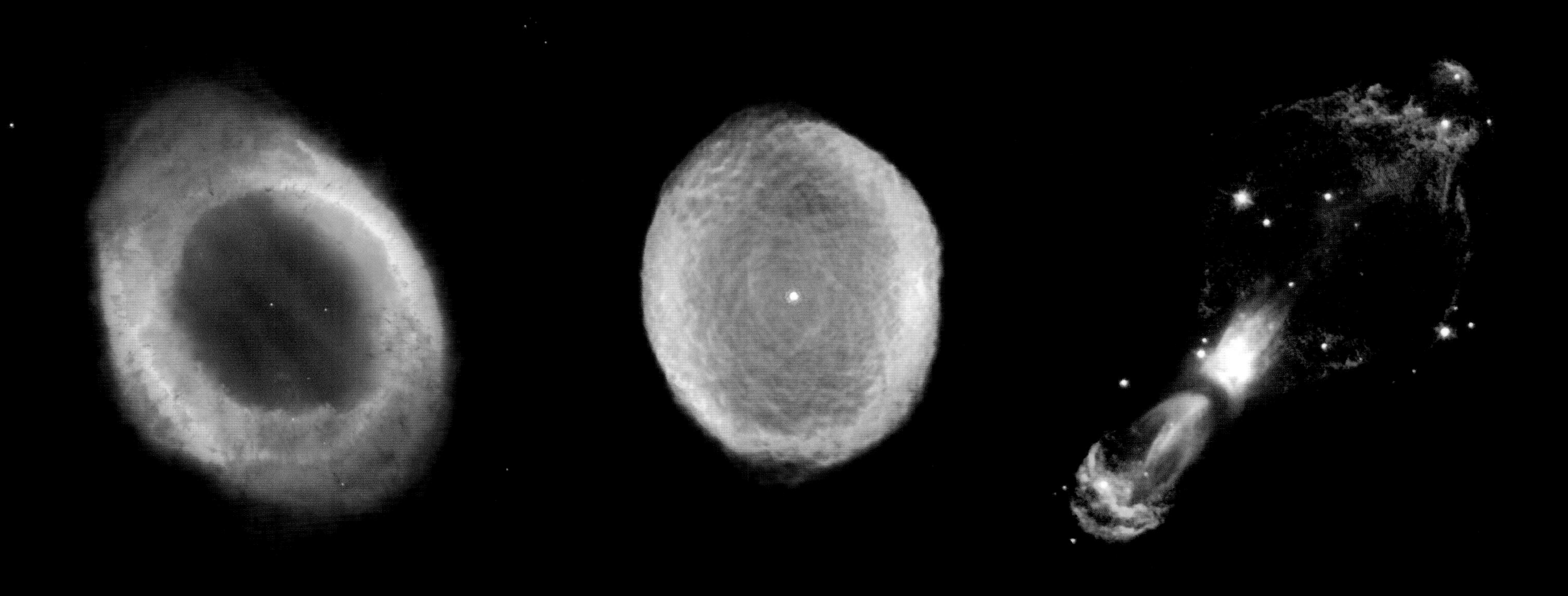

4

6

7

[4] M57 **PLANETARY NEBULA**

The Ring Nebula

First catalogued more than 200 years ago, the Ring Nebula was thought to be the classic planetary nebula. Now, however, astronomers know that ring-shapes are just one form a planetary nebula can take. At infrared wavelengths, [5] a beautiful web work of gaseous petals appears around the main Ring Nebula structure. This displays the fact that the central star began losing gas long before the formation of the prominent rings.

DISTANCE 2 THOUSAND LY

SIZE 1 LIGHT YEARS

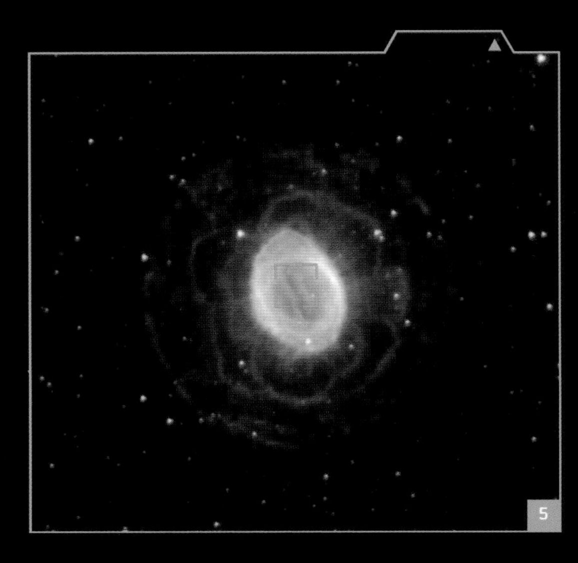

5

[6] IC 418 **PLANETARY NEBULA**

The Spirograph Nebula

The red glow in this delicately structured nebula comes from nitrogen gas, the green shows hydrogen and the blue traces oxygen.

DISTANCE 2 THOUSAND LY

SIZE 0.2 LIGHT YEARS

[7] OH231.8+4.2 **PLANETARY NEBULA**

Rotten Egg Nebula

Astronomers have detected large quantities of sulphur in this planetary nebula. The gas hydrogen sulphide is responsible for the smell of rotten eggs; hence the nebula's nickname.

DISTANCE 5 THOUSAND LY

SIZE 1.4 LIGHT YEARS

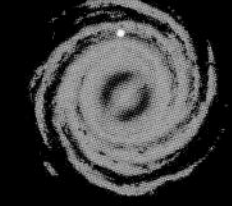

NGC 7293 **PLANETARY NEBULA**

The Helix Nebula

This is one of the finest examples of a planetary nebula available to astronomers. It is relatively close by and, whilst it looks like a bubble, analysis shows that it is more like a cylinder of glowing gas more than one trillion kilometres long. At its very centre lies the exposed nuclear core of the dead star. It glows incandescently as a white dwarf, its radiation exciting the surrounding gas to glow.

At infrared wavelengths [1], the shells are revealed to be knots of gas, which each have a long tail blown out behind them. These cometary knots are colour-coded with blue-green heads where they are being excited by shocks and ultraviolet radiation from the central star. The tails appear redder because the heads take the brunt of the onslaught.

Shifting to longer wavelengths of infrared can bring the dust content of the system into view [2]. Here, the outer gases are rendered in red and blue, while in the centre of the nebula, near the white dwarf star itself, there is a circle of dense red surrounded by a fainter red halo. The halo is made up of the very last traces of the star's gas being blown off into space whilst the red disc is dust surrounding the red dwarf. Evaporating comets that survived the death of the star, only to be vaporized by the intense ultraviolet radiation from the exposed nuclear heart, are thought to have deposited the dust.

DISTANCE 650 LIGHT YEARS

SIZE 5.75 LIGHT YEARS

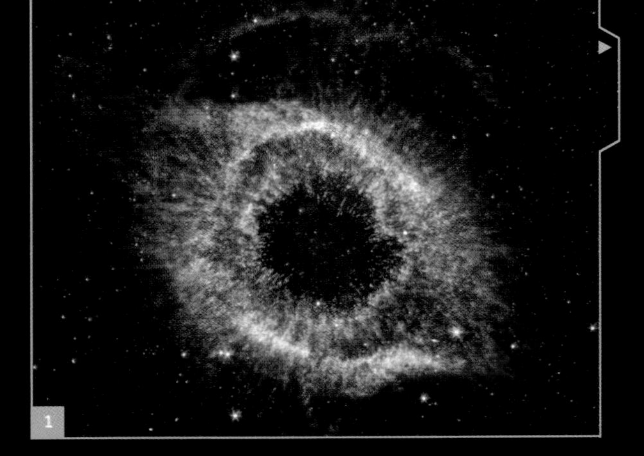

1

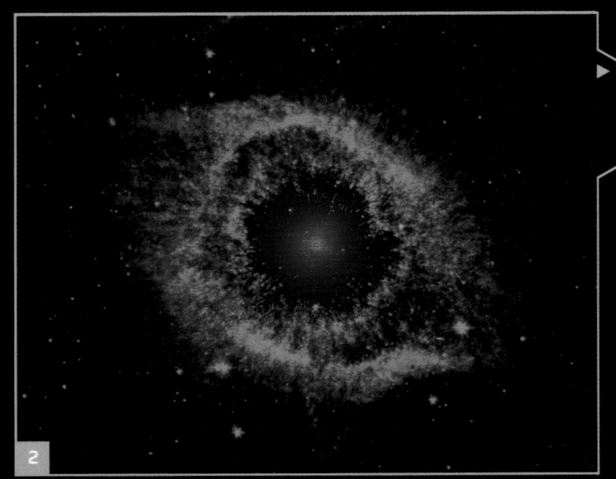

2

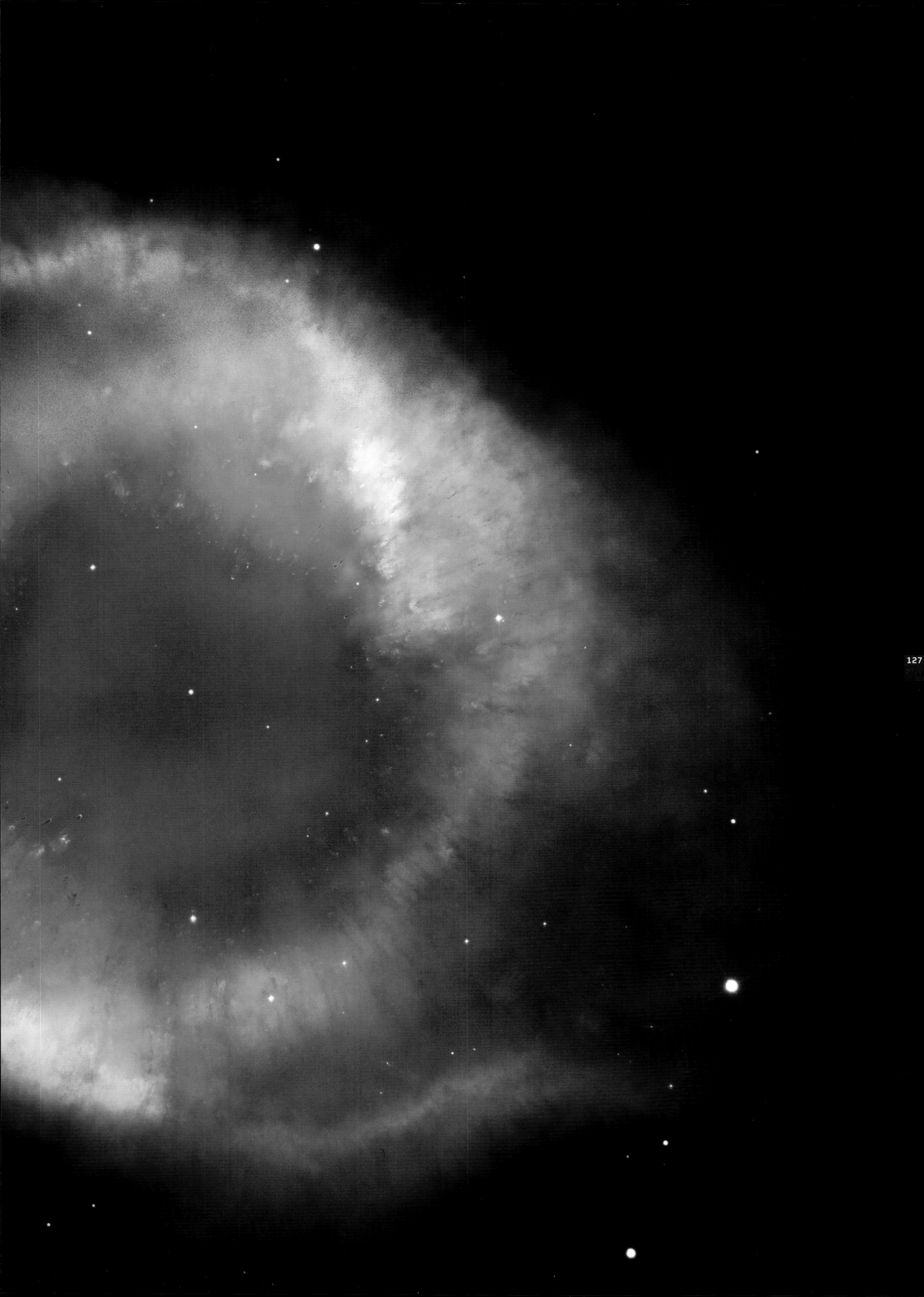

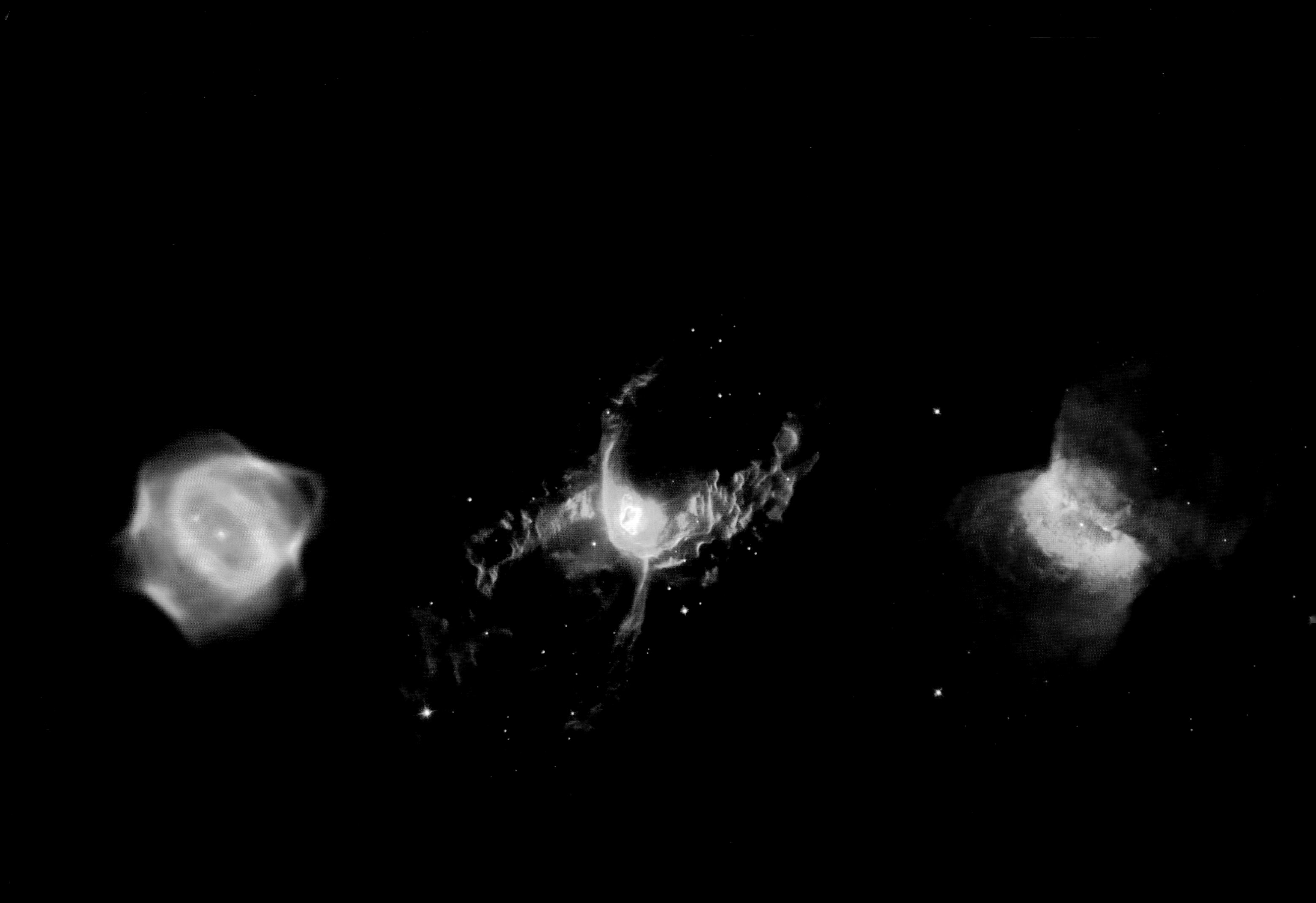

1

2

3

[1] HEN-1357 PLANETARY NEBULA
Stingray Nebula
Astronomers estimate this planetary nebula is just 20 years old, making it the youngest known. As a result it is still ten times smaller than most planetary nebulae.

DISTANCE 18 THOUSAND LY

SIZE 0.2 LIGHT YEARS

[2] NGC 6537 PLANETARY NEBULA
Red Spider Nebula
At the centre of this nebula is one of the hottest known white dwarfs. It is shining at 500,000 Kelvin, a temperature ten times higher than most 'hot' white dwarfs.

DISTANCE 3 THOUSAND LY

SIZE 1.3 LIGHT YEARS

[3] NGC 2346 PLANETARY NEBULA
A red giant star, engulfing a smaller companion star, has sculpted this planetary nebula.

DISTANCE 2 THOUSAND LY

SIZE 0.3 LIGHT YEARS

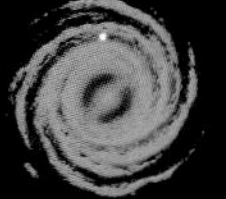

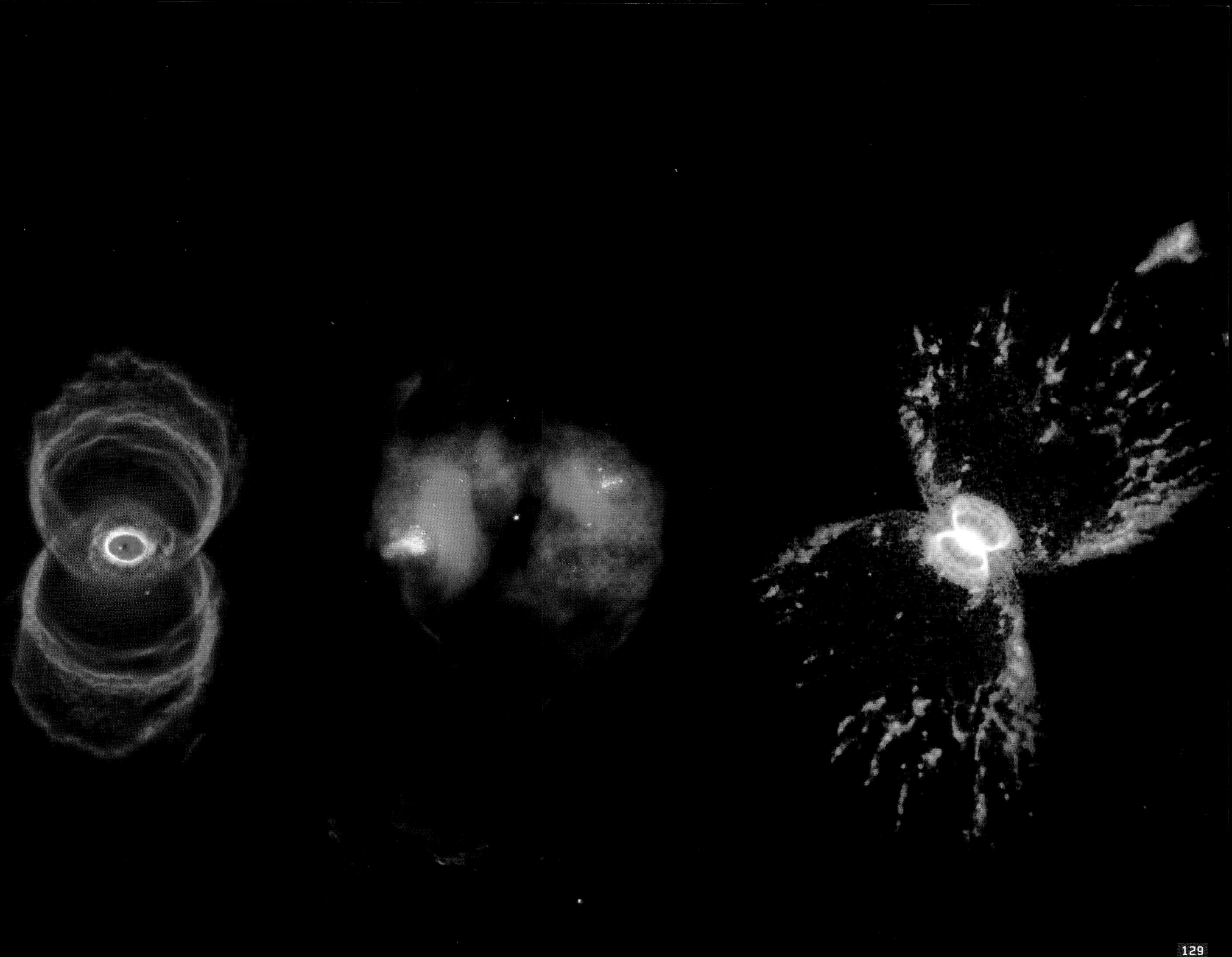

4

5

6

[4] MYCN18 PLANETARY NEBULA
Hourglass Nebula
What at first appear to be loops are actually hourglass shapes of gas, with the top lobe tilted towards us.

DISTANCE	SIZE
8	0.3
THOUSAND LY	LIGHT YEARS

[5] NGC 2371 PLANETARY NEBULA

Dense knots of gas show up in this planetary nebula as pink dots. The large 'bolts' of pink emission are the shock front caused by a jet emitted by the dying star.

DISTANCE	SIZE
4.3	1.6
THOUSAND LY	LIGHT YEARS

[6] HE2-104 PLANETARY NEBULA
Southern Crab Nebula
Two stars are interacting at the centre of this planetary nebula and creating these large outflows of material.

DISTANCE	SIZE
2	2
THOUSAND LY	LIGHT YEARS

White Dwarfs

At the heart of any planetary nebula lies a white dwarf star. This celestial corpse is a tightly packed sphere of spent star-fuel that was once the energy generating heart of the star. Once the planetary nebula has dissipated, the white dwarf is left alone to slowly cool as its remaining heat radiates into space. Such bare white dwarfs have typical temperatures of between 8000 and 40,000 Kelvin. They are notoriously difficult to spot because, despite the fact that they contain about the same mass as the Sun, they are only about the size of the Earth.

[1] NGC 2440 **PLANETARY NEBULA**

Energized by the central white dwarf star, glowing ridges of gas curl around this complex planetary nebula. At its centre, sits a seething white dwarf star. Newly exposed to the outside Universe, this white dwarf is losing energy rapidly. At the moment it burns five times hotter than most, at 200,000 Kelvin.

DISTANCE 4 THOUSAND LY — SIZE 1.3 LIGHT YEARS

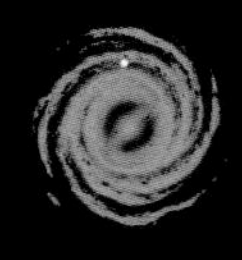

[2, 3] ALPHA CANIS MAJORIS B

WHITE DWARF STAR

Sirius B

The tiny dot of light to the lower left of the main star [2] is the white dwarf star, Sirius B. It orbits the central star, Sirius A, once every 50.1 years and is now around 120 million years old. The gravity at the surface of Sirius B is a staggering 400,000 times that of Earth.

Its surface temperature of 25,000 Kelvin is hot for a star but in stellar terms its surface area is small, at around the same as Earth. So it is 10,000 times dimmer than its companion star, Sirius A, at visible wavelengths. Switch to X-rays, [3] however, and the situation is reversed. Now Sirius B is the brighter of the two. Sirius A's surface temperature of 10,000 Kelvin, is insufficient to produce many X-rays at all.

DISTANCE 8.6 LIGHT YEARS — MASS 0.98 SUNS — LUMINOSITY 0.03 SUNS

[4, 5] NOVA CYGNI 1992 **NOVA**

White dwarfs in binary star systems can become catalysts of tremendous explosions called novae. This pair of images shows the evolution of a ring of debris thrown out by a nova in the constellation Cygnus. Image [4] was taken in 1993, 15 months after the build up and detonation of material on the surface of the white dwarf. Seven months later, image [5] shows that the ejecta had clearly expanded even further, propelled onwards by the force of the original blast. Because novae explosions do not destroy the underlying white dwarf, more gas can fall onto its surface and build up again, resulting in another nova explosion at a later date.

DISTANCE 10.5 LIGHT YEARS — MASS 1 SUNS — LUMINOSITY 100 SUNS

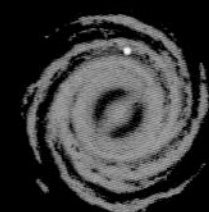

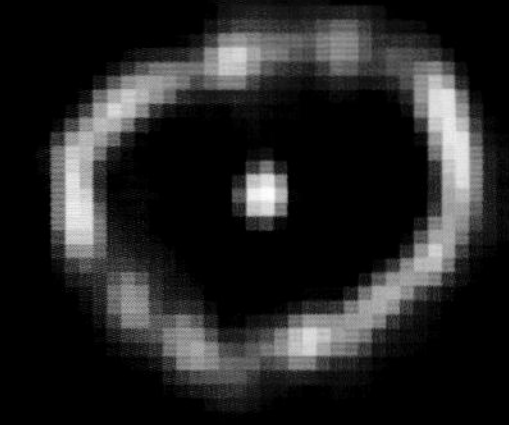

5

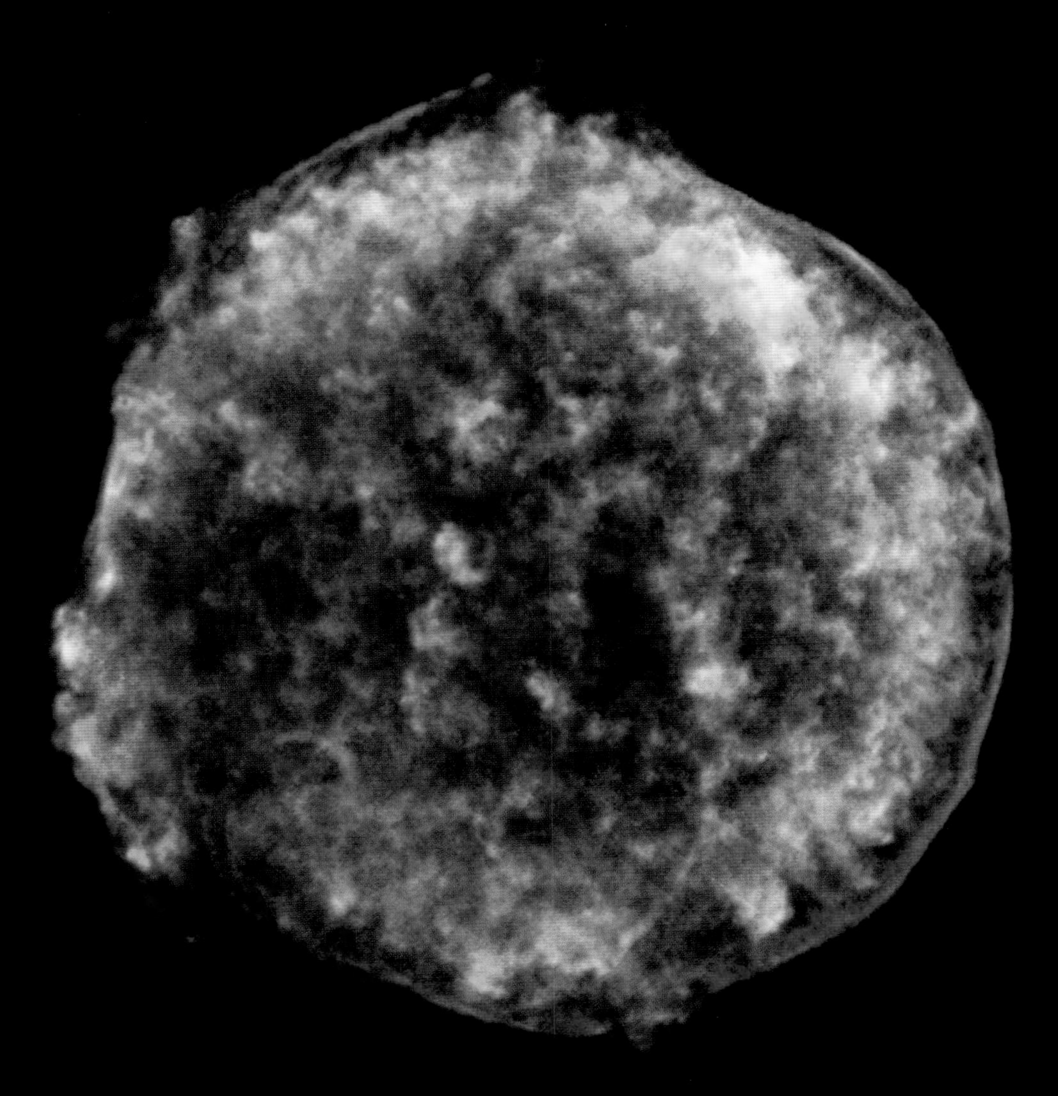

6

[6] 3C 10 **SUPERNOVA REMNANT**

Tycho's supernova remnant

In 1572, the Dutch astronomer Tycho Brahe observed a supernova burst in the night skies. Now, thanks to his descriptions of its location, modern astronomers have found what they think are the remains. This X-ray picture shows that 400 years have done little to still its violence. This expanding bubble of multimillion-degree gas was once a white dwarf star that pulled too much gas from a companion star and blew itself to pieces as a result.

DISTANCE 7.5 THOUSAND LY

SIZE 24 LIGHT YEARS

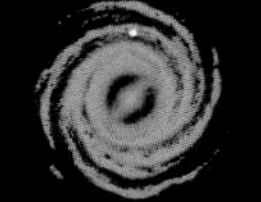

[7] SN1994D **SUPERNOVA TYPE IA**

Supernova 1994D occurred in the very outer edges of the lenticular galaxy NGC 4526. It is thought the total explosion of a white dwarf star was the cause. Circling another, more normal star, the white dwarf wrapped itself in layers of hydrogen, just as a nova does. However, it went too far and instead of the detonation of just its surface layers, it blew up catastrophically when the pressure inside mounted so much that it ignited a runaway nuclear fusion reaction.

DISTANCE 55 MILLION LY

MASS 1.38 SUNS

LUMINOSITY 5 BILLION SUNS

7

1 2

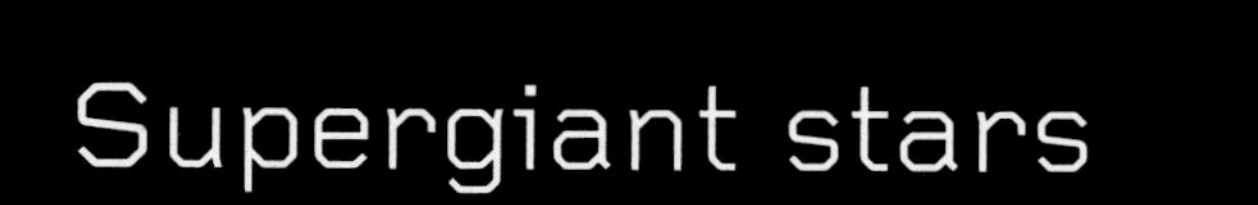

Supergiant stars

The largest stars announce their intention to explode by emitting tremendous gusts of luminous gas. Each celestial hiccup usually contains more mass than our entire planet – just a drop in the ocean for the central star.

[1] M1-67 **EMISSION NEBULA**

Wolf-Rayet stars each contain around 20 solar masses, so they are some of the larger stars known. They possess a surface temperature of between 25,000 and 50,000 Kelvin, which makes them extraordinarily powerful emitters of ultraviolet radiation. This one, WR 124, illuminates the outer layers it has thrown off over the last 10,000 years, as a prelude to exploding completely.

[2] G0.15-0.05 **NEBULA**

The Pistol Nebula

This may be the most luminous star known. At a searing 10 million times the luminosity of the Sun, the Pistol Star is generating so much energy that it can barely hold itself together. As a result it is suffering recurrent outbursts that strip successive layers off the star, flinging them into space. The latest eruption has shed nearly ten times the amount of matter in our Sun. There's plenty more though; the Pistol Star still contains between 100 and 200 solar masses.

DISTANCE 25 THOUSAND LY SIZE 4 LIGHT YEARS

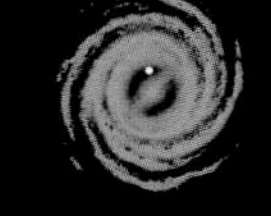

[3] HD 12545 **RED GIANT STAR**

XX Triangulum

The red giant star XX Triangulum is revealed to have one hemisphere cooler than the other. It is thought magnetic fields on the star are the cause. This giant cool patch has a surface area far larger than our entire Sun (to scale, on the right). Such a red giant star is getting ready to enter the final stages of its life.

DISTANCE
1.08
THOUSAND LY
DIAMETER
10
SOLAR RADII
LUMINOSITY
100
SUNS

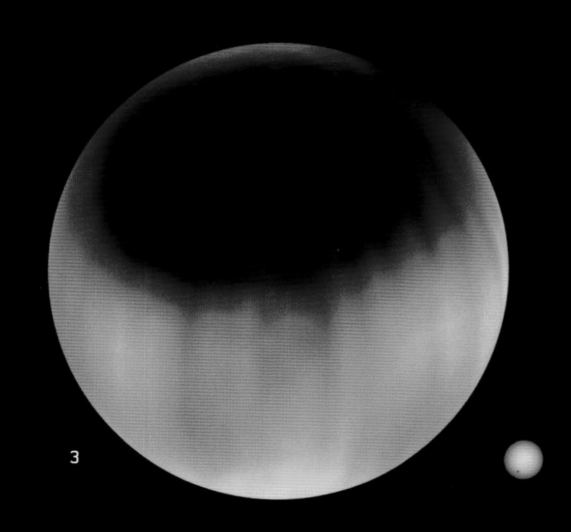

3

[4] NGC 3372 **EMISSION NEBULA**

Carina Nebula

These veils of colourful gas are home to one of the most massive stars in the Galaxy. The radiation from this star, Eta Carinae, lights up the entire nebula. An eruption on the star around 160 years ago created the central Homunculus Nebula.

[5] NEBULA

Homunculus Nebula

At the centre of the Homunculus Nebula is the blue hypergiant star Eta Carinae. Similar in size to the Pistol Star, Eta Carinae is the next star in our Galaxy that most astronomers consider likely to explode as a supernova. The dumbbell shape centred on the star, known as the Homunculus Nebula, is the result of a huge eruption earlier in the star's life.

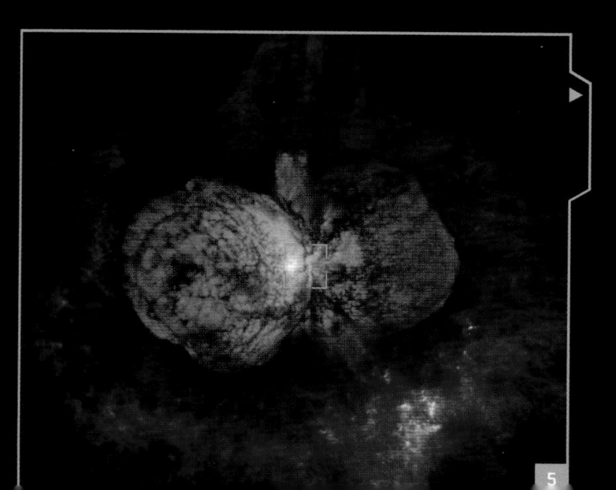

5

4
5

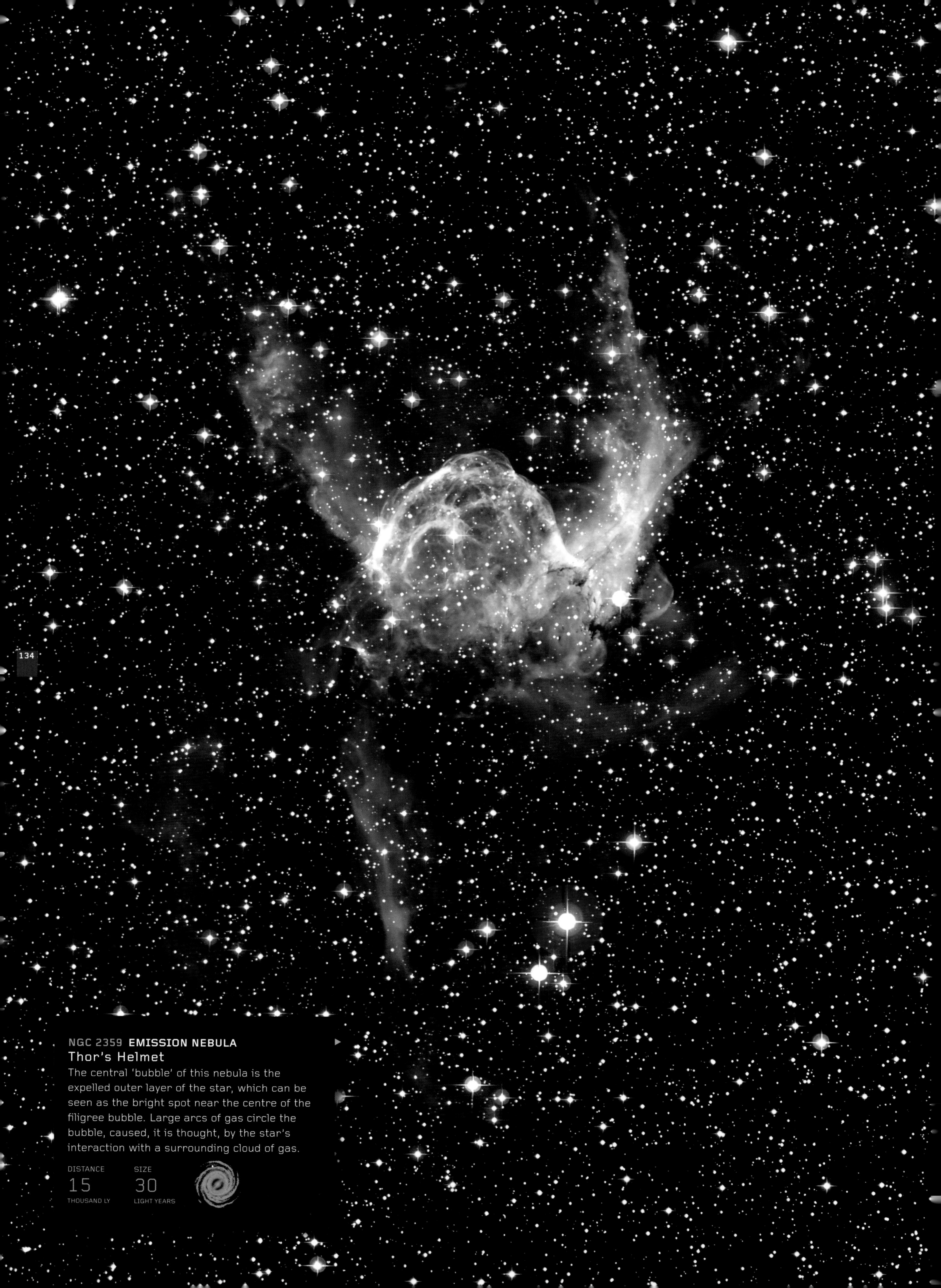

NGC 2359 **EMISSION NEBULA**

Thor's Helmet

The central 'bubble' of this nebula is the expelled outer layer of the star, which can be seen as the bright spot near the centre of the filigree bubble. Large arcs of gas circle the bubble, caused, it is thought, by the star's interaction with a surrounding cloud of gas.

DISTANCE
15
THOUSAND LY

SIZE
30
LIGHT YEARS

NGC 6888 **EMISSION NEBULA**

Crescent Nebula

The Crescent Nebula formed around 400,000 years ago, when a red supergiant star began to cast off its outer layers, exposing the hot inner regions of the star. Now classified as a Wolf-Rayet star, its welter of ultraviolet radiation bombards the discarded outer layers, causing them to glow.

DISTANCE
5
THOUSAND LY

SIZE
25
LIGHT YEARS

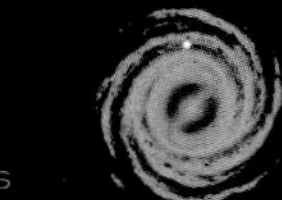

Supernovae

Eventually a star can take no more. Energy generation falters in its core and initiates a sequence of events that results in the catastrophic explosion of the star. The star's life ends with a final flash of glory, never more to grace the night.

[1] NGC 1559 BARRED SPIRAL GALAXY
Supernova SN 2005df is the bright star that appears to hang just to the left of galaxy NGC 1559 [2]. This galaxy is something of a supernova factory. There have been two previous supernovae recorded in the last few decades: SN 1984J in 1984 and SN 1986L in 1986. This is remarkable because the Milky Way, seven times bigger than NGC 1559, is only expected to produce a supernova every 50 years and this small galaxy has had three in half the time.

DISTANCE	SIZE
50 MILLION LY	14 THOUSAND LY

[3] NGC 2403 SPIRAL GALAXY
Supernova SN 2004dj [4], despite residing in another galaxy, is bright enough to be mistaken for a star belonging to the Milky Way – as the larger star to its left does. Here, it has been captured blazing with 200 million times the intensity of our Sun. The luminosity allows astronomers to estimate the mass of the original star to be around 15 times than of the Sun. It is one of the first deaths in a cluster of stars called Sandage 96, whose total mass is calculated to be 24,000 times that of the Sun.

DISTANCE	SIZE
11 MILLION LY	60 THOUSAND LY

[5-8] NGC 2770 SPIRAL GALAXY
Whilst observing the fading X-ray aftermath of SN2007uy [5, 6], astronomers serendipitously caught the first burst of a new supernova, SN2008D [7, 8]. This is the first time the flash of X-rays that presage the optical explosion have been detected in a supernova.

DISTANCE	SIZE
90 MILLION LY	95 THOUSAND LY

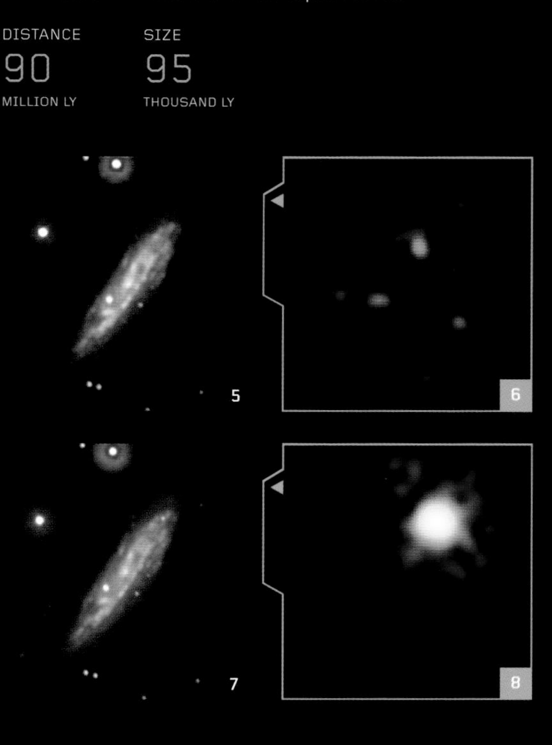

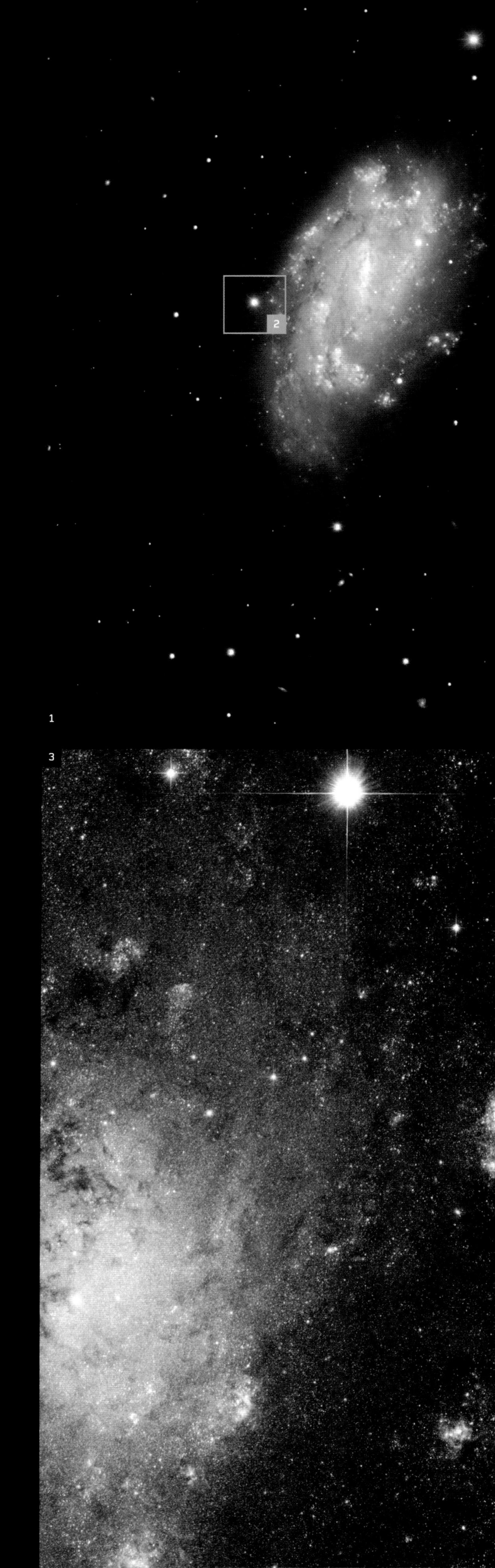

SUPERNOVA 1987A SUPERNOVA

The nearest supernova in modern times occurred on 23 February 1987. Labelled supernova 1987A, it exploded in the satellite galaxy, the Large Magellanic Cloud. Supernovae are classified according to the year they are discovered and then a letter denoting the order in which they occurred. So SN 1987A was the first supernova discovered in 1987.

This wide-scale image is 130 light years across and shows the supernova in its galactic context. There are a number of nearby stars, probably siblings of the supernova, shining brightly. Each of these blue stars is some six times heavier than the Sun but probably not quite massive enough to become a supernova.

Astronomers have now tracked the explosion for more than 20 years. The inset image [9] shows an inner ring of debris lighting up in 2004. The debris must have been expelled earlier in the star's life. Astronomers estimate that this took place 20,000 years ago, as the prelude to it going supernova. Now, the blast wave from the supernova proper, moving at millions of kilometres per hour, has smashed into the ring and set it glowing. The first bright blob appeared in 1996. Since then, the ring has been steadily brightening.

DISTANCE	SIZE
160 THOUSAND LY	9.5 LIGHT YEARS

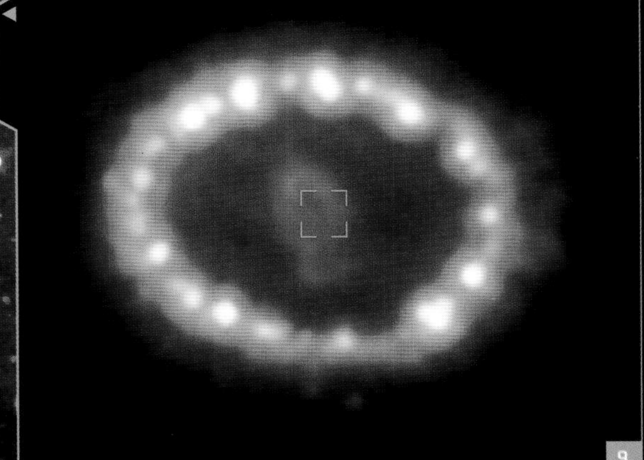

IC 443 SUPERNOVA REMNANT

A speeding neutron star is captured in this combined X-ray and optical image of the supernova remnant IC 443. A distinct bubble of gas from the supernova is expanding in one direction, whilst the neutron star itself appears to be speeding off in another [1]. A neutron star is often given a kick by its supernova event but, in this case, the stellar corpse is moving at right angles to the direction of the rest of the debris. Astronomers do not know why this is the case.

DISTANCE 5 THOUSAND LY

SIZE 72 LIGHT YEARS

Stellar corpses

After the supernova has faded, the big question is: what remains of the star? Will it be a tiny neutron star or the king of celestial weirdness, a black hole? Both objects are so small that astronomers face an incredible challenge just to locate them.

[2] RX J0822-4300 **NEUTRON STAR**
Surrounded by the shattered remains of the star it once lay at the heart of, this neutron star is the progeny of a supernova that exploded 3700 years ago [3]. It is emitting so many X-rays that, despite the fact it is just 10 kilometres in diameter, it can be seen by the Earth-orbiting X-ray telescope Chandra. Comparing X-ray images taken six years apart shows that the neutron star has moved noticeably in that time. The stellar corpse is rocketing through space at nearly 5 million kilometres per hour.

DISTANCE	DIAMETER
7 THOUSAND LY	10 KILOMETRES

[4] Black hole passing
The intense gravitational field of a black hole has the ability to focus light, rather like a lens. This is a simulation of what a black hole would do to our view of the Milky Way if it floated through our Solar System, close to Earth. Light passing close to the black hole would be focused around it, causing the circular distortion. The simulation relies on a black hole of 10 solar masses at a distance of just 600 kilometres from Earth. In reality, such a close encounter would be disastrous for the planet. At the very least, Earth would be pulled out of its orbit around the Sun. Most likely it would fall into the black hole and be devoured.

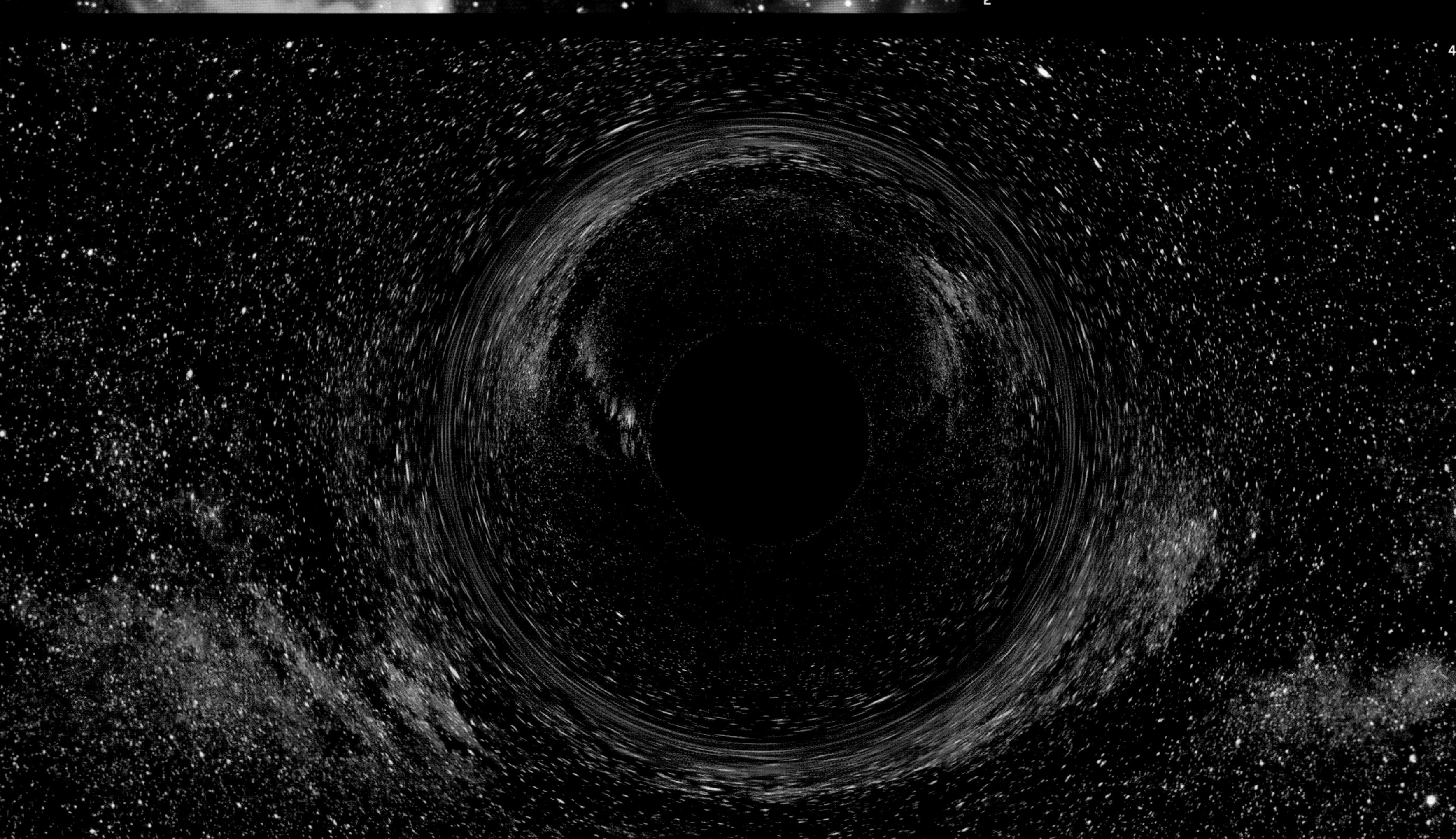

M1 **SUPERNOVA REMNANT**

The Crab Nebula

Up until a thousand years ago, the Crab Nebula appeared as a giant star. Then its nuclear fuel ran out and it gave up the fight against gravity. Japanese and Chinese astronomers, and probably Native Americans, noted the star's demise in 1054AD as it lit up the night skies in a supernova explosion.

In the main image, colours represent the dominant chemicals: red wisps in the outer part of the nebula are oxygen, and green filaments are sulphur. The eerie blue glow in the Crab Nebula's interior is emission powered by a rapidly spinning neutron star at the nebula's heart. Known as a pulsar, it spews high-speed particles into the surrounding gas, pumping up its energy and making it glow.

At X-rays the swirling gas of particles around the pulsar is revealed [1]. The pulsar is the bright white dot in the centre of the image. Putting all the data together allows the central whirling mass to be seen in context with the rest of the nebula [2]. X-rays are shown in light blue, optical wavelengths are in green and dark blue, whereas the infrared is displayed in red.

DISTANCE 6.5 THOUSAND LY

SIZE 7 LIGHT YEARS

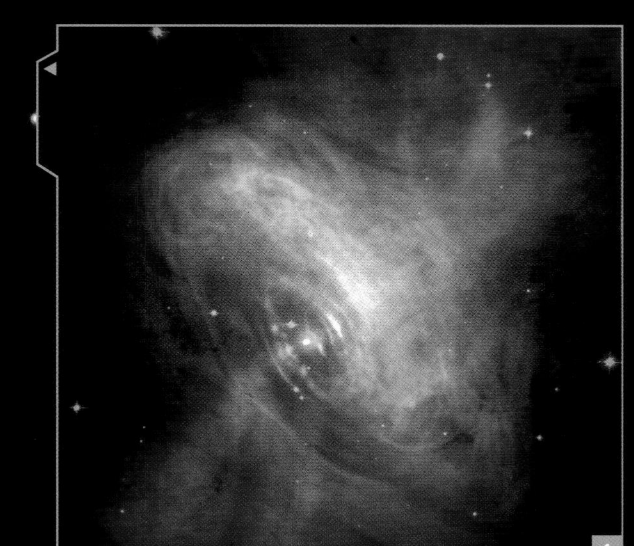

1

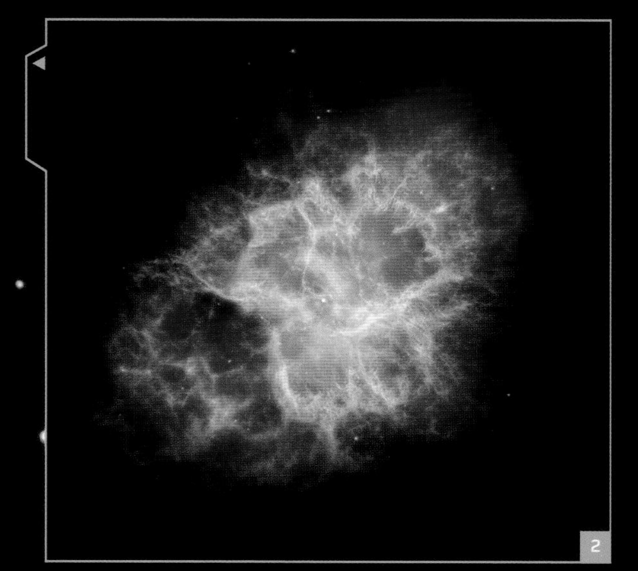

2

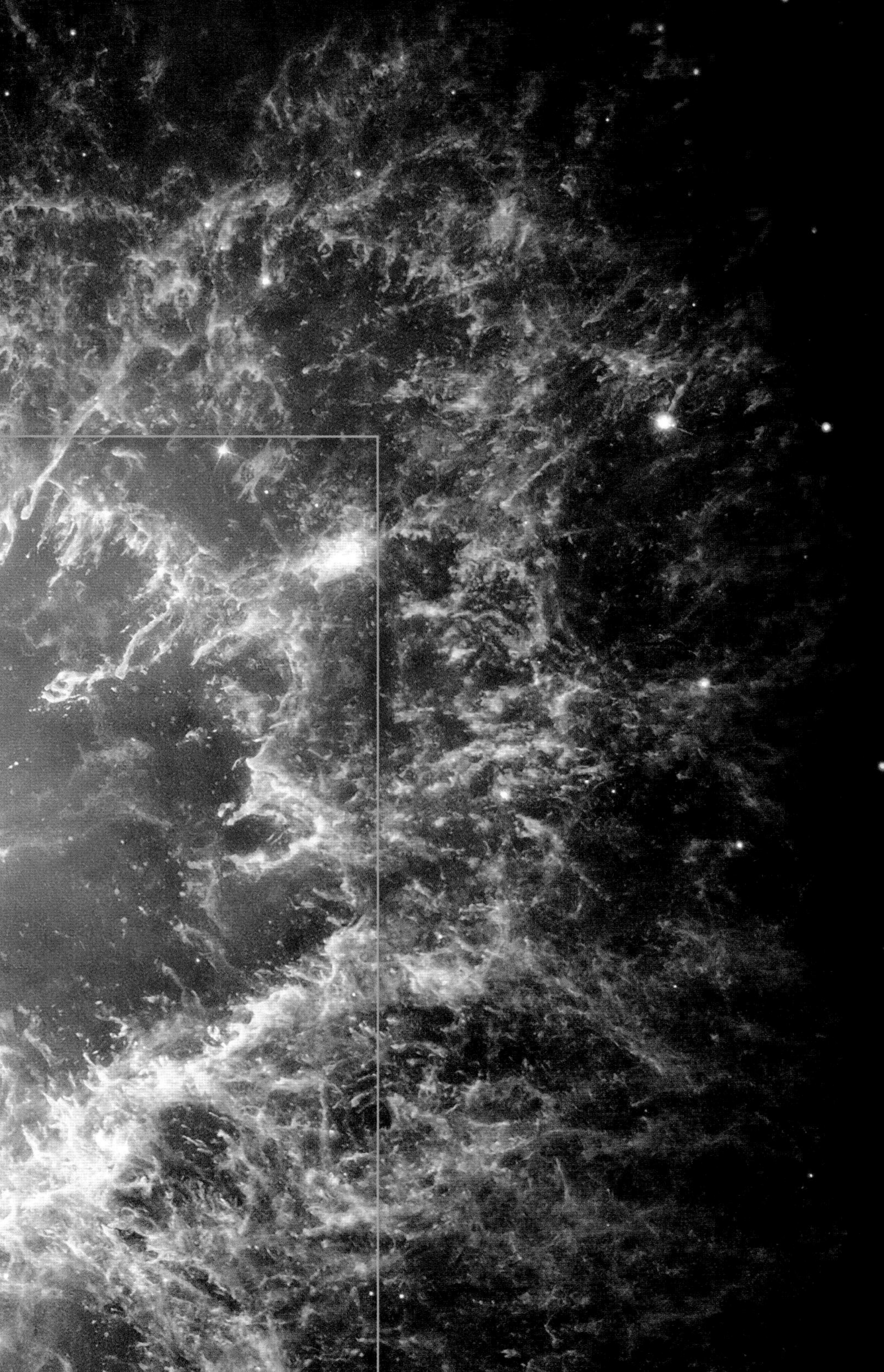

1

REBIRTH_

The death of a star is not the end. Instead, it begins to spread its influence over the surrounding space. In the case of a low mass star, this influence is gentle as the outer layers of the star drift through the planetary nebula stage and then merge with the other gases in space. For a high-mass star, the explosive supernova phase has a big impact, helping to trigger new star formation throughout the Galaxy.

Away from the denser clouds, the gas and dust of interstellar space is known as the diffuse interstellar medium, composed of a patchwork of bubbles that have been inflated by exploding stars. There are distinct phases in the evolution of a supernova remnant. During the first phase, the expanding cloud of stellar debris sweeps up surrounding gas to form a dense shell. Driven outward by the colossal explosion, supernova debris can reach velocities approaching one percent of the speed of light, or around 3000 km/s. As high-velocity debris ploughs into the gathering shell, its temperature rises to 10 million Kelvin initiating the second phase, in which the shell starts to glow. The third phase sees the expanding bubble slow and the shell begin to lose heat. Finally, the fourth phase occurs when the ejecta velocity has slowed down so much that it merges back into the general flow of the interstellar medium again.

Our Solar System just happens to find itself travelling through a supernova bubble at the present time. Known as the Local Bubble, it has an elongated shape, some 300 light years in length. Inside, the density of hydrogen is only about one tenth of the average figure for the rest of the Galaxy. Astronomers estimate that a supernova explosion some time within the last few million years, and perhaps as recently as 300,000 years ago, created the Local Bubble.

The Sun shares its niche with a few thousand other stars and perhaps the dead core of the star that exploded to create the Local Bubble in the first place. Geminga was detected in 1972, as a powerful source of gamma rays. It was positively identified as a neutron star in the 1990s and dated to be some 300,000 years old. Although that is a little young compared to estimates of the Local Bubble's age, Geminga must have once been at the heart of a supernova and some astronomers think that it could have been the one that gave rise to the Local Bubble.

There are other supernova bubbles nearby as well. These have been called Loop I, Loop II and Loop III. They show up prominently at radio wavelengths and each one touches the Local Bubble.

As a supernova bubble expands, it piles up the interstellar matter like a snowplough. If this shockwave strikes a molecular cloud, it can compress the cloud so much that star formation is initiated within it. Thus, the death of one star can lead to the formation of a whole generation of new stars.

Seeding space

In addition to injecting energy into the interstellar medium, the supernova also seeds space with heavy chemical elements. The low mass planetary nebulae do this to a lesser extent, too.

The collapse of a high-mass star's core initiates an apocalyptic process that liberates more energy than the star itself was capable of producing during its lifetime. In a supernova explosion atoms are flung together with enough energy to be forged into heavier and heavier chemical elements, creating all the elements heavier than iron – including the radioactive ones.

The brightness of the supernova climbs and climbs, until it outshines all the other stars in the Galaxy for a few weeks and the radioactive elements come into their own. As they decay,

NGC 6960 SUPERNOVA REMNANT

The Veil Nebula

The Veil Nebula is an arc of a much larger supernova remnant known as the Cygnus Loop [1]. At the time of the explosion, astronomers estimate that it would have been a searing star, rivalling the crescent moon in brightness. The ring-like shape is caused by the shockwave from the explosion snow-ploughing gas in front of itself.

DISTANCE 1.5 THOUSAND LY

SIZE 50 LIGHT YEARS

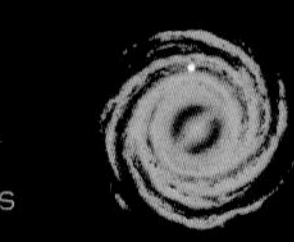

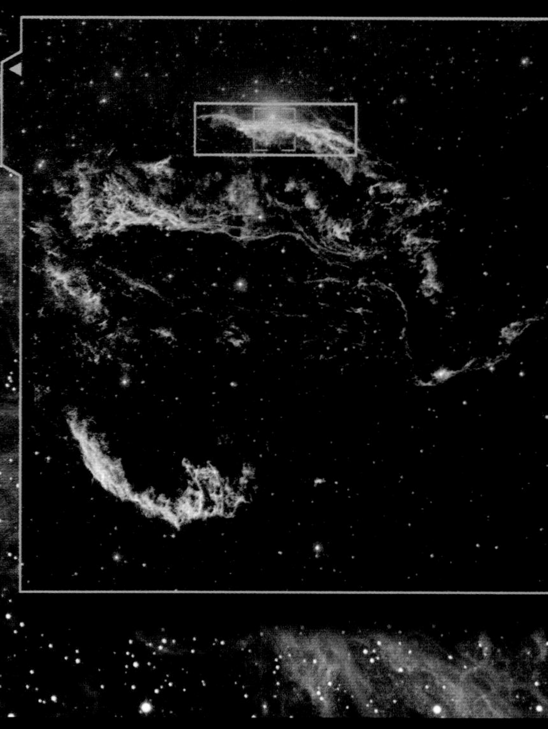

they inject more energy into the expanding cloud of supernova debris, keeping it glowing for months afterwards, while the supernova remnant spreads newly formed elements far and wide.

The antimatter fountain

In 2001, astronomers were stunned to discover a fountain of antimatter pouring out of the centre of our own Galaxy. They described it as like finding a new room in a house you've lived in all your life. The first hints of this strange fountain were seen in the 1970s but it took until 2001 for spacecraft to clearly see its towering shape. It was detected at gamma-ray wavelengths and, to start with, no one could think what could possibly cause this much antimatter to be created in the centre of the Galaxy.

Antimatter is the opposite of matter. For every type of matter particle, there is an antimatter counterpart with exactly opposite properties except mass. Mass is only ever positive but the electrical charge and other particulate properties can be reversed. For example, the antimatter counterpart of the electron is called the positron. Whereas the electron has a negative electrical charge, the positron is positively charged. Positrons should not be confused with the positively charge matter particle, the proton. They are completely different. Protons are much heavier, are made of quarks and have their own negatively charged antimatter counterpart – the anti-proton.

Whenever an electron meets a positron, the pair annihilate each other in a burst of gamma rays. It was just such gamma rays that betrayed the antimatter fountain, which extends for 10,000 light years across space. Matter is being annihilated at an astonishing rate in the antimatter fountain. Every second, it destroys enough matter to generate 10,000 times the Sun's luminosity.

One of the possible models for the fountain hypothesizes that its supply of antimatter is created by the vast energies unleashed during a supernova explosion. In the crowded stellar neighbourhoods of the galactic centre, supernovae should be reasonably frequent, providing a steady stream of antimatter. Another solid theory sees antimatter created when binary stars transfer mass between one another, particularly in systems where matter is flowing from a normal star to a neutron star. In the strong gravitational field of a neutron star, velocities and therefore energies are high, allowing antimatter to be created.

If a supernova occurs near the top or bottom of the galactic disc, the explosion can burst out of the disc, spewing hot gas into the galactic halo. These clouds of gas w eventually rain back down onto other parts o the Galaxy's disc, spreading newly synthesiz elements far and wide.

A supernova remnant is usually a rich mix unburned hydrogen and helium from the sta outermost layers and the heavier elements that have been forged both during the star's life and in the supernova itself. It is these chemicals that make planets, and ultimately life, possible in the Universe.

Elements like silicon make rocks possible, t metals form planetary cores, and life itself is based upon the so-called CHNOPS elements carbon, hydrogen, nitrogen, oxygen, phosphorus and sulphur. All of these, with th exception of hydrogen, must have been forge in a massive star. This is why, as the well-known phrase goes, we are all stardust. Or look at it another way, we're all nuclear was

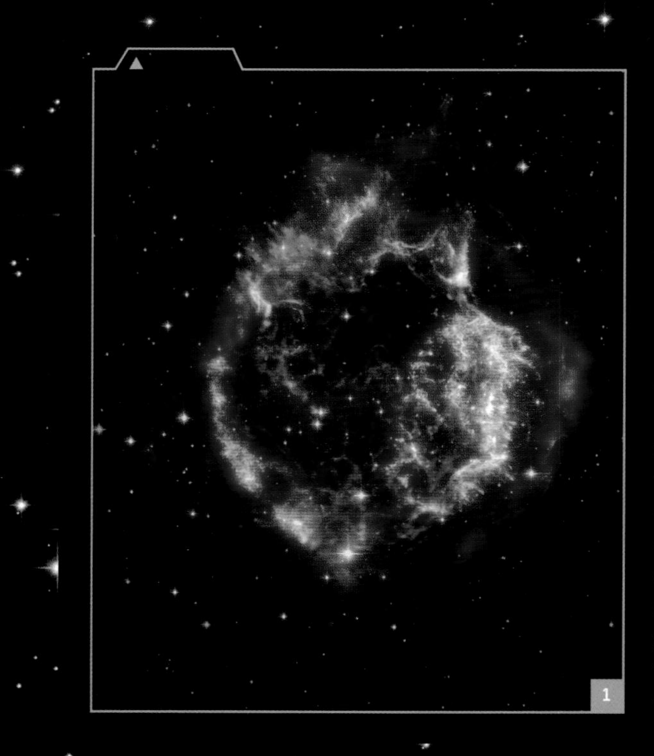

3C461 SUPERNOVA REMNANT

Cassiopeia A

Following a supernova 340 years ago, an expanding shock wave now heats the interstellar medium as it charges through space. Green filaments are rich in oxygen, red and purple represent sulphur, and blue ones are comprised mostly of hydrogen and nitrogen.

But these bright colours are the cosmic equivalent of a ripple on a pond. X-ray and infrared images help to fill in the gaps [1], showing that the after-effects of the explosion are still strongly felt everywhere in the once-bright star's vicinity. The X-rays are shown in blue and reveal multimillion-degree gas, excited by the explosion of the star. Red represents dust glowing in the infrared and the visible light is shown as yellow.

At only 10,000 light years from the Earth, this supernova should have created a blazing star in the sky, easily visible to the naked eye. Yet, there are no such historical records. The only possible sighting is from the British astronomer John Flamsteed who may have seen it at the limit of naked eye visibility on 16 August 1680.

Perhaps the supernova was blanketed by layers of gas that it had already thrown off in outbursts as a prelude to its ultimate detonation. Maybe these absorbed the light from the blast and prevented it from becoming a celestial beacon.

DISTANCE 10 THOUSAND LY

SIZE 10 LIGHT YEARS

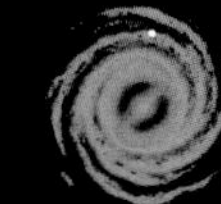

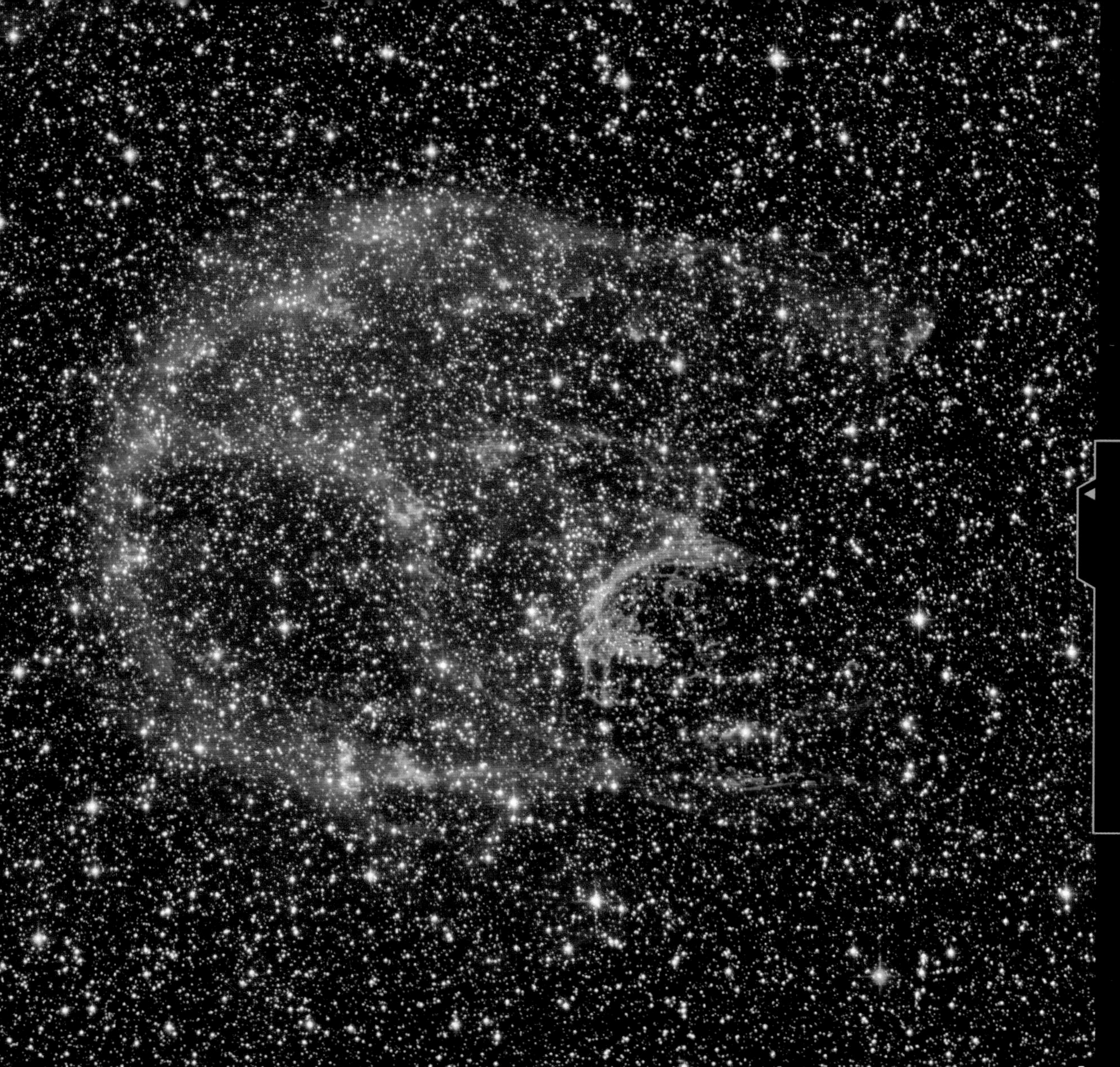

2

[2] N132D **SUPERNOVA REMNANT**

In visible light, this 3000-year-old supernova remnant is losing its potency, but at X-ray wavelengths [3] the inner cauldron of super-heated gas still shines out brightly.

DISTANCE	SIZE
160 THOUSAND LY	80 LIGHT YEARS

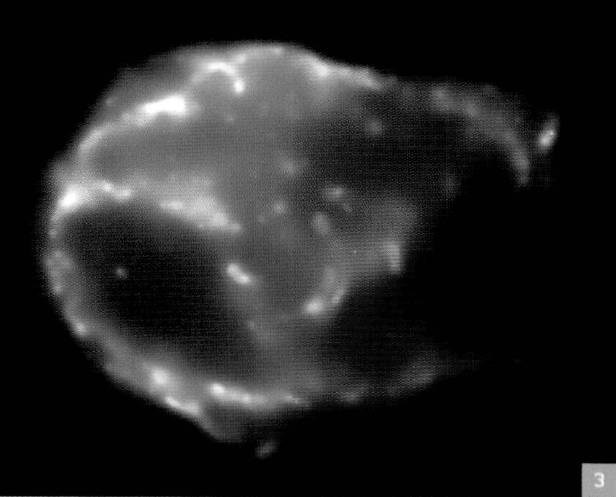

3

4

[4] IC 443 **SUPERNOVA REMNANT**

The Jellyfish Nebula

An old supernova remnant, perhaps dating back 30,000 years, IC 443 is the result of the failing blast wave being rejuvenated by ploughing into a molecular cloud. The interaction has set bright arcs of hydrogen gas glowing.

DISTANCE	SIZE
5 THOUSAND LY	72 LIGHT YEARS

[5] SN 1006 **SUPERNOVA REMNANT**

This is the remains of a star that exploded in 1006 AD. For a while, it was brighter than the planet Venus in the night sky. In those days, such occurrences were called nova, for new stars. We now know that it was exactly the opposite. It was not the birth of a new star but the death of an old one, scattering its nuclear products into space.

DISTANCE	SIZE
7.2 THOUSAND LY	73 LIGHT YEARS

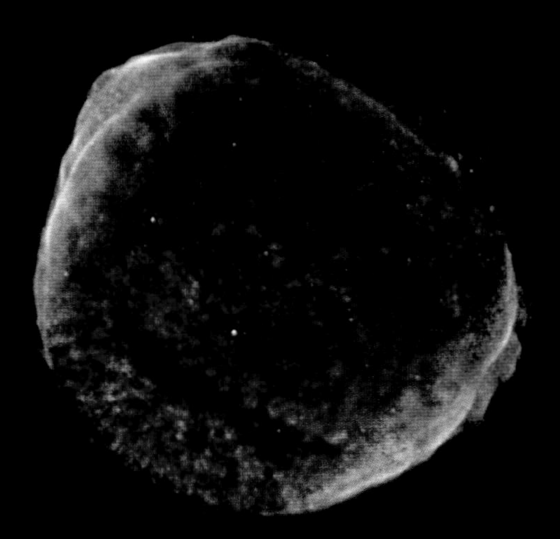

5

NGC 2736 **SUPERNOVA REMNANT**

The Vela Supernova Remnant

The shredded remnants of this star have been flung in graceful arcs of emission across one of the Milky Way's dense star fields. The whole supernova remnant is enormous, spanning nearly 16 times the diameter of the full moon. Unfortunately, this magnificent sight is too faint to be seen by the unaided eye.

DISTANCE
815
LIGHT YEARS

SIZE
113
LIGHT YEARS

04

SOLAR SYSTEMS_

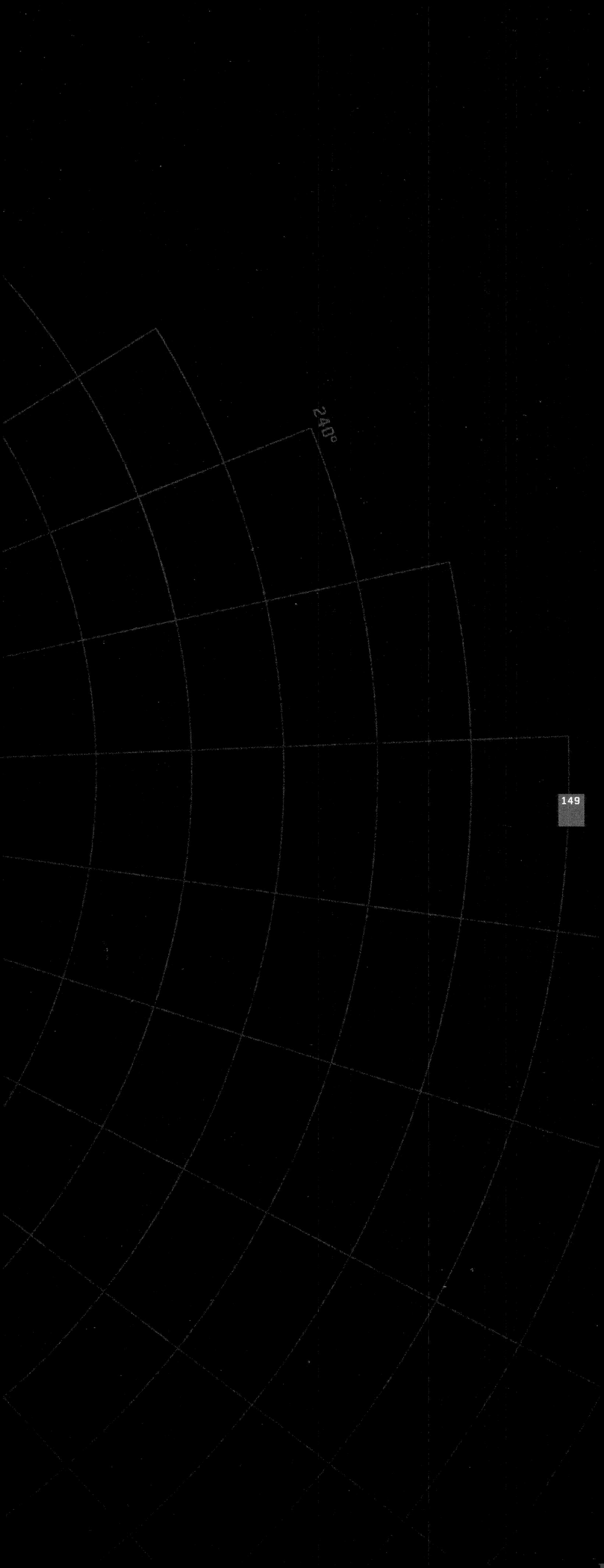
240°

PLANETS_

According to our current knowledge of physics, planets appear to be an essential by-product of star formation. As the cloud of gas that becomes a star shrinks under the force of its own gravity, so it changes shape. Instead of simply compressing itself into an ever-tighter ball until it ignites, the gas cloud flattens into a disc shape.

It does this because it is rotating. As the cloud contracts, so the rotation speeds up, creating an outward pull called the centrifugal force. This is the same foce that tries to tug passengers outwards when a car drives quickly round a bend.

In the case of a rotating cloud of gas, the greatest amount of centrifugal force is generated along the equatorial regions because this is where the cloud is rotating the fastest. This force resists gravity and so the cloud collapses more slowly around its equator than at its rotation poles. The result is that the sphere of gas flattens into a disc. This is the same process that causes much larger gas clouds that collapse in on themselves to form entire galaxies.

Planet formation

Although the vast majority of the mass still accumulates at the centre of the disc, where the star is busily forming, the matter in the disc is far from stagnant. As it circulates around the forming star, so it gradually clumps together. Initially, this is a gradual process because the dust grains are not sufficiently large enough to attract each other through gravity. Instead, they must rely on random collisions to bring them into contact with each other.

It may be that larger scale clumps form in the disc as whole areas begin to contract in a miniature version of the process that caused the star to form in the first place. In these locations, the collision rate between dust grains would be enhanced and greater conglomerations of matter would be built more quickly.

Eventually, the dust grains build up into asteroid-sized objects known as planetesimals. These are now large enough to attract each other through the force of gravity, so building even bigger objects. As they come together, there is a fine line between higher speed collisions that break the planetesimals into fragments and the lower speed impacts that allow them to coalesce.

In a coalescence event, one planetesimal bumps into the other with just enough force to melt the two objects into a single, larger celestial object. This process continues until bodies between the sizes of the Moon and Mars are formed. These are called planetary embryos and they populate a forming solar system in large numbers. Computer simulations suggest that in the inner Solar System alone, there may once have been 50 or more of these nascent planets.

The planetary embryos then embark on an enormous tug of war, in which they attract and merge with each other to form fully-fledged planets. Some of them will almost certainly be flung out of the gravitational reach of their star through near misses rather than collisions. As they fall together on similar orbits, the two planetesimals pull on each other through gravity. This usually means that the forerunning planetesimal is slowed down whereas the approaching one is speeded up.

If they miss rather than hit, the speedier planetesimal can sometimes find itself travelling so fast that it escapes the pull of its parent star. If this happens, it will escape from the solar system altogether and go into orbit around the centre of its galaxy. Such orphaned worlds have not yet been identified in deep space because they are so small and dim, but they are predicted by theory and a name for them has been proposed: planetars. The name reflects the fact that they are planetary bodies that find themselves on similar orbits to the stars.

Victoria crater, Mars
In September 2006, NASA's Mars Exploration Rover Opportunity arrived at the rim of the Victoria Crater and before descending its slopes, paused to capture the panoramic view that greeted it. The crater is about 750 meters in diameter and 70 metres deep. See also p.190.

Eventually the number of planetary embryos dwindles as the final planets bulk up and the solar system becomes more or less fixed in its configuration. As for the variety these configurations can take, astronomers are just beginning to get their first glimpses.

For most of history, the only solar system that astronomers have been able to contemplate has been our own. Since 1995, however, telescope technology has allowed us to detect large planets around nearby stars. Planets are mostly found by the small gravitational tug that they give their central star, making them appear to wobble under the gaze of a telescope.

Planets around other stars

The first planets discovered around Sun-like stars were a complete surprise because they turned astronomers' expectations completely

a half times closer to its parent star than Mercury is to our Sun. Yet the planet is nearly 2700 times more massive, containing half the mass of Jupiter.

This makes astronomers think that the planet must be a gas giant, rather than some extraordinarily large rocky body – which leads to another mystery. It seems impossible that a gas giant planet could form so close to the central star. The intense heat of the young star should have blown away the light gases required to form such a planet.

Astronomers therefore had to revise their thinking about how planets formed. In particular, computer simulations showed that if the disc nurturing the planet is particularly dense, it could rob the planet of orbital energy. If this happened, the planet's orbit would shrink and so the planet would appear to spiral inwards, coming to rest near its

of them large planets close to their star. The tally rises continually thanks to a number of projects that are currently running across the world. So far, no solar systems like ours have been detected. This may be because our technology is currently accidently geared towards finding large planets close to their stellar parents. As our equipment improves, perhaps we will start discovering solar systems more closely resembling our own.

Building a solar system

Astronomers can pick up vital clues about the formation of our Solar System by looking at its final arrangement, the state of the planetary surfaces and the chemical composition of the various bodies. For the rest of the story, they have to look out into space and try to catch young stars in the process of forming their own solar systems.

[1, 2] Forming planets in Orion
Astronomers have discovered a menagerie of forming solar systems within the Orion nebula. These can be split into stable and unstable systems. The stable systems [1] are young stars that are surrounded by a dark disc of matter from which planets will form. These are located well away from the high-mass stars that have already formed in the nebula.

The unstable systems are those unlucky enough to be situated near the high-mass stars. These forming planetary systems [2] are being 'blowtorched' by the perpetual torrent of ultraviolet radiation from the large stars. Will they survive to become planetary systems? Only time will tell.

[3] BETA PICTORIS **MAIN SEQUENCE STAR**
Beta Pictoris is estimated to be somewhere between 8 and 20 million years old, making it a young adult star, past its tempestuous youth. It has a dusty disc surrounding it, shown here by the light it scatters from the central star, which is blocked out to make the fainter disc visible. The disc extends more than 75 billion kilometres away from the central star. Such distances in our Solar System are way beyond the planets, and reach out into the Kuiper belt and scattered disc regions.

DISTANCE	DIAMETER	MASS	LUMINOSITY
63 LIGHT YEARS	1.4 SOLAR RADII	1.7 SUNS	8.6 SUNS

[4] HD 107146 **YELLOW DWARF STAR**
HD 107146's disc is almost face-on and contains one-tenth the mass of Earth in dust. In both cases, there could be fully formed planets embedded within the dust as well. This would vastly boost the mass of each disc.

Astronomers believe that our own Solar System would resemble either AU Microscopii or HD 107146 if viewed from a distance, although it would be significantly fainter because our Solar System contains between 1000 and 10,000 times less dust. Perhaps this is because these two systems are between 30 and 250 million years old, whereas our Solar System is 5 billion years old.

DISTANCE	DIAMETER	MASS	LUMINOSITY
88 LIGHT YEARS	1 SOLAR RADII	1 SUNS	1.1 SUNS

[5] AU MICROSCOPII **RED DWARF STAR**
Even completely mature stars have dusty discs. They are 10–100 times thinner than the discs around young stars and are thought to be composed of the dust liberated by evaporating comets. Collisions between asteroids also help to keep the disc topped up. AU Microscopii's disc is seen edge on and, for all its apparent grandeur, it is only estimated to total about the same mass as the Moon.

DISTANCE	DIAMETER	MASS	LUMINOSITY
32 LIGHT YEARS	0.6 SOLAR RADII	0.5 SUNS	0.03 SUNS

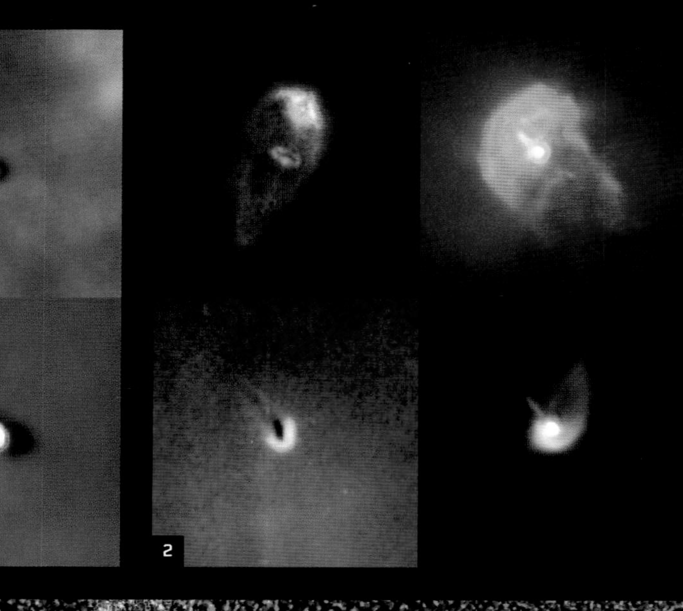
1 2

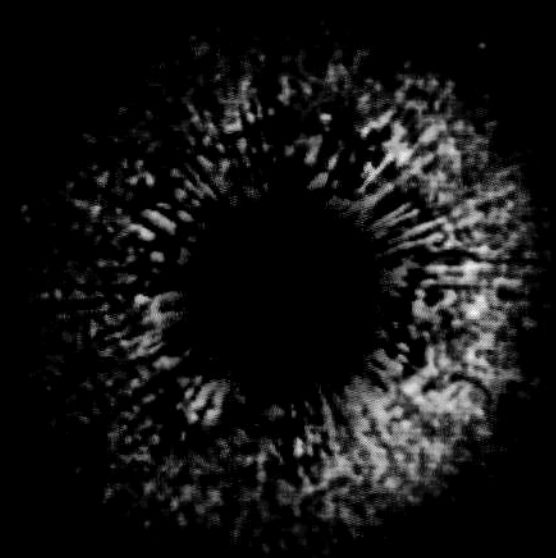
4

Planet factory

The Orion Nebula has proved a fruitful hunting ground for astronomers seeking forming solar systems. There are thousands of infant stars in this collapsing gas cloud and many are now known to have dusty discs of planet-forming material around them.

Our Solar System

Taken as a whole, our Solar System is a remarkable place in its own right. All roads of enquiry lead to the conclusion that it formed some 4.5 billion years ago. There is also evidence that a nearby supernova triggered the process. It comes in the form of meteorites that contain signs of the unmistakable decay of radioactive elements, many of which have short half-lives on the astronomical timescale.

For example, aluminium-26 decays into magnesium-26 with a half-life of 740,000 years. This means that in 740,000 years, half the radioactive aluminium will have transformed itself into magnesium. In another 740,000 years, half the remaining aluminium will have become magnesium, and so on.

Aluminium-26 is produced in large quantities during a supernova explosion. An analysis of meteorites found on Earth has shown that many of them once contained this isotope. This indicates there must have been a good supply of Aluminium-26 in our cosmic neighbourhood while the Solar System was forming. With such a short decay time, the likelihood is that a nearby supernova explosion unleashed an expanding shockwave that compressed a local gas cloud, triggering its collapse and the formation of the Solar System. The same supernova also seeded the cloud with heavy elements synthesized during the explosion, which were ultimately incorporated into the planets as well as the meteorites of the Solar System.

Central hub

The Sun is the central hub of the Solar System, containing 99 percent of its mass but less than one percent of its rotational momentum. With the planets, the situation is exactly reversed. Whilst they contribute just one percent to the mass of the Solar System, they carry almost all of its rotational momentum as they sweep through their respective orbits.

There is an intriguing question that periodically vexes astronomers concerning the arrangement of the planetary orbits. Why should they be spaced as they are? In the 18th century, this question particularly fascinated astronomers. A German astronomer, Johann Daniel Titius, found a mathematical relationship that appeared to predict the distances of the planets. Another German astronomer, Johann Elert Bode, was also gripped by this idea and promoted it widely.

At this time Uranus and Neptune, the two outer planets, were unknown. Also, astronomers had yet to set eyes on the asteroids. The Titius-Bode law, as it became known, was thought nothing more than a curiosity until William Herschel discovered the seventh planet Uranus during 1781. Astonishingly, its distance could be deduced from the Titius-Bode law.

This sparked a frenzy of interest as the same law predicted a planet between Mars and Jupiter, where astronomers finally found the asteroid belt. In 1888, Neptune was discovered using Newton's law of gravity. This planet did not fit into the Titius-Bode scheme however, and belief in its validity as a true law of nature diminished.

Nowadays, most astronomers believe that the planetary distances are just a result of random events during the cataclysmic collisions that built the planets during the origin of the Solar System. Yet some astronomers have claimed that one other system of planets in particular does follow a variation of the Titius-Bode law.

Only when greater numbers of solar systems are found will we be able to fully test whether Titius-Bode is a coincidence or a strange fact that needs a physical explanation.

The habitable zone

There is a special set of orbits in the Solar System, which is where Earth finds itself. Known as the 'habitable zone', in this region of space heat from the Sun is sufficient to keep water liquid on a planetary surface. In our Solar System, the habitable zone can be thought of as roughly extending between the orbit of Venus and the orbit of Mars, neatly straddling the Earth.

Venus, at the inner edge of the habitable zone, is too hot whereas Mars at the outer edge is too cold. Earth is just right, leading some astronomers to refer to it as enjoying a 'Goldilocks orbit'. The habitable zone of any system will be determined by both the luminosity of the star and the size of the planet. So, whereas Venus might have become a habitable planet if it had existed further out in the Solar System, it is not certain that Mars would have been clement even if it had been closer. This is because Mars is so small that its

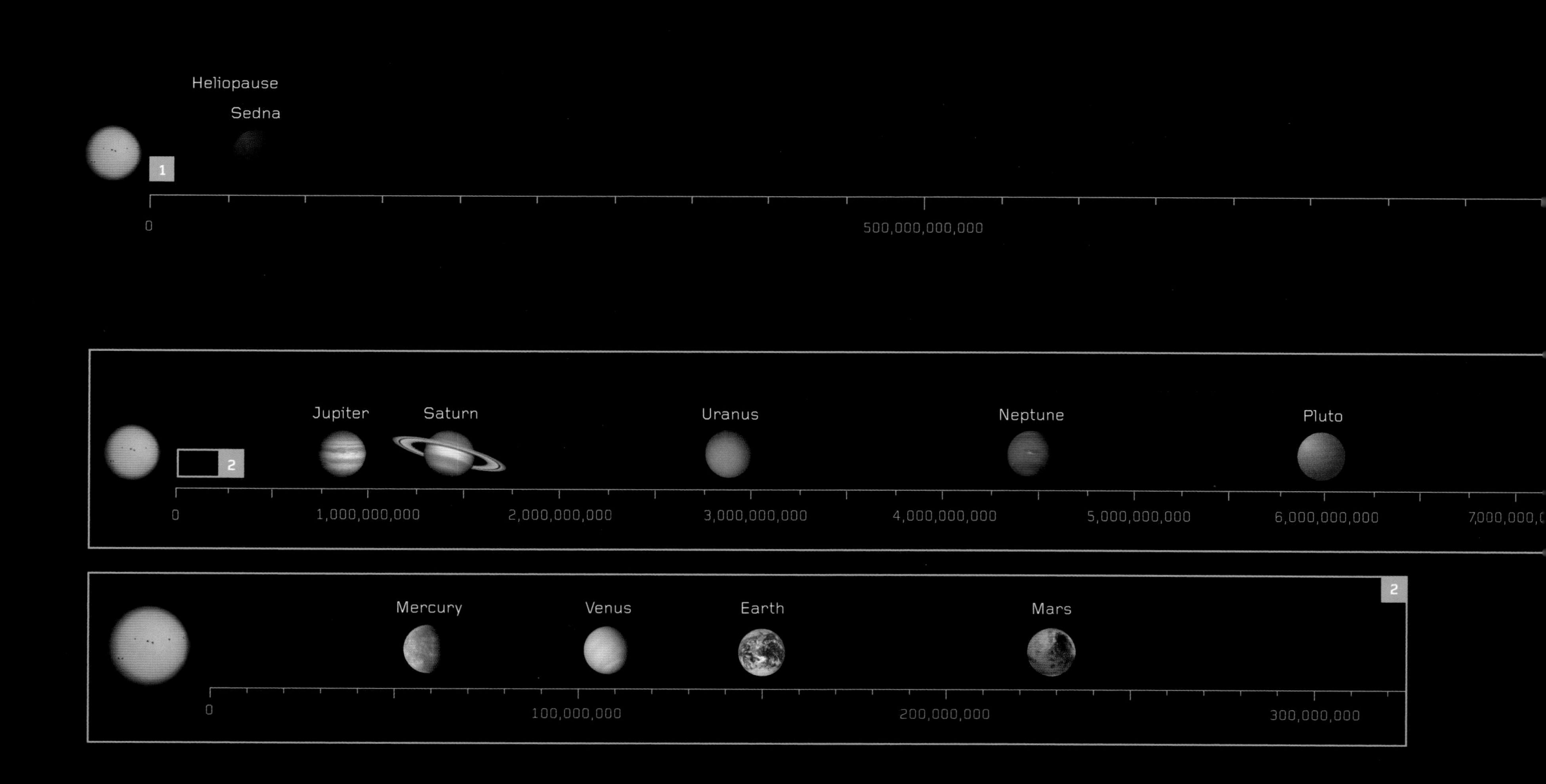

atmosphere is thin. Its diminutive size also prevents it from generating a protective magnetic field such as Earth's.

Planetary arrangement

Our Solar System splits up into two remarkably tidy planetary regions, each one delineated by a zone of debris. This is thought to be significant and gives away the density of matter that was found in the original disc surrounding the young Sun, and out of which the planets formed.

The rocky planets are found within reach of the Sun and the gas giants are found in the colder outer reaches. The asteroid belt is a zone of rocky debris that sits beyond the rocky planets and houses the leftovers from the process of inner planet formation. A similar zone, the Kuiper belt sits beyond the gas giants and holds their unwanted ingredients, including the dwarf planet, Pluto.

Another important boundary, though an incorporeal one, is the heliopause. This is where the Sun loses its grip on the particles that fill space within the Solar System and they become swept up in the general flow of the interstellar medium.

In the furthest reaches of the Solar System are the true vagabonds. These are the scattered disc objects and the Oort cloud inhabitants. Mostly icy asteroids, some larger bodies, such as Eris and Sedna also exist here. Occasionally, objects can fall from these outer regions into the inner zone. Heated by the Sun, these distant visitors can become comets and light up the night sky with their icy brilliance, but they can also pose a danger to Earth.

The risk of collision between the Earth and another celestial body is an ever-present concern. The famous comet astronomer Edmond Halley publicly talked of this possibility in the 17th century. Indeed, the impact of a comet fragment devastated a region the size of a large city in Siberia, Russia, during June 1908. Luckily, no one was killed because the area is so remote. Nevertheless, it highlights the threat from space. Nowadays, telescopes constantly scan the skies, looking for perilous objects.

Astronomers currently track some 100,000 objects in the Solar System. That figure is set to soar to 10 million as dedicated survey telescopes come on line over the next few years. Their discoveries should herald the largest jump in the known population of the Solar System in history.

Of all the objects that astronomers keep a wary eye on, Apophis currently tops the list. It is a near-Earth asteroid that was discovered in 2004, and for a brief time caused concern that it might actually be on a collision course with our planet. The impact was set to take place in 2029 with Apophis spanning some 250 metres, making it around five times larger than the Tunguska meteorite.

Thankfully, as more astronomers trained their telescopes on the threatening object, so they measured its position and movement with ever-greater precision and the threat of the impact diminished to almost insignificant levels. Nevertheless, astronomers plan to track this object carefully.

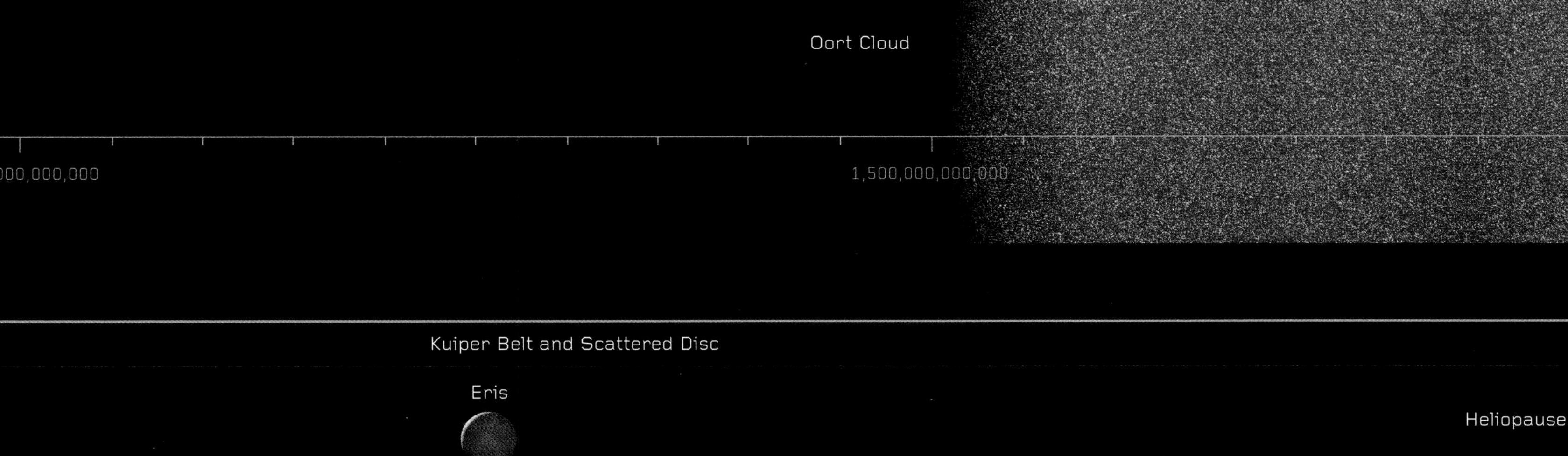

SUN_

The glowing surface of the Sun radiates a prodigious quantity of light and heat into space. The dark blotch of several sunspots can be seen on this image. These transitory blemishes come and go on the Sun and are a barometer of solar activity though not, as once thought, a precise measure. Sunspots are created by invisible magnetic fields that spontaneously burst out of the surface of the Sun, cooling their surroundings.

The lighter mottled regions towards the right-hand limb of the Sun are called faculae. These are luminous hydrogen filaments that are usually found near sunspots or in regions where sunspots have been or are about to appear.

The darkening round the edges of the Sun indicates that it is a gaseous body, rather than a celestial object with a solid surface.

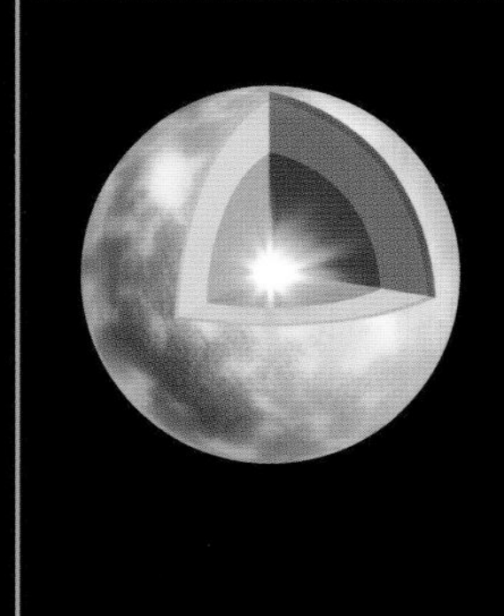

SUN'S INTERIOR
The Sun's core is where nuclear reactions take place. Surrounding this is a tightly packed region of gas known as the radiative zone. The outermost layer is the convective zone where the gas rolls over and over. At the top is the visible surface.

DISTANCE GALAXY CORE	DIAMETER	MASS	ROTATION PERIOD	MEAN SURFACE TEMPERATURE
26	1.4	333	25.4	6000
THOUSAND LY	MILLION KM	THOUSAND EARTHS	DAYS	KELVIN

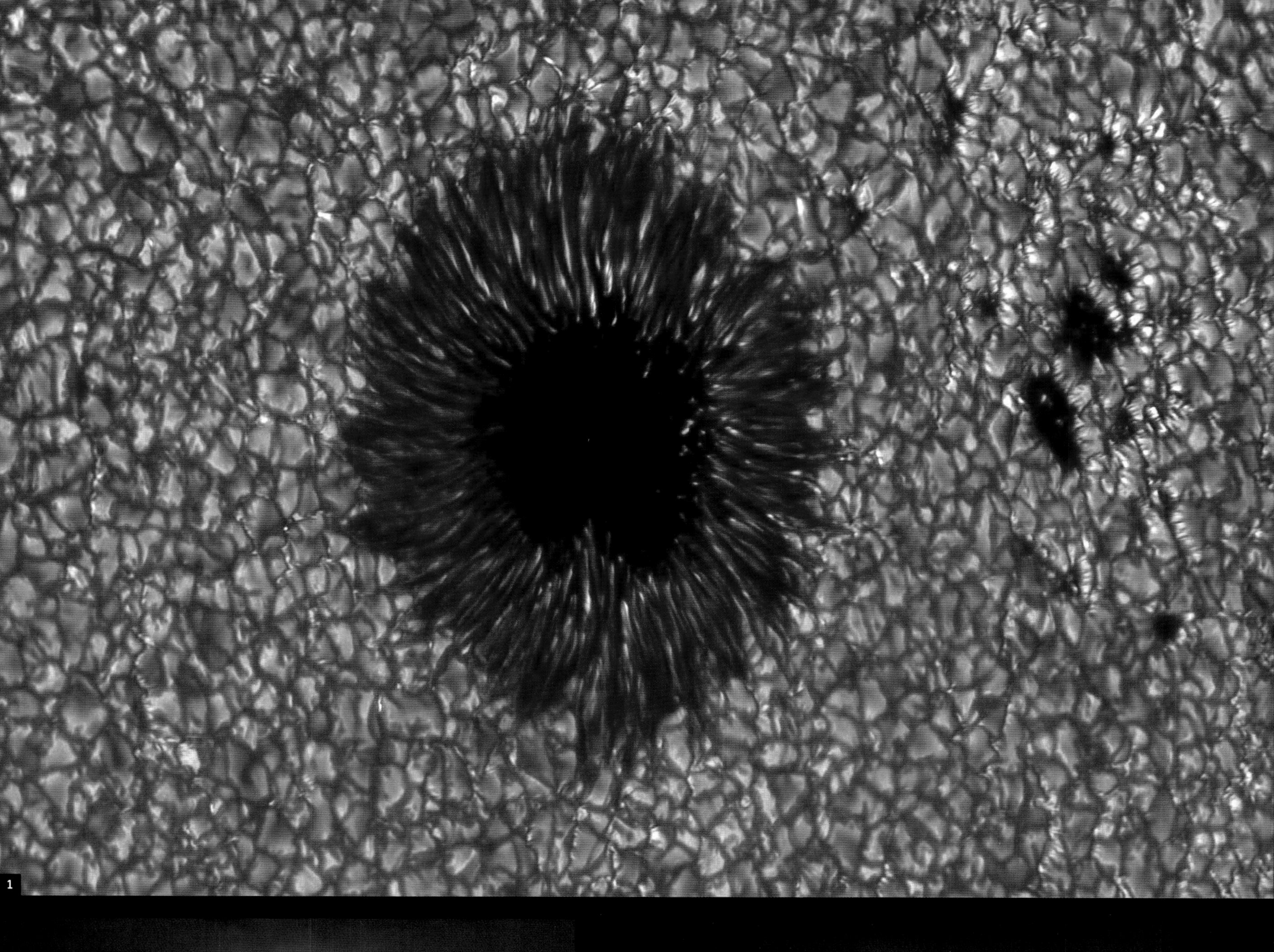

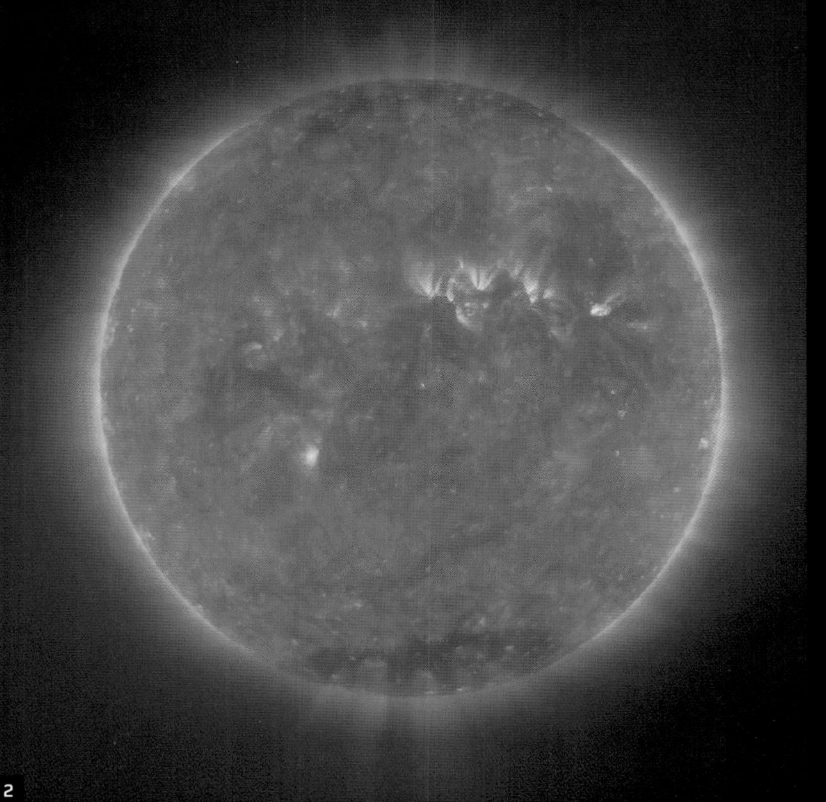

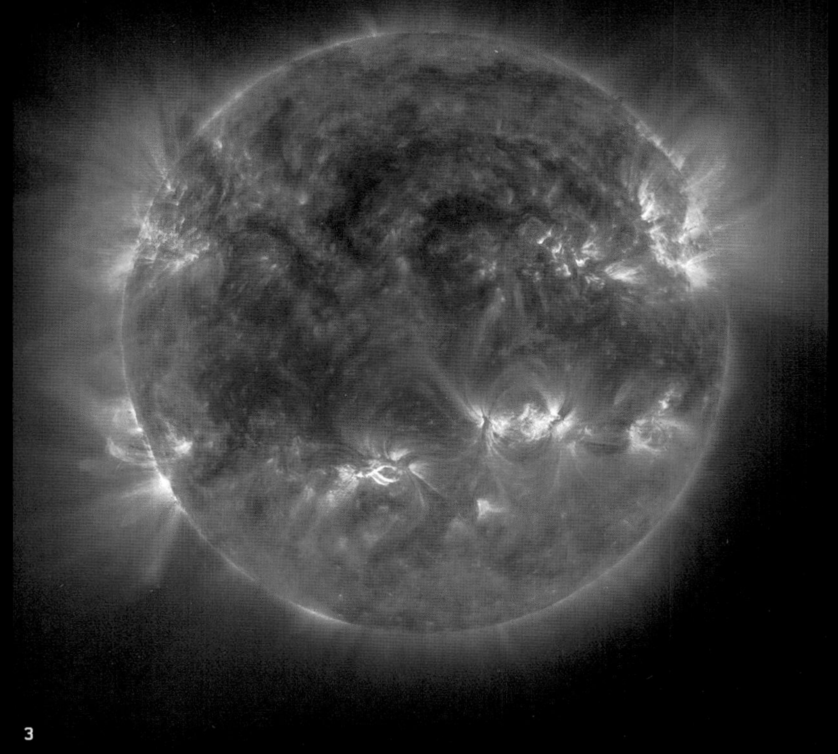

[1] Sunspot close-up
A sunspot sits on the boiling surface of the Sun. It is a region of cooler gas, about half the brightness of its surroundings. Therefore, it appears dark in contrast. The penumbra is the striped fringe surrounding the truly dark centre, known as the umbra.

The texture of the solar surface is called the granulation. Each of these cells is a pocket of convecting gas 1000 kilometres in size, boiling upwards rather like the rolling motion seen in boiling milk.

[2, 3] The solar cycle
Solar activity ebbs and flows in a cycle that lasts approximately 11 years. These images are taken at ultraviolet wavelengths and show the outer atmosphere of the Sun. Known as the corona, this gas has an average temperature of around 1.3 million Kelvin. In image [2], taken in 1997, the corona is relatively calm. About two years later, image [3] was taken. This time solar activity has bloomed and the corona is a knotted mass of active regions.

1

Solar activity

The incandescent gas at the surface of the Sun is caught in the grip of great forces. Gravity and magnetism fight it out to rule the movement of the gases here. Tremendous magnetic explosions can fling billions of tonnes of gas into space, where it collides with the planets triggering aurorae.

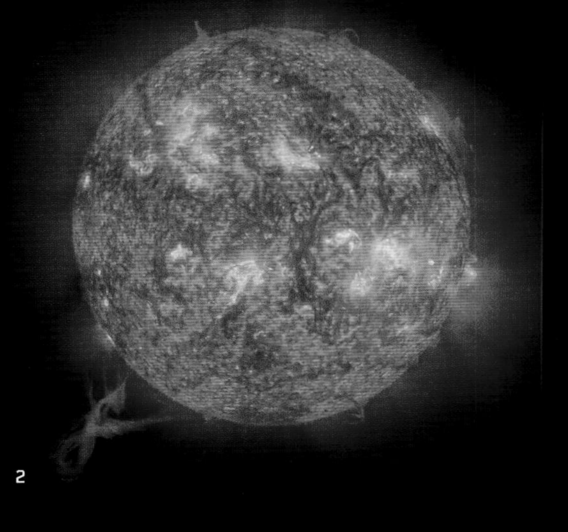

2

3

[1] Hot loops of gas

Hot loops of gas are guided by the Sun's magnetic field up into the solar atmosphere and down to the surface again. This loop complex spans more than 30 times the diameter of the Earth. The image was taken at very short ultraviolet wavelengths, near the boundary with X-rays.

[2] Twisted prominence

Prominences are gargantuan extensions of relatively cool gas that hang suspended in the Sun atmosphere. This twisting prominence was captured on 18 January 2000.

[3] The Sun's handle

This huge handle-shaped prominence is a dense bridge of cooler gas. Sometimes these structures drain back down onto the solar surface. On other occasions, they can erupt and escape into space.

◂ Tortured surface

This view shows the contorted field of gas around a sunspot. White areas are the hottest gas, at just over 6000 Kelvin, whilst black is the coolest, at around 5000 Kelvin. Every feature in this image traces the structure of the magnetic field underlying the solar surface.

Inner world

The crater-scarred face of Mercury, the Solar System's innermost planet is glimpsed in this crescent view. Its superficial resemblance to the Moon is all the more pronounced when it appears under this illumination.

The lack of atmosphere has left its surface frozen in time, showing us how the planet appeared back around 4 billion years ago when the Solar System's planet formation was complete.

ROCKY WORLDS_

The inner Solar System is the home of four rocky planets, sometimes referred to as terrestrial planets because of their superficial resemblances to the Earth. In order of increasing distance from the Sun, the rocky worlds are Mercury, Venus, Earth and Mars.

Earth is the biggest, with Venus running a close second, then Mars and finally Mercury, now the smallest planet in the Solar System following Pluto's relegation to dwarf planet status. A terrestrial planet distinguishes itself because it is primarily made of rocks and metal. Atop three of these solid spheres are relatively tenuous atmospheres.

In addition to the four rocky planets of the inner Solar System, the largest asteroid Ceres, now classified as a dwarf planet, can be thought of as a terrestrial dwarf planet. Pluto on the other hand, is a different type of object because it contains large quantities of ice as well as its quota of rock and metal.

Formation

It would appear to be no accident that the rocky planets exist in the inner Solar System. Here the temperature of the young Sun was so fierce that the only solid matter able to condense out of the gases in the collapsing nebula consisted of materials with high melting points, such as rocks and metals. Once condensed they conglomerated with the help of their mutual gravity and grew to become the planets of today.

Both Venus and Earth have permanent atmospheres. They scour the planets' surfaces whilst simultaneously protecting them from the harsh environment of outer space. On the other two rocky worlds it is a different story; Mars's atmosphere comes and goes depending on which season the planet is experiencing, and Mercury has no atmosphere whatsoever.

All rocky worlds have a solid surface – something that space probes can land on, or maybe even humans can walk across one day. With a surface comes the whole panoply of geography and geology to study.

The surface of each planet is a mirror into its past. Craters on the surface betray a sluggish world of little activity, either volcanic or meteorological, that would wipe the craters away. Volcanoes are an indication of inner heat, signifying stocks of radioactive elements that even today are keeping the interiors in a partially molten condition. Earth is volcanic for sure; there are eruptions every day somewhere on our planet. Of the others, Venus is almost certainly still volcanic, Mars was volcanic once because extinct volcanoes can be found on its surface, and Mercury probably was but only in the very early stages of its existence, and then it did not build towering volcanoes but spilled its lava in lakes.

The past and present volcanic activity on the rocky worlds is an excellent measure of the internal conditions.

Internal conditions

Each rocky world is expected to be composed of layers resulting from the titanic collisions that welded its planetary building blocks together. In their molten or semi molten state, the densest material fell to the centre of each world, whilst the lighter matter rose to the top.

So the metals formed the cores of the rocky worlds. On top of these solid foundations, a thick mantle of rocky material formed, culminating in the crust and the solid surface of the world.

Solid or fluid, the condition of each rocky body's metallic core probably determines whether the planet has an appreciable magnetic field or not. Earth has the largest magnetic field, a vigorous force field that lifts high above the planet and protects us from an onslaught of solar radiation.

Mercury too has a magnetic field, which is a great puzzle. The planet is so small that astronomers had expected it would have long since radiated away any internal energy. This should have led to the interior solidifying and stilling the convection currents needed to generate the field. However, against all the odds, Mercury displays a magnetic field, albeit just one percent as strong as the Earth's. How it is generated, no one yet knows.

Just as puzzling is that Venus does not have a magnetic field, certainly not an appreciable one. Being about the same size as Earth, Venus might have been expected to have a similar strength magnetic field. Instead, it has almost nothing; and astronomers currently have no way of explaining its absence.

Mars's magnetic field appears to be generated by magnetic rocks in the crust of the planet. These were imprinted with the planet's intrinsic magnetic field as they solidified from lava flows. Now, even though the core of Mars has frozen to the point where it can no longer generate a magnetic field, the crustal rocks still carry its imprint and influence.

Each rocky world shares striking similarities and displays huge differences. Piecing together their histories, to see where their evolution converges and then diverges again, is the work of the planetary scientist.

Superearths

Astronomers have discovered a number of planets around other stars that seem to be 'superearths'. They have measured them as being up to twice the diameter of the Earth, so still too small to be a gas giant, yet containing up to ten times the mass of the Earth, the largest rocky planet in our Solar System.

This makes them dense worlds and pumps their surface gravity up to over twice the strength of Earth's. That would be enough to pull down mountain ranges. Each of these planetary heavyweights will contain a rich stock of radioactive material, generating heat and probably driving a super-charged volcanic system. Astronomers have not as yet been able to analyse the atmosphere of a superearth. It could be anything from a thick blanket, producing a perpetual orange twilight, to a virtually non-existent mist with most of it frozen to the planet's surface.

These are truly exotic worlds. What makes them important is that they are the first examples of predominantly rocky planets that have been found outside our Solar System. How they formed is a puzzle but there are already two competing theories.

The first is that they formed in just the same way as the rocky planets in our own Solar System but they grew larger because there was more material in the disc surrounding the young star. The second idea is that the superearths are the cores of planets that should have been gas giants, but for some reason either the nebula was starved of gas and ice or their atmospheres were evaporated away as the planets migrated closer to their central star.

If the latter formation idea is true, it means that there are superearths in our own Solar System, but they are just buried inside the gas giants Uranus and Neptune. Astronomers estimate that in the heart of each planet lies buried a bulk of rocks and metals containing some five times the mass of the Earth.

Superearths have also been found in an unexpected place in the cosmos: around the dead heart of a star. In 1991, three planets were inferred to exist around a pulsating neutron star called PSR B1257+12. One is a small rocky world but the two outermost planets both contain approximately four times the mass of the Earth. Perhaps these were once gas giant planets that had their atmospheres scorched off by the supernova blast that transformed their parent into a neutron star.

MERCURY_

Despite its appearance as the archetypal rocky world, Mercury might actually be better referred to as a metallic planet. That's because, despite its rocky upper layers, Mercury is the densest planet in the Solar System. Perhaps this is because it formed in the very hottest environment available: right next to the Sun. Here, many rocks were prevented from solidifying, leaving Mercury to become a little world with a giant metallic heart.

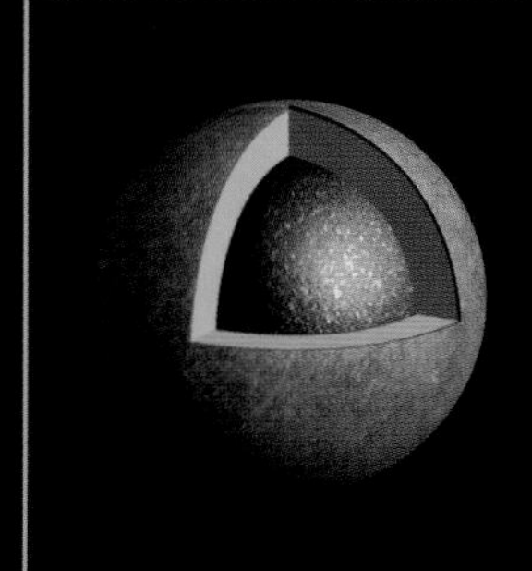

MERCURY'S INTERIOR
Mercury's enormous core of iron and nickel occupies 42 percent of its volume and accounts for 70-80 percent of its mass. Overlying the core is a mantle of rocks that supports the crust and the desolate surface.

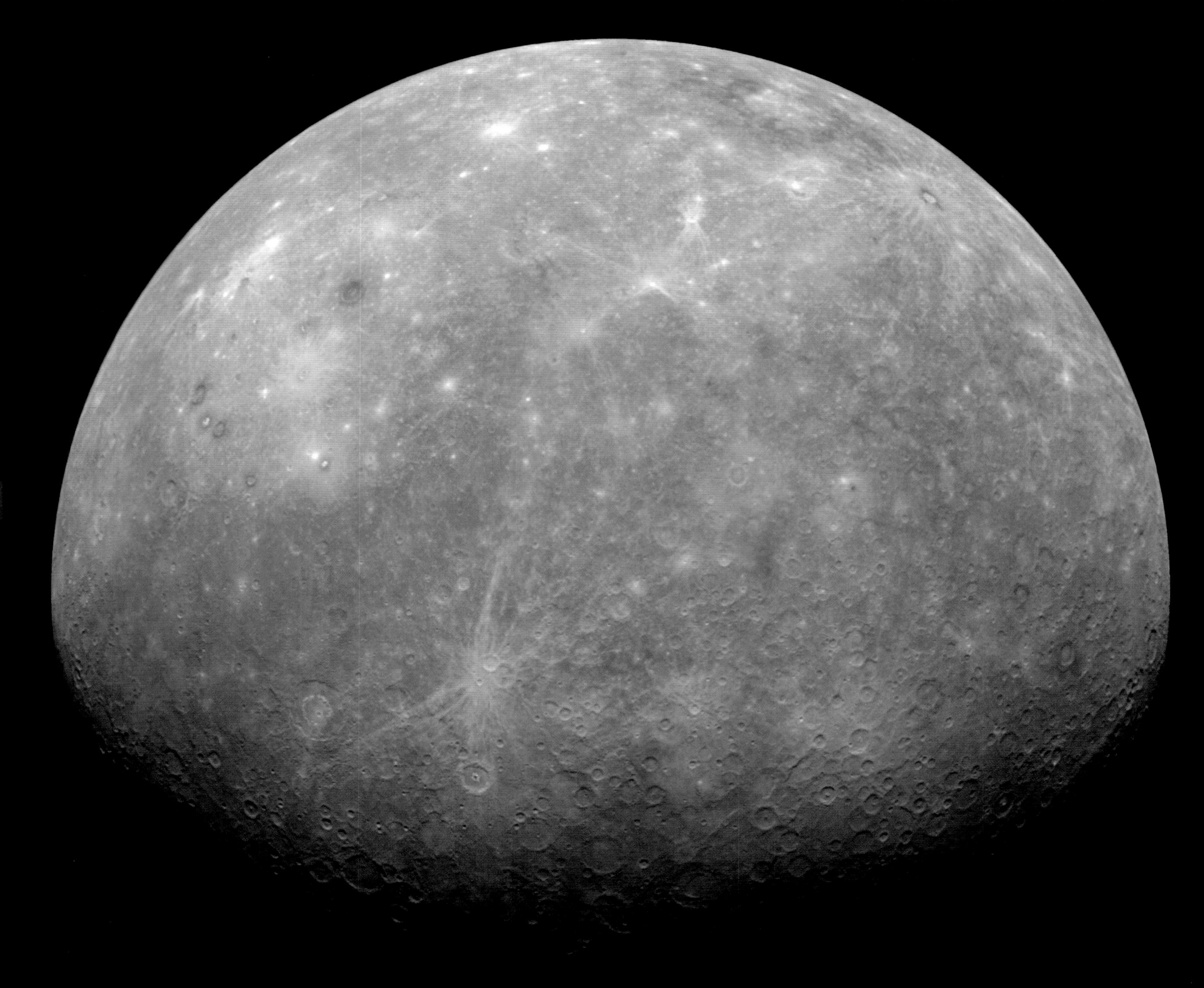

DISTANCE	DIAMETER	MASS	ROTATION PERIOD	ORBITAL PERIOD	MEAN SURFACE TEMPERATURE
58	4.9	0.05	59	88	340
MILLION KM	THOUSAND KM	EARTHS	DAYS	DAYS	KELVIN

Gibbous Mercury

Mercury is a place of subtle colour differences; nevertheless they reveal important information about the surface. Bright spots with a bluish tinge are relatively recent impact craters. Some have bright rays extending from them, composed of crushed rock. The large circular, light-coloured area in the upper left of the image is the Caloris basin, an enormous impact crater. It is so large it is usually referred to as a basin rather than a crater. The colour hints that there is a compositional difference between the basin floor and the surroundings. The interior of Caloris also hosts several dark-rimmed craters made by subsequent impacts.

[1] Dark halos

Two of the larger craters here appear ringed in halos of dark material. This is either darker subsurface material that has been thrown out by the impact, or rocks melted together and 'splashed' out by the impact; such melted rocks often appear dark.

[2] Weird terrain

This jumbled region of Mercury's surface is exactly opposite the Caloris Basin, on the other side of the globe. That fact leads planetary scientists to think that shock waves from the impact that formed Caloris travelled right the way through the planet. When they reached the other side, they caused tremendous upsets of material, which sculpted this weird hilly terrain.

[3] Fractured floor

The floor of the Caloris basin is riddled with fractures. This indicates that at some time in the past, the entire floor was forced upwards by activity within the planet. The craters can be seen superimposed on the fractures, indicating that the craters are more recent.

[4] Surface history

Planetary scientists can tell in which order a planet accumulated its surface features. For example, this image of Mercury shows at least five different historical events. The large crater to the lower left measures about 230 kilometres in diameter and has a prominent crater, about 85 kilometres across, nestled inside it. These craters were subsequently filled with volcanic lava that reached to the rim of the larger crater. Next, a fault line appeared across the crater, caused by compression as Mercury cooled and shrank a little. The last major episode in the history of this region is the impact that formed the large crater at the top of the image. This event threw ejecta across the region, creating smaller craters. Some of these are visible atop the fault line.

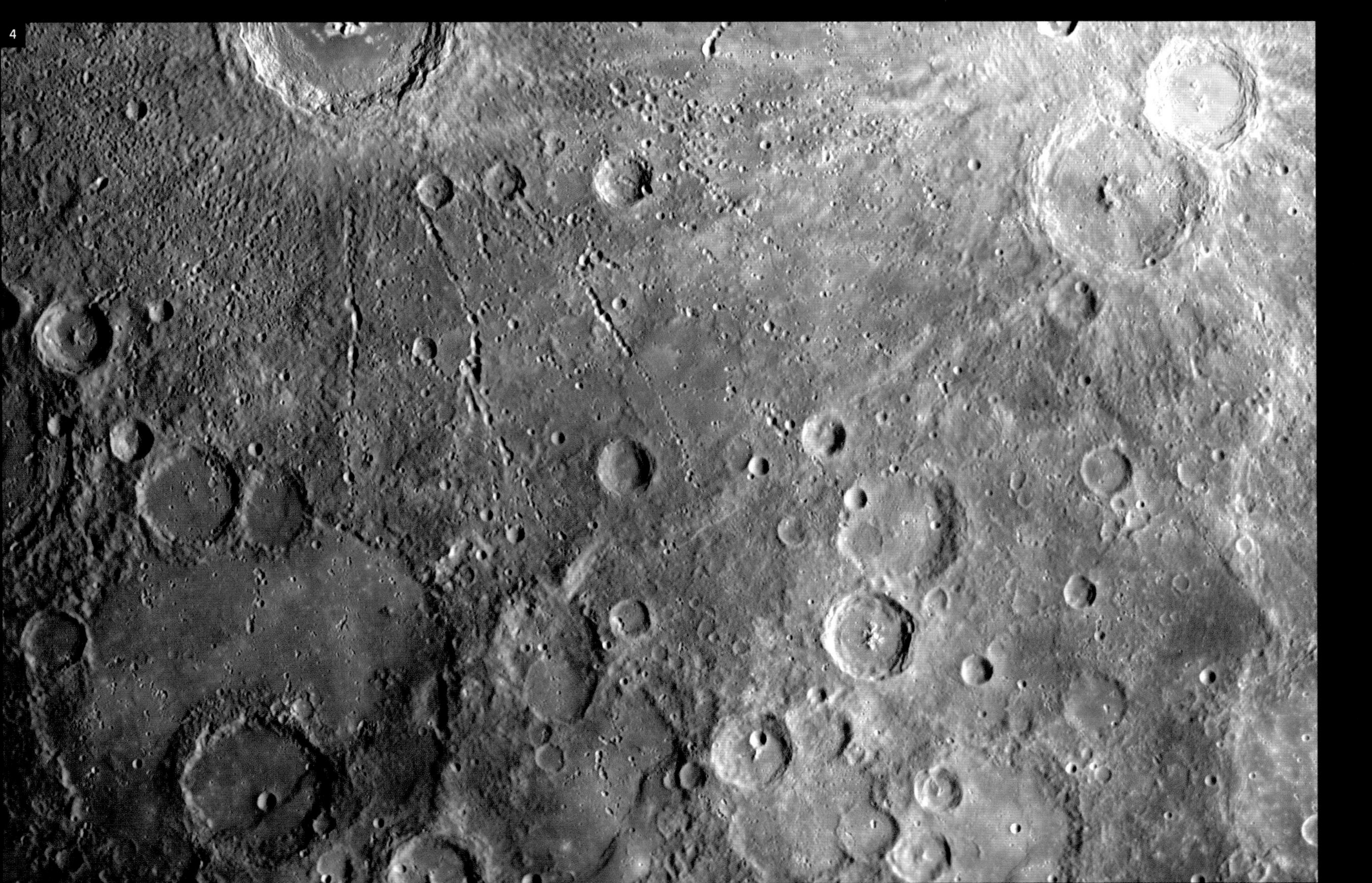

VENUS_

In terms of mass and size, Venus is virtually Earth's twin. The atmosphere of Venus, however, has driven the planet far away from the clement conditions that our world enjoys.

Venus approaches closer to Earth than any other planet, halving the distance between our world and Venus's nearest rival, Mars. As such, Venus shines brilliantly when it appears in the skies of Earth. It is only seen at twilight because it orbits closer to the Sun than Earth. Hence, it is often referred to as the evening star or the morning star, depending upon which end of the day it is visible.

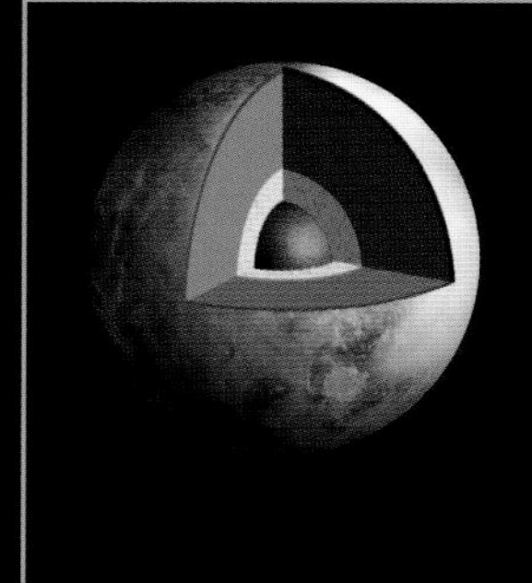

VENUS'S INTERIOR
Venus's interior is similar to Earth's. Its metal core is mostly solid, covered by a deep mantle of rocky material and a thin, dry crust. The water that once existed on Venus has long since been baked out.

DISTANCE	DIAMETER	MASS	ROTATION PERIOD	ORBITAL PERIOD	MEAN SURFACE TEMPERATURE
108	12.1	0.8	243	225	735
MILLION KM	THOUSAND KM	EARTHS	DAYS	DAYS	KELVIN

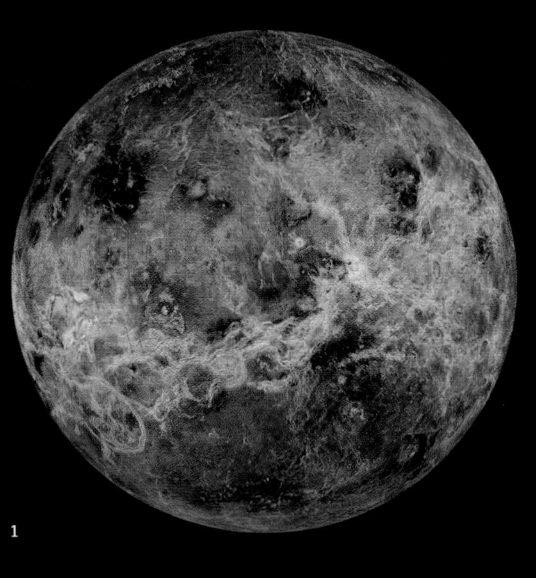

1

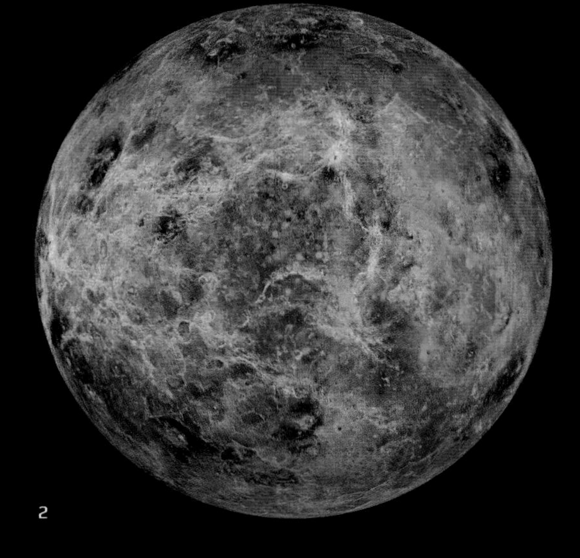

2

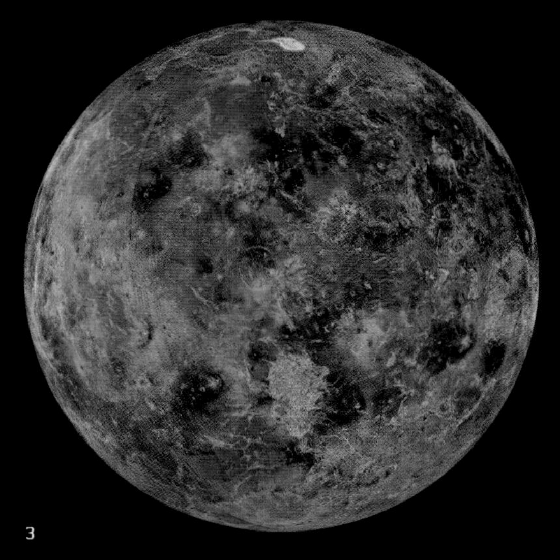

3

Beautiful Venus

Venus is perpetually shrouded in blankets of pastel clouds. They have continuously trapped solar heat inside the atmosphere and created a runaway greenhouse effect. The resulting temperature at the surface of Venus soars higher than 400 °Celsius, hotter than a kitchen oven.

[1-4] Maps of Venus
Although ordinary cameras cannot penetrate the cloud decks at Venus and see the surface below, radars have been used to map the planet. This sequence shows successive hemispheres of Venus, constructed from radar data. The false colours signify different heights at the surface. They have revealed a surface that lies halfway between that of Mars and Earth in terms of craters. There are fewer craters on Venus than on Mars but more than on Earth. Even so, there are not as many craters on Venus as scientists expected. Something must be erasing them. That something is thought to be volcanic activity.

[5] Scorching surface
This panoramic view of the surface of Venus is looking towards the feet of Russian lander Venera 13. The sky is just visible as the orange triangles in the top corners of the images. The rock-strewn inferno was so hostile that the spacecraft stopped working after only two hours. Venus's sulphuric acid rain has probably now eaten away most of the spacecraft.

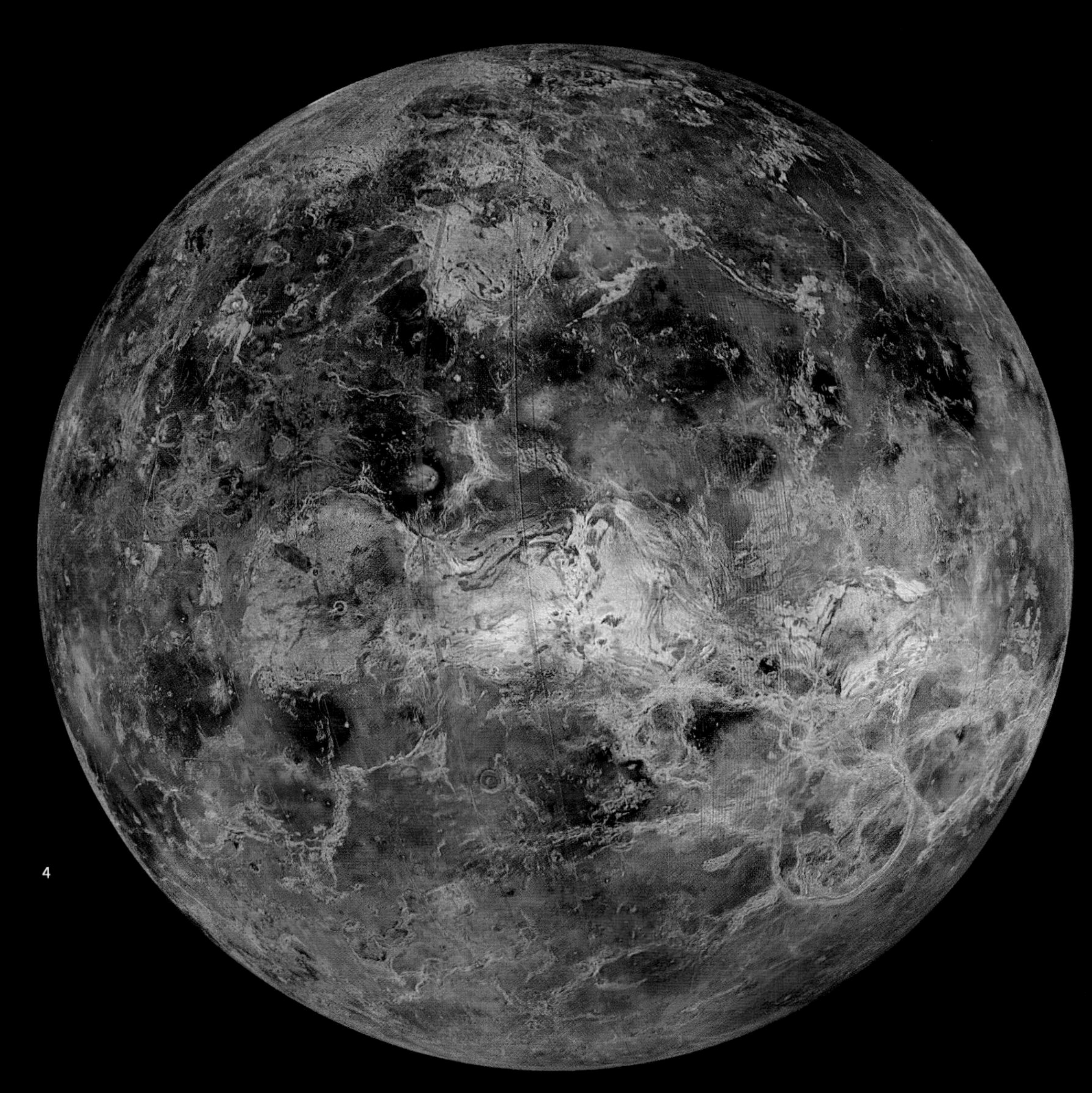

4

5

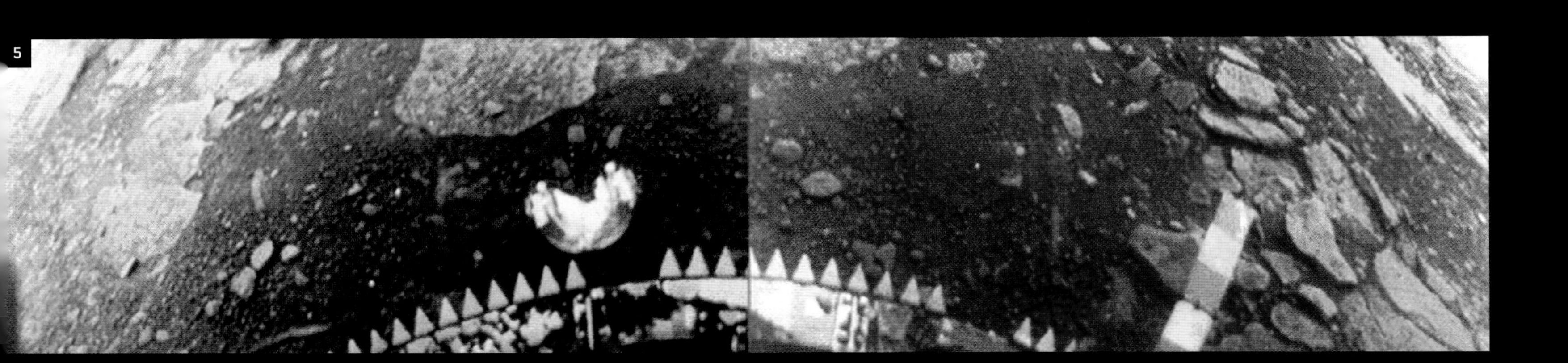

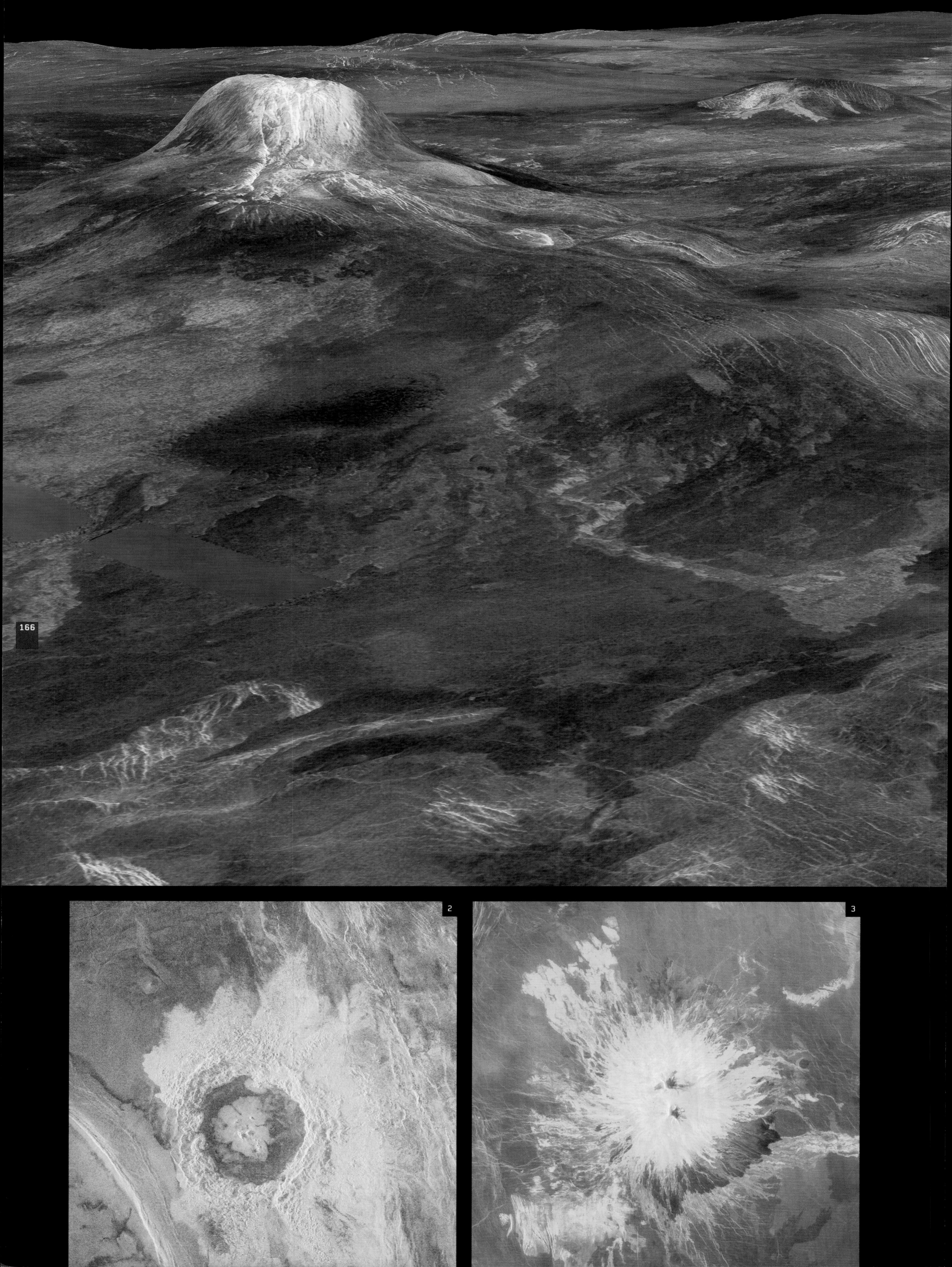
2
3

Geology of Venus

There are plenty of volcanic structures on Venus. They speak of a highly active past and hint that the volcanism may not yet be over. Planetary scientists have still to confirm that Venus is volcanically active, but they are 90 percent certain it is. Short-lived volcanic chemicals have been discovered in the atmosphere and lightning has been observed over the mountain peaks. Infrared instruments that can just about see through the clouds are currently being used to scan for heat coming from any active lava flows that may be snaking across the surface.

[1] Eistle Regio
Dominated by two volcanoes, Eistle Regio sits near the Venusian equator. The two volcanoes are Gila Mons (left) and Sir Mons (right). Bright flows of solidified lava trail the flanks of both volcanoes.

[2] Dickinson Crater
One of the few craters that survives on Venus, Dickinson Crater is interesting because it is not encircled by ejecta. Rather, it blankets the ground only on three sides. The western direction (left) is relatively clear. This may indicate that the asteroid that created this 43-kilometre-wide crater arrived from the west, travelling at a shallow angle.

[3] Sapas Mons
Overlapping lava flows have repeatedly covered this 650-kilometre-wide area to the north of Venus's equator. Seen from directly overhead, the brighter flows are rougher and therefore appear paler in these radar images. The thick Venusian atmosphere gradually works to erode this into smoother, darker terrain.

[4] Maat Mons
Another large Venusian volcano, Maat Mons towers in this radar image. Although the elevation has been considerably stretched for emphasis in this photo, the volcano does reach an altitude of 8 kilometres. Shown in true perspective, it would be revealed as a shallow-sided volcano.

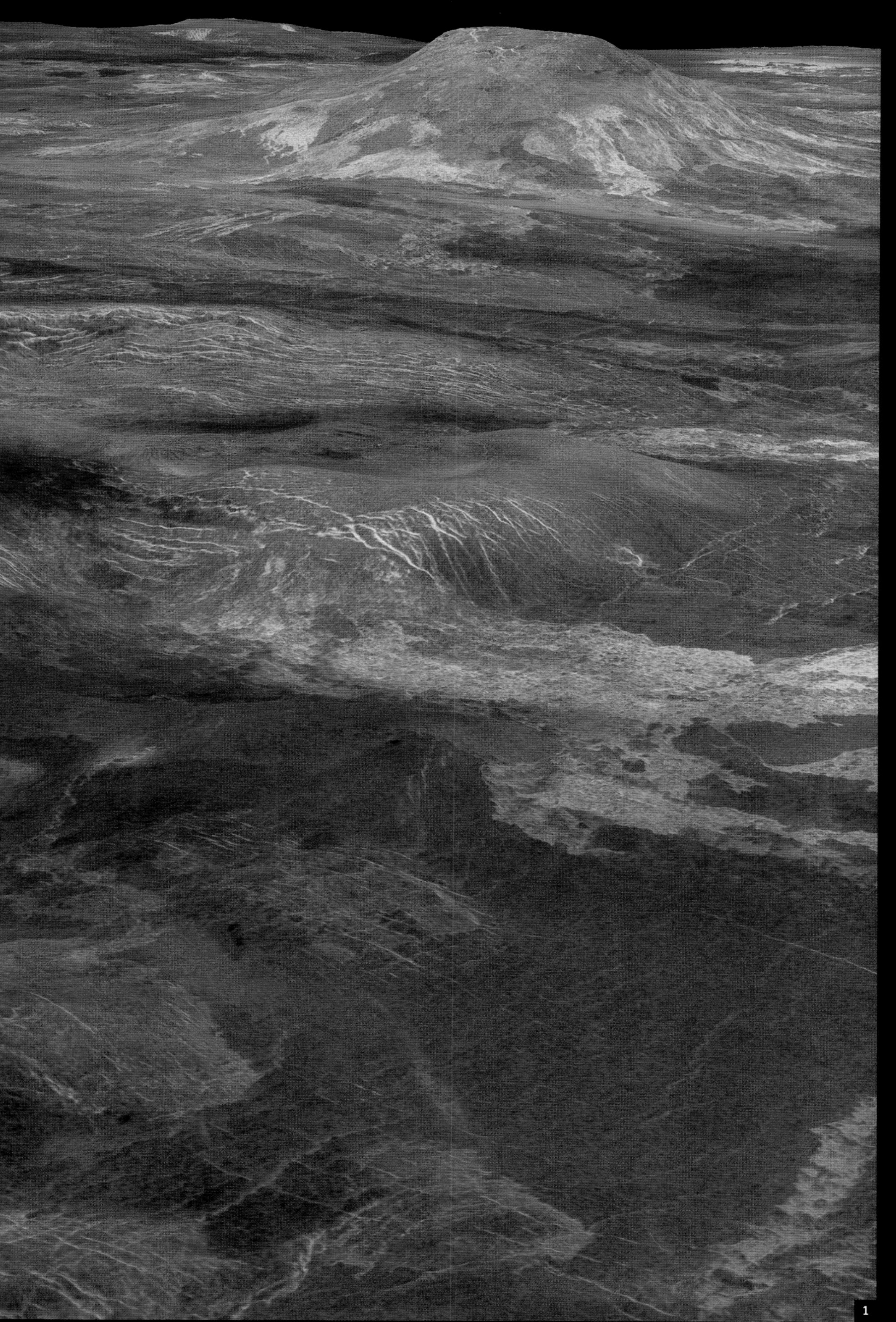
1

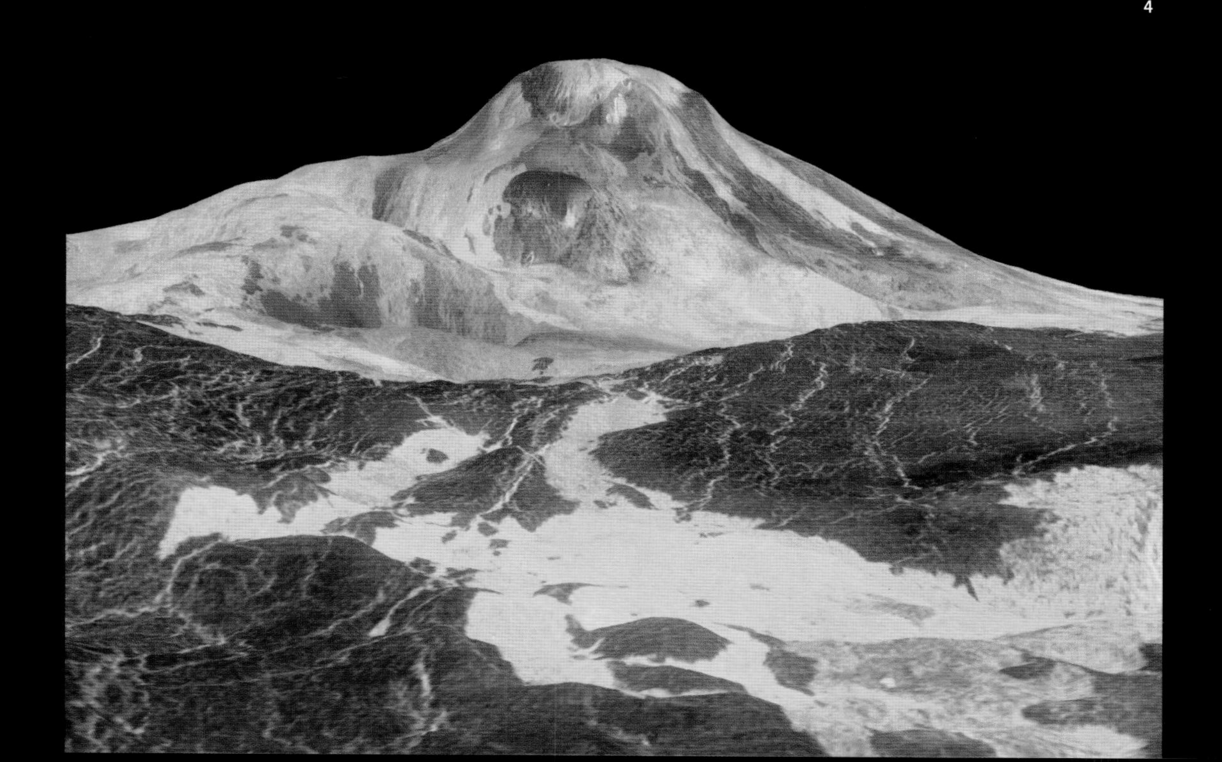
4

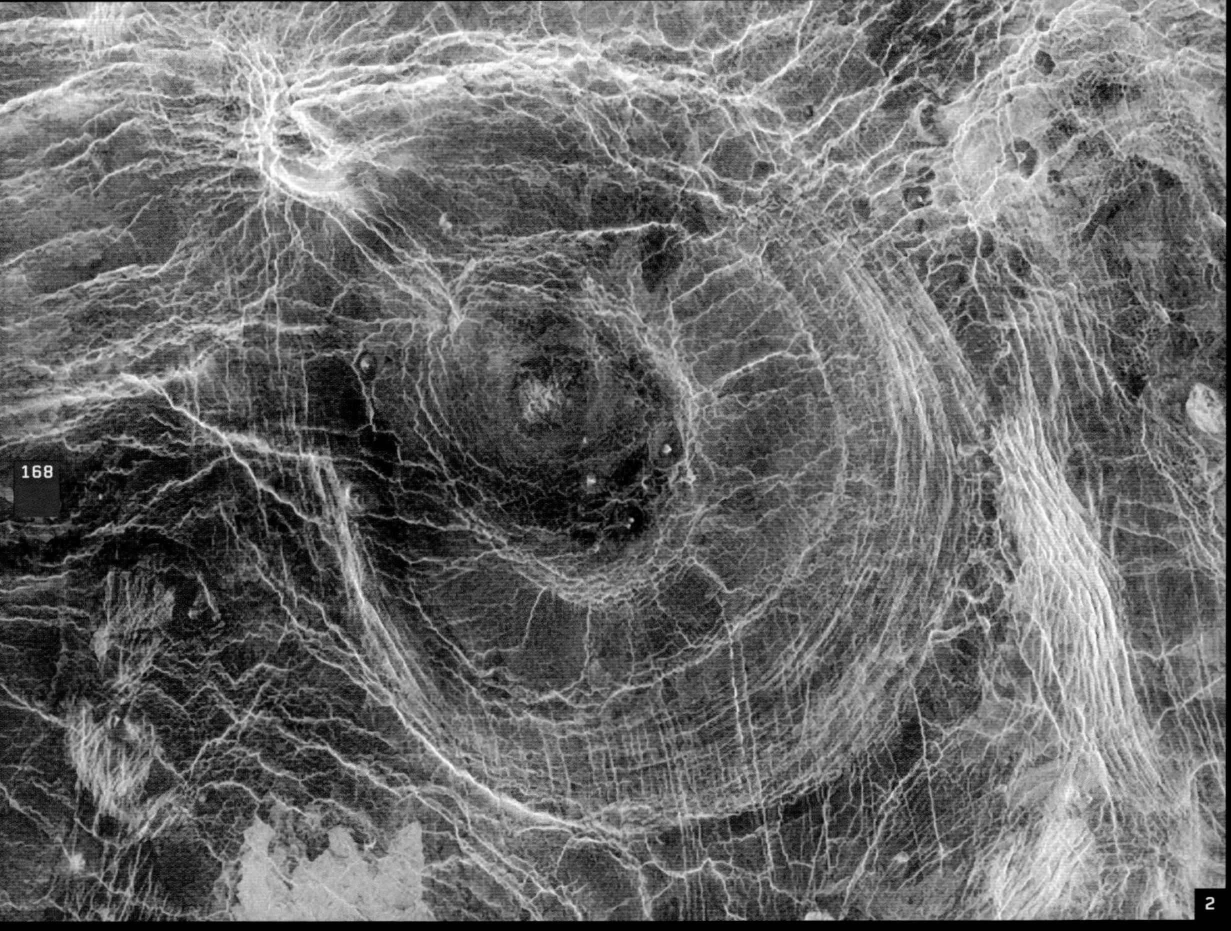

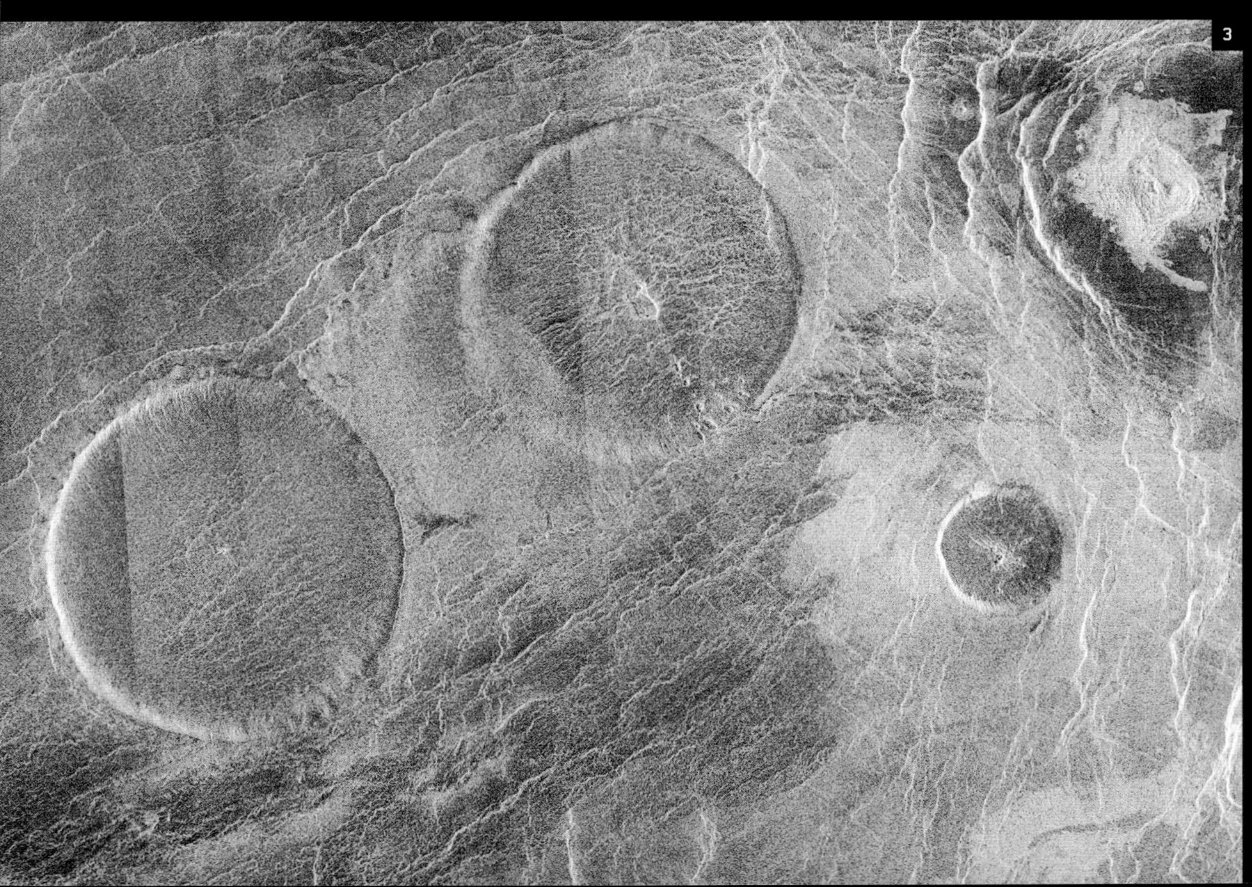

[1] Latona Corona
Coronae are circular features on Venus that were pushed upwards by rising domes of magma inside the planet. This is the eastern half of Latona Corona, which stretches across 1000 kilometres in total. Bright fractures within the corona appear to radiate away from its centre toward the rim.

[2] Arachnoids
These are large structures that so far have been found only on the surface of Venus. Russian scientists chose the term because of their resemblance to spider webs. Each arachnoid displays a complicated pattern of concentric oval fractures. More than 30 such features have been identified on Venus, with some spanning over 200 kilometres. It is possible that they are sn exotic relative of the volcano.

[3] Pancake domes
The prominent circular features here are volcanic domes, each one about 65 kilometres in diameter. They both have a broad, flat top and are less than a kilometre in height. These pancake domes are a type of volcano unique to Venus. They form from the eruption of a particularly viscous lava.

Venusian weather

Venus's dense atmosphere possesses a dynamic weather system. At the cloud tops, winds speeds reach 350 kilometres per hour, which is faster than hurricanes on Earth. At the surface, however, the wind is usually no more than a breeze. This is because the atmosphere is denser than the Earth's and so the lower layers are heavy and sluggish.

[4] Cloudy Venus
Venus has the thickest atmosphere of all the rocky planets. The pressure at the surface is over 90 times that of Earth's atmosphere. Whereas the clouds present an impenetrable blanket at optical wavelengths, the ultraviolet view of Venus shows more structure. Near the equator (right in this image) the clouds are patchy, giving a lacy appearance. At the mid-latitudes, the clouds become streaky and over the poles the clouds become an almost featureless haze called the polar cap.

[5-8] Polar vortex
At each rotation pole of Venus there is a vortex of gas. It is created when high-altitude gas from the warm equatorial region travels polewards, loses its heat and so sinks back to the lower levels of the atmosphere. This sequence of four images shows the rotation of Venus's southern hemisphere over a two Earth-day period in 2007. The green dot marks Venus' south pole.

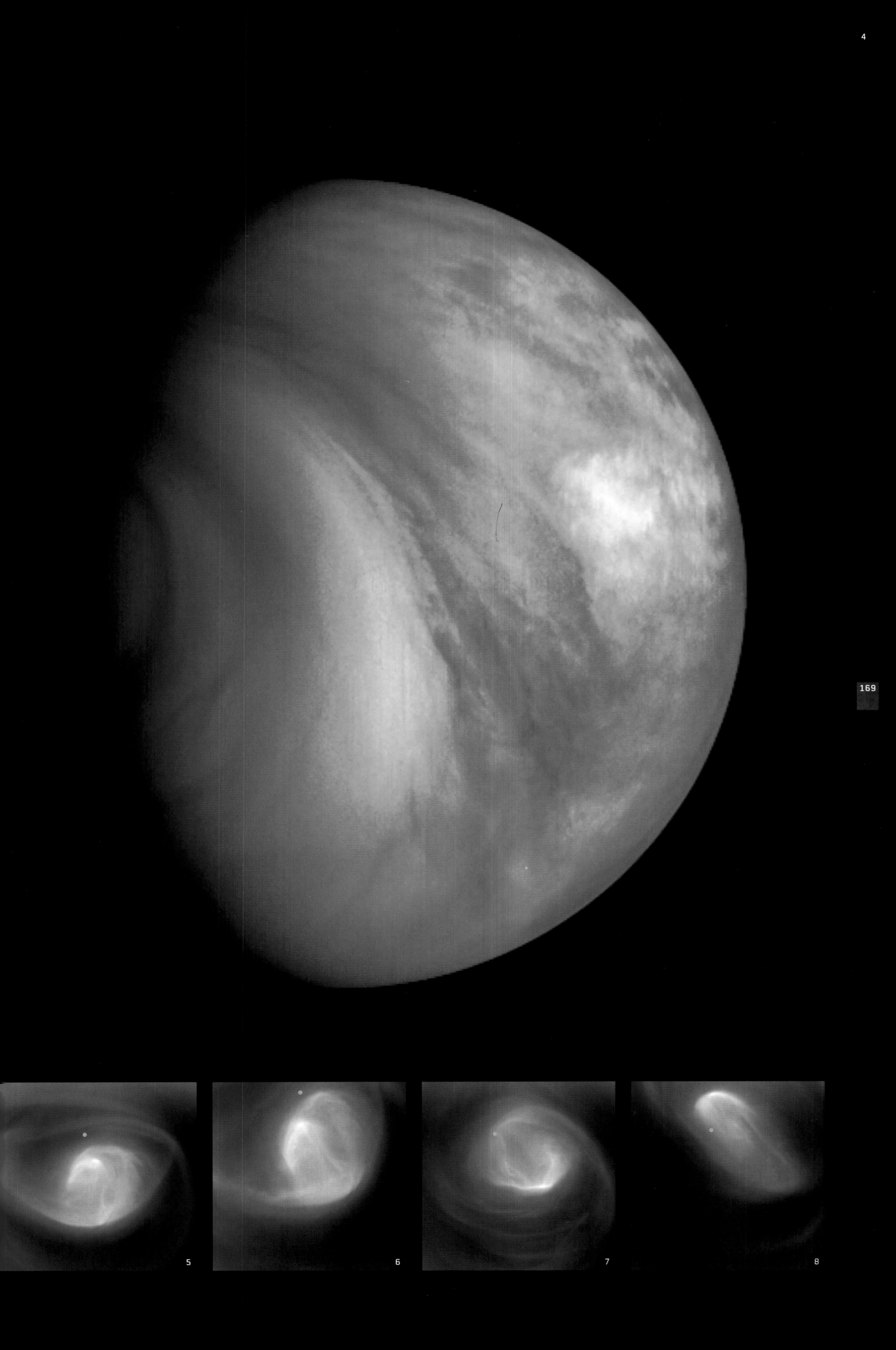
4
5
6
7
8

EARTH_

Earth means more to us than any other planet because it is our home. Scientists explore its many aspects from pole to pole, cataloguing its rich diversity of plants and creatures, and its amazing geology.

As a result, our knowledge of the Earth is becoming so detailed that it sometimes makes it more difficult to see it as a celestial object on a par with the other planets. Images from space make this easier, as we see the planet as a whole, rather than the parochial view we gain from the surface.

Earth is certainly a dynamic, beautiful world with a rich tapestry of interactions, many of which are similar to the other planets but, of course, one is unique: the widespread proliferation of life on its surface.

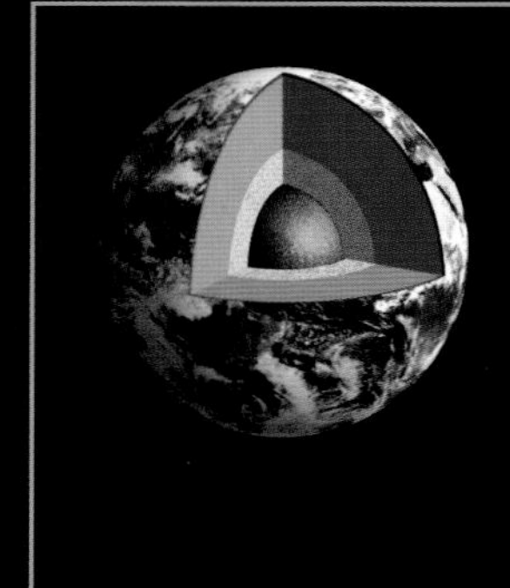

EARTH'S INTERIOR
Earth's iron-nickel core is split into two regions: the solid inner core and the partially molten outer core, where the Earth's magnetic field is generated. Atop this are a partially molten mantle of silicate material and a thin crust of rocks.

DISTANCE	DIAMETER	MASS	ROTATION PERIOD	ORBITAL PERIOD	MEAN SURFACE TEMPERATURE
150	12.7	1	24	365	288
MILLION KM	THOUSAND KM	EARTH	HOURS	DAYS	KELVIN

Home world

The largest of the terrestrial planets, a whisker ahead of Venus in terms of diameter, the Earth orbits the Sun in a nearly circular path. It takes our world approximately 365.25 days to complete this trek, measuring our year. As it does so, in just under 24 hours it rotates about its axis, giving night and day.

[1] Water world

Two thirds of the planet's surface is covered with water, forming the seas and oceans. Science fiction writer Arthur C. Clarke once remarked how much more appropriate it would be to call our planet Ocean instead of Earth. This image shows why. Viewed from the correct angle above the Pacific Ocean, virtually all the land disappears from sight.

[2-4] Seasonal changes

The Earth does not spin completely upright. In common with most of the other planets, its rotation axis is tilted. In Earth's case, the tilt is 23.4 degrees and gives the planet its seasons. When the northern hemisphere is titled towards the Sun, so it is northern summer. At the same time, in the southern hemisphere, it is winter because that hemisphere is tilted away from the Sun.

This tilt defines the location of the tropics and the Arctic and Antarctic Circles. The tropics are any location where the Sun will pass directly overhead at some stage during the year, so they are found within 23.4 degrees of the equator. The Arctic and Antarctic circles are defined as locations within which the Sun spends part of the year never setting. They are found within 23.4 degrees of the poles. When the Sun is never setting on one polar region thereby providing perpetual daylight, it is never rising on the other, leading to a period of perpetual night.

The seasonal cycle has a great effect on the appearance of the Polar Regions, especially the Arctic where the ice sheets advance and retreat in sympathy with the amount of solar radiation they receive. In January [2], when there is a period of perpetual night, the ice and snow creeps down across the continents, covering much of Canada, Scandinavia, Siberia and Alaska.

In April [3], the ice begins to retreat, revealing tundra and grasslands that begin their cycle of reproduction. By the time July arrives, summer has set in [4] and the Sun remains in the sky for months on end, the ice and snow is mostly confined to Greenland and the high Canadian Arctic.

Then, as autumn arrives, the snow and ice begin to return and the cycle starts again.

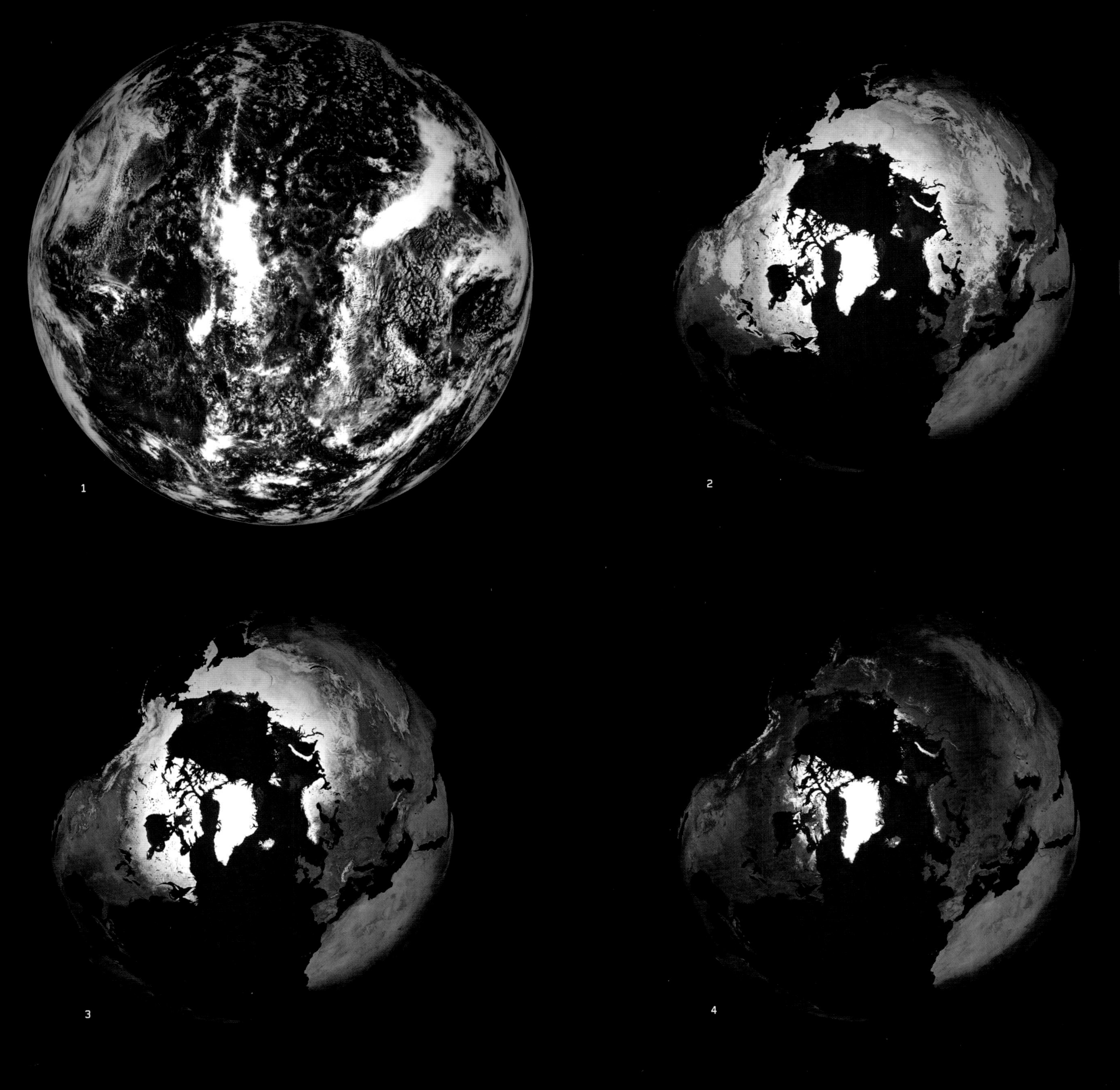

1 2 3 4

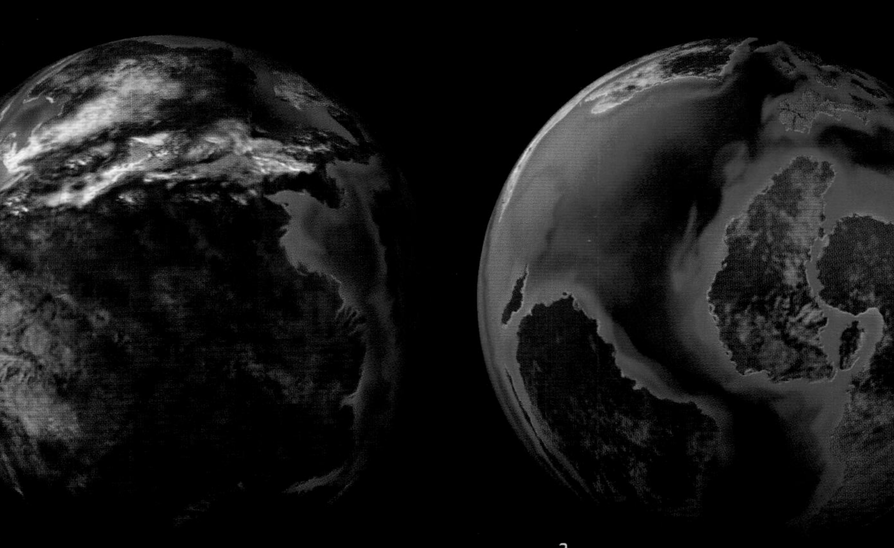

1 2

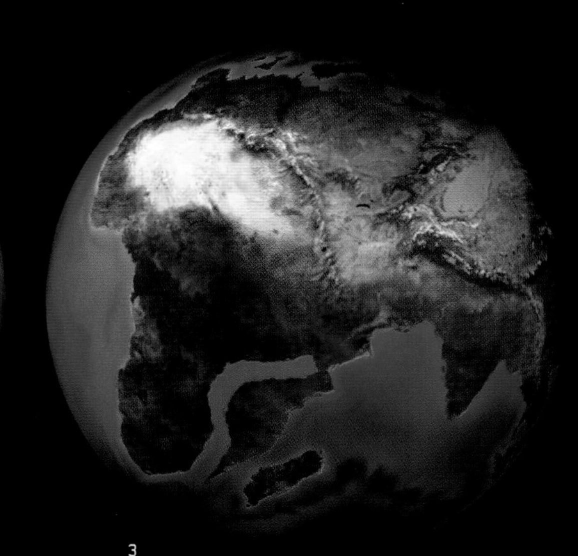

3

A restless planet

Earth's surface is not a solid shell. Instead its crust is fractured into a number of geological plates. These move, guided by the slow but perpetual forces at work inside the planet. Hence, over millions of years, the arrangement of the continents changes.

[1-3] The changing face of the Earth

Two hundred and seventy million years ago [1], most of the Earth's land masses were huddled together forming a supercontinent called Pangaea, surrounded by an enormous ocean known as Panthalassa. On land, Life was beginning to thrive, with the appearance of lizards, amphibians, insects and reptiles but the dinosaurs were still some 40 million years in the future.

By 65 million years ago [2], Pangaea had broken up and Panthalassa was being divided into separate oceans and seas. The dinosaurs had enjoyed a long existence but their reign was coming to an end. Eventually, the slow migration of the continents would produce the familiar arrangement we instantly recognize as Earth today.

Continental drift is an ongoing process and so the Earth will continue to change. In 50 million years' time [3], Africa will have closed the Mediterranean Sea and collided with Europe. Meanwhile, the Americas will have drifted further away.

[4] New rocks

As the plates move around the Earth, so the crust is recycled. This occurs either when plates are pushed up into mountain ranges, which are then eroded away, or when they are driven down into the Earth's interior, where they are melted and catapulted back to the surface as volcanic lava. Where plates are moving apart, so new rocks are created on the ocean floor. Volcanic lava spills upwards and solidifies to become new crustal rock. In the process, it is imprinted with the direction and strength of Earth's ever changing magnetic field. Geologists use this to tell the age of the rocks and can thus chart continental drift. In the image below [4], the youngest rocks have been colour-coded red and the oldest blue.

4

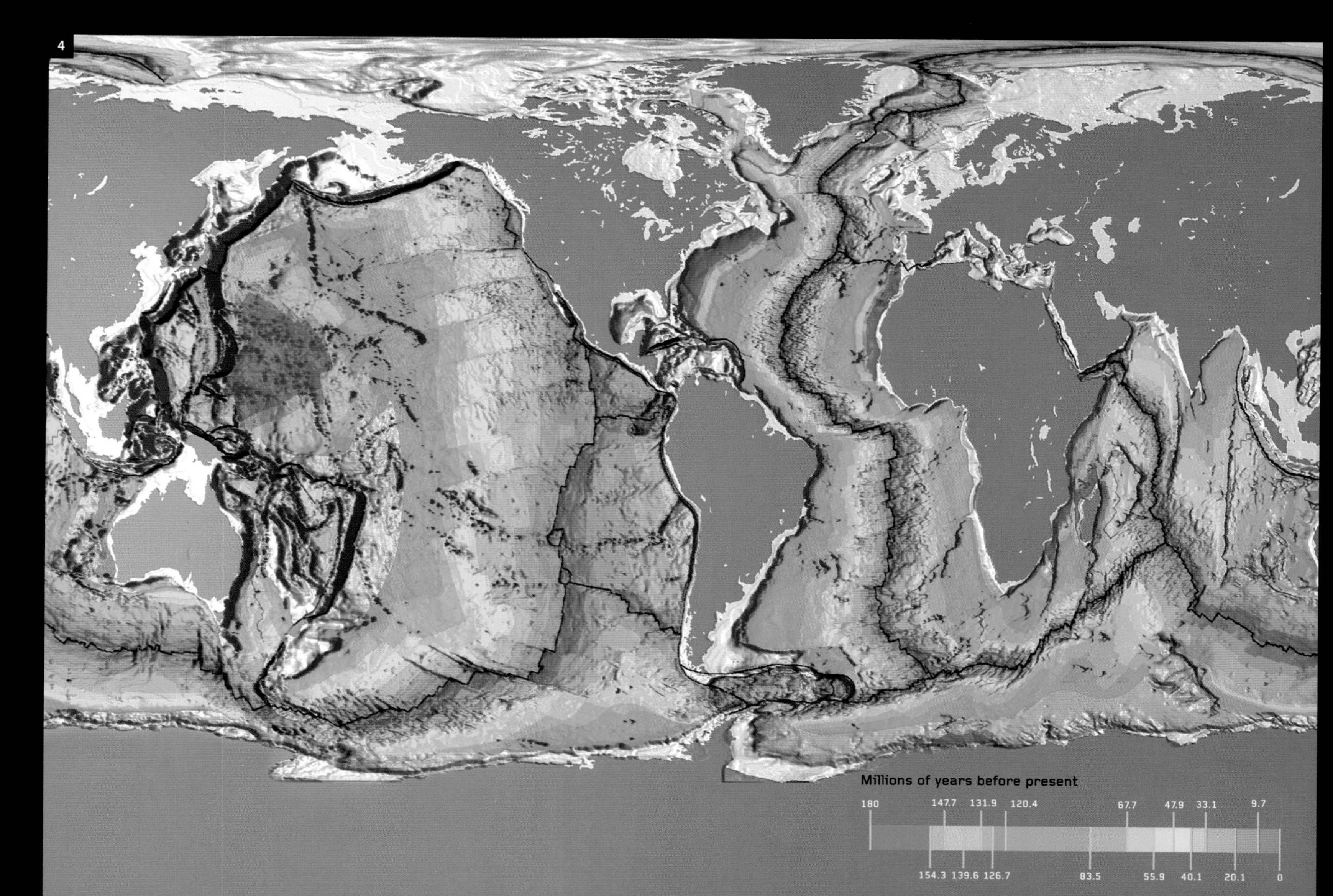

Mount Everest

The collision of India into Asia has pushed up the surrounding rocks into the extraordinary Himalayan mountain range. The most famous of these peaks is Mount Everest, the highest mountain in the world. The mountain range is young, having begun forming some 50 million years ago when India finally closed the Tethys Ocean, which separated it from Asia. Moving at 15 centimetres per year, the mountains are still being pushed upwards. The weather then erodes the rocks into jagged peaks.

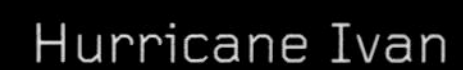

Hurricane Ivan

Looking down from the International Space Station, astronauts saw Hurricane Ivan as it swept through the Caribbean. It grew to become the strongest storm of the 2004 Atlantic hurricane season and caused grave damage to the islands of Grenada, Jamaica, Grand Cayman and Cuba. It also swept across southern states of America, spawning 117 tornados. The top wind speeds recorded in this hurricane were 260 kilometres per hour.

2

3

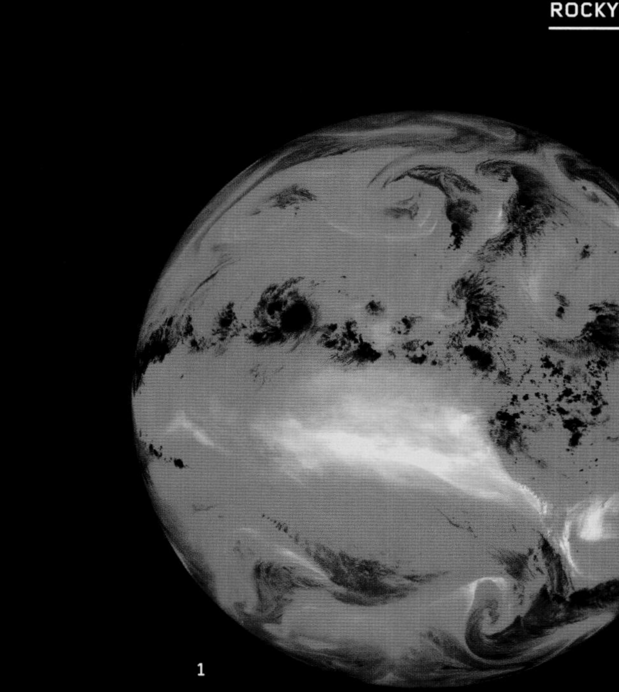

1

Wind and weather

The Earth's atmosphere is powered by the influx of solar radiation and the rotation of the Earth. Together, these two awesome powers stir the atmosphere, sometimes into a frenzy of activity.

[1] Water vapour

Water vapour absorbs infrared radiation and then re-emits it again. So this infrared image of Earth reveals the extent of water vapour in the atmosphere of the Earth. Bright areas are loaded with more water vapour than dark areas. It can be seen swirling and cascading with the wind patterns.

[2-4] Sand dunes

As the winds whip across the Earth, so they interact with the surface. Nowhere is this more obvious than in deserts, where the sands can be sculpted into ever-moving dunes. Dunes come in a variety of shapes and sizes.

In image [2], the Rub Al Khali Desert in Saudi Arabia displays lines of crescent sand dunes. These form when the sand supply is small and a single wind direction prevails. Elsewhere in the Rub Al Khali Desert, where there is plenty of sand and a predominant wind direction, longitudinal dunes tend to form [3].

The sand dunes in the Grand Erg Oriental, near the border between Tunisia, Libya and Algeria in North Africa, have a peculiar form like that of a jellyfish [4]. They are the result of winds blowing from many directions. Each dune is approximately 100 metres in height and 2 kilometres long.

[5] Ozone hole

Ozone is comprised of three oxygen atoms joined together in a molecule. It performs a vital function in the atmosphere because it filters out wavelengths of ultraviolet radiation harmful to living things. In the 1980s, polar scientists discovered that a hole in the ozone layer of our atmosphere opens every spring over the Antarctic. Shown here, the quantity of ozone is represented by the height of the contour, giving a graphic sense of the hole.

This hole has been linked to the widespread use of chlorofluorocarbons in manmade products. Such chemicals have largely been phased out now, and The World waits to see if the ozone hole will recover.

4

5

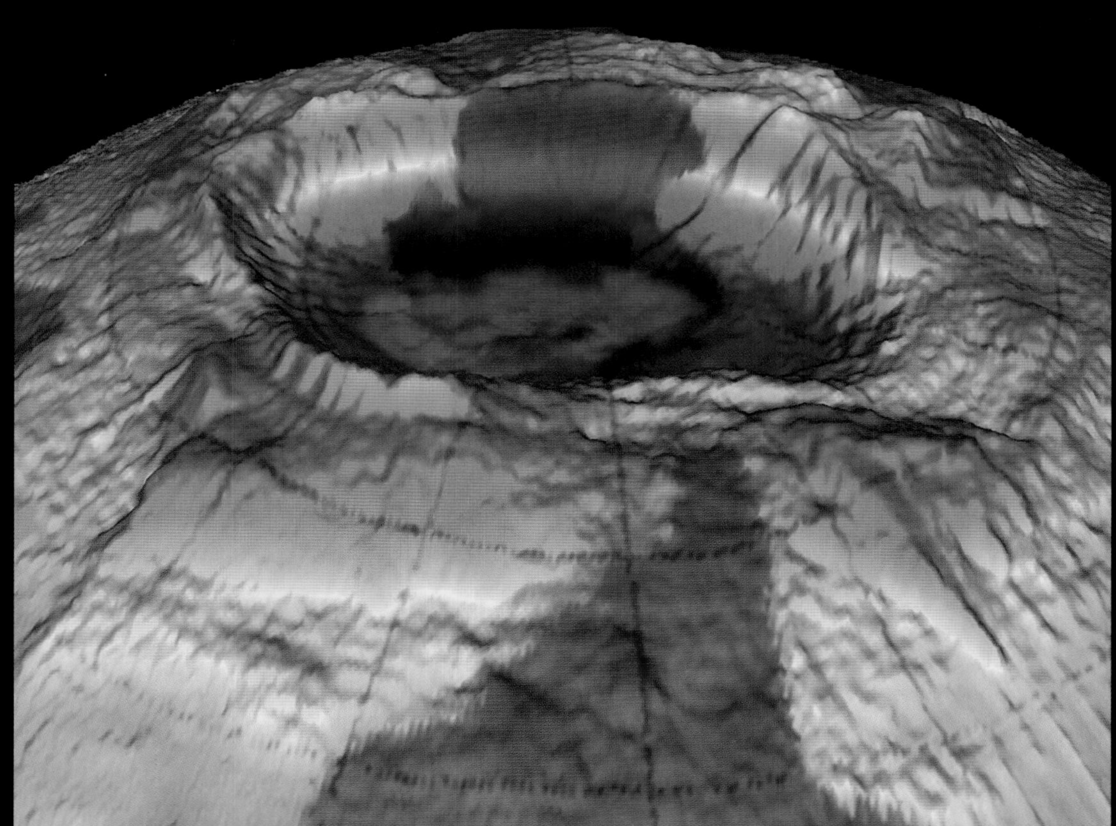

1

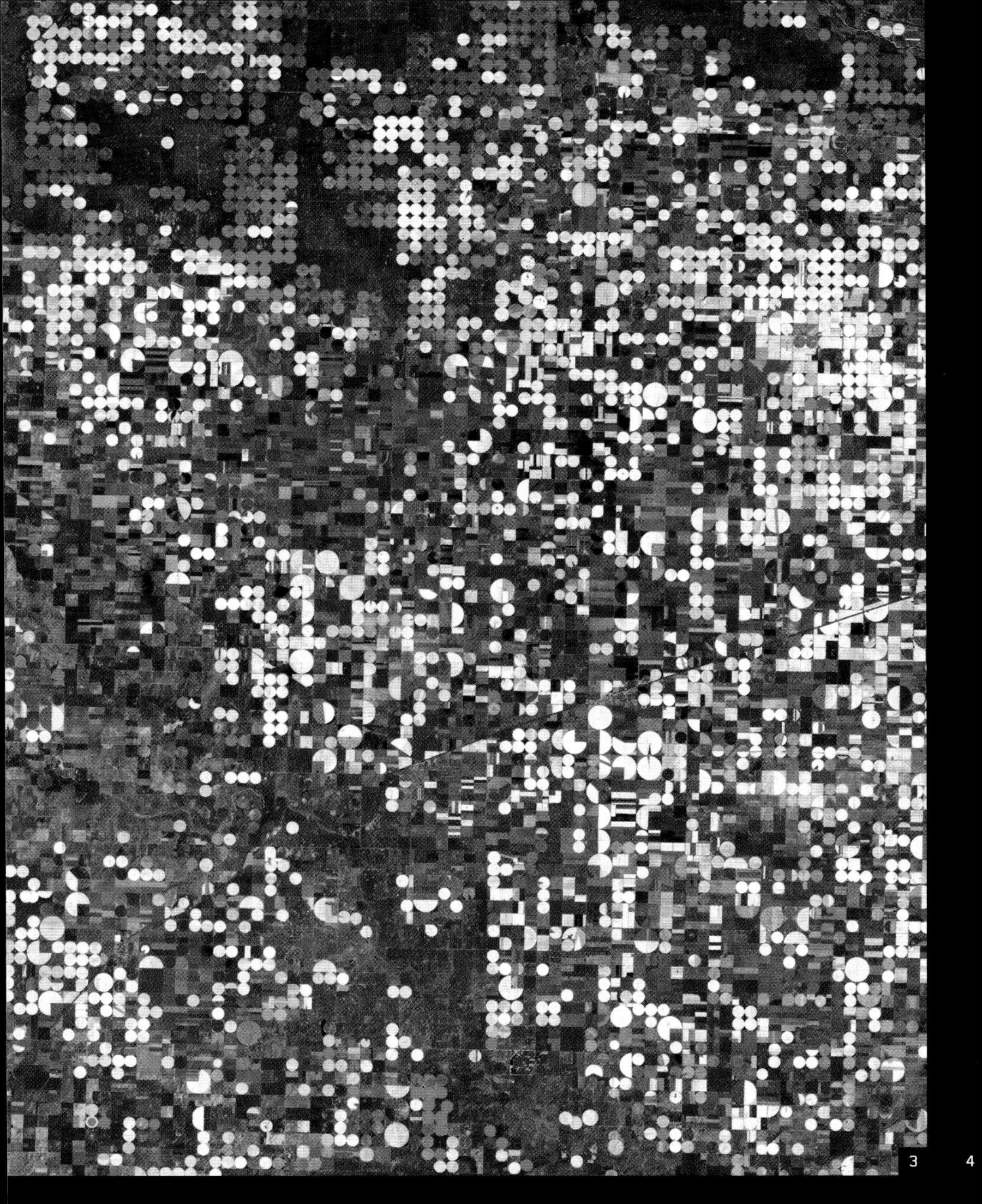

3

4

Life on Earth

If there is one thing that sets Earth apart from its celestial siblings, it is the widespread presence of life on our world. Earth appears to sit in an orbital sweet spot where it receives just as much energy as it needs to keep water liquid on our surface.

2

[1] Phytoplankton bloom
Water is considered essential for life. Indeed, there is an enormous proliferation of both simple and complex life in the ocean. One of the most visible clues to life's presence on Earth comes not from humans but from tiny, water-borne organisms known as phytoplankton. They thrive on sunlight, much as plants do, and feed from the nutrients found in the water. In this image, the phytoplankton has bloomed, creating rich swirls of green in the ocean off western Iceland. Such sudden proliferations happen when the sea conditions are right. In this case, cooling water has plunged to the ocean floor, stirring up nutrients from the depths to feed the simple creatures.

[2] Human signals
Humans mostly betray their presence by the stray emissions from their technology. This includes pollution pumped into the atmosphere but is not confined to harmful emissions. For example, radio transmissions are leaking from our planet all the time, making us like the noisy neighbours who won't turn the radio down. This image shows another wasteful emission from the trappings of civilization: light. This view of the Earth shows the light emitted by cities across Europe and Asia.

[3] Kansas's fields
From orbit around the Earth, the changes that mankind has brought to the surface of the planet become much more noticeable. This is part of Kansas that has been converted to large-scale agriculture. The fields are mostly circular because mechanical devices that pivot from a central point are irrigating them. Colours have been used to code where the field is still growing (red) or whether it has been harvested (white).

[4] Black Smokers
Deep in the ocean there are hot-water vents called 'black smokers'. Here, water that has seeped down through the bedrock has been heated by volcanic activity and shot back up into the cold surrounding ocean. On its journey back upwards, it dissolves a multitude of chemicals that cause the black colour of the water jets. Amazingly, scientists have discovered a plethora of bacterial life clustered around these hot vents, feeding off the chemicals found in the water. Analysis shows that they are some of the earliest living cells on the planet to develop. Could these be the sites where life began on our world? Scientists are investigating the possibility.

MOON_

Earth's natural satellite is unique. Although not the largest moon in the Solar System, it is the largest moon in proportion to its parent world by a long way. Planetary geologists and astronomers believe that it may have been formed in a giant impact that nearly destroyed Earth. According to computer simulations, if the Earth were struck a glancing blow by a Mars-sized planet around 4.6 billion years ago, it would not shatter our world but would throw a colossal cloud of debris into orbit. This then accumulated to form the Moon.

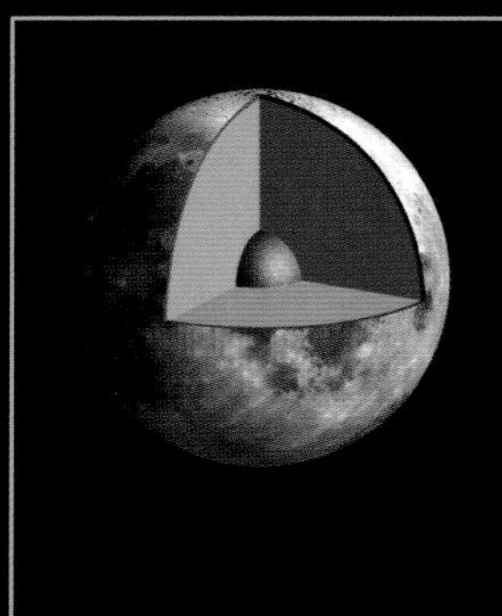

LUNAR INTERIOR
The Moon possesses a small core of metallic substances. This supports the theory that it accumulated from rocky debris following an impact. Above the core, there is a deep mantle of solid rocks and then a crust.

[1, 2] Lunar composition

At visible wavelengths, the Moon's face is a patchwork of greys [1]. This image was taken by a passing spaceprobe, looking down onto the Moon's north polar region. The Humboldtianum Basin, a 650-kilometre impact structure partly filled with dark volcanic deposits, is seen at the centre of the image. The north pole itself is just inside the shadow zone, about a third of the way from the top left of the illuminated region.

The dark lunar 'seas' are the obvious feature of the sun-lit side. To the upper left is Mare Imbrium; to the middle left is Mare Serenitatis; to the lower left is Mare Tranquillitatis. Mare Crisium completes the gathering and is the dark circular feature toward the bottom of the image. The dark lava plains of the Marginis and Smythii Basins can be seen at the lower right.

False colouring the image, according to the various wavelengths of light reflected from the surface gives a different view that reflects the minerals and composition at the surface [2]. Bright pinkish areas are highland materials, such as those surrounding the oval, lava-filled Mare Crisium toward the bottom of the picture. Blue and green to orange shades indicate volcanic lava flows. To the left of Crisium, the dark blue Mare Tranquillitatis is richer in titanium than the green and orange Mare Serenitatis above it. Light blue colours represent thin mineral-rich soils, associated with relatively recent impacts, with the youngest craters having prominent blue rays extending from them.

The identities of surface chemicals and minerals are important both for testing theories of lunar formation and as possible resources for astronauts to use on future Moon bases. The fact that the lunar surface is rich in rare metals such as titanium has led some to propose that mining operations on the Moon could be profitable.

Beneath the surface, the bulk composition is where the biggest clue to the Moon's formation lies. Taken as a whole, the Moon is remarkably light, containing mostly rocky material and minerals. This is surprising because, if the Moon and Earth formed side by side, they should be made of exactly the same proportions of rocks to metals. Yet they are not sufficiently different for astronomers to think that the Moon formed elsewhere and was just captured by Earth's gravity.

The impact origin theory explains the mild differences because, after the blow some of the heavier material, the metals, fall back to the Earth whilst the lighter matter, the rocks, stay in space to form the Moon.

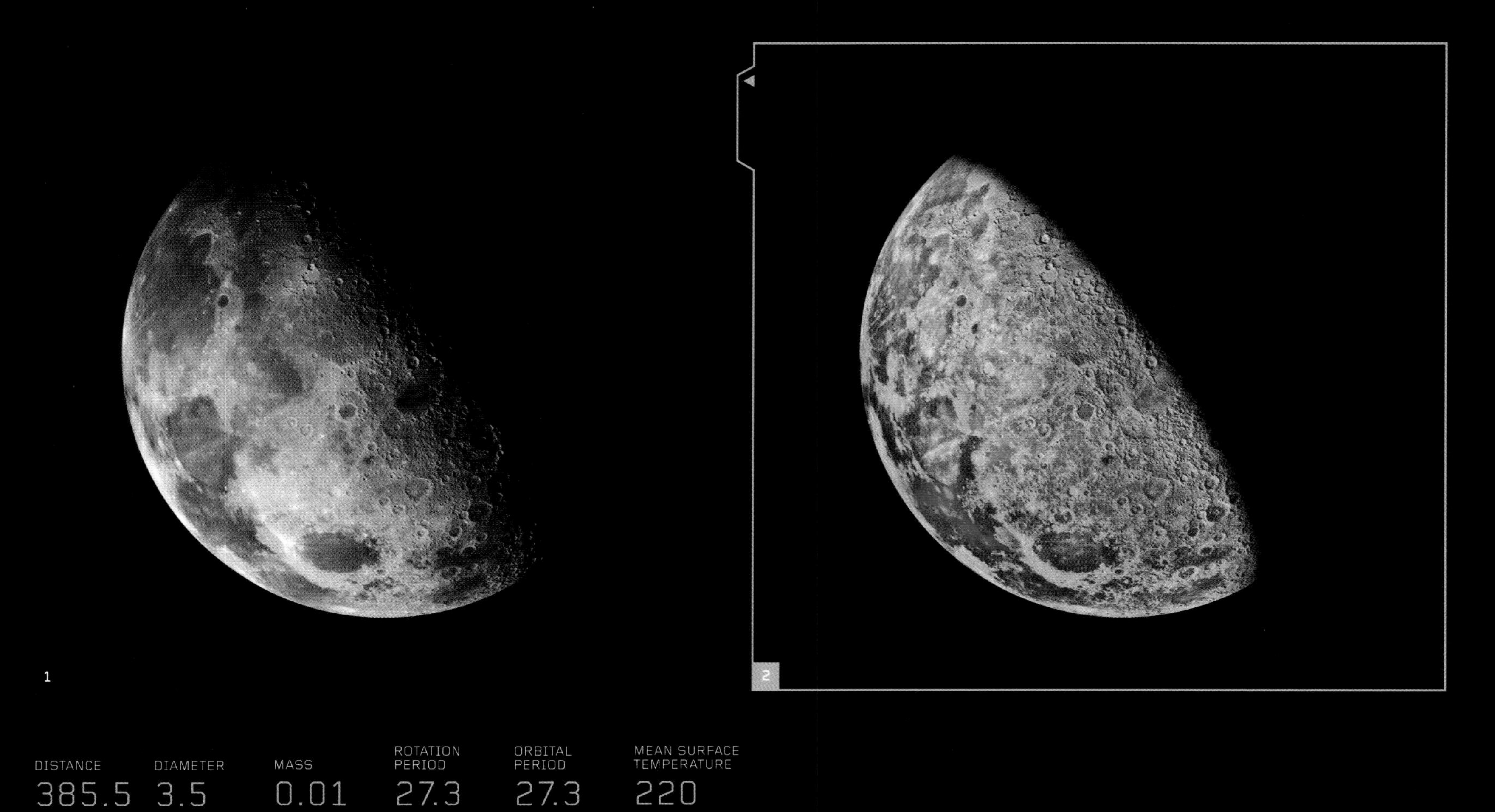

1

2

DISTANCE	DIAMETER	MASS	ROTATION PERIOD	ORBITAL PERIOD	MEAN SURFACE TEMPERATURE
385.5	3.5	0.01	27.3	27.3	220
THOUSAND KM	THOUSAND KM	EARTHS	DAYS	DAYS	KELVIN

As the Apollo 17 spacecraft rounded the Moon, it saw a crescent-shaped Earth rise over the lunar limb. The sight reversed the usual roles of these two celestial bodies to human eyes.

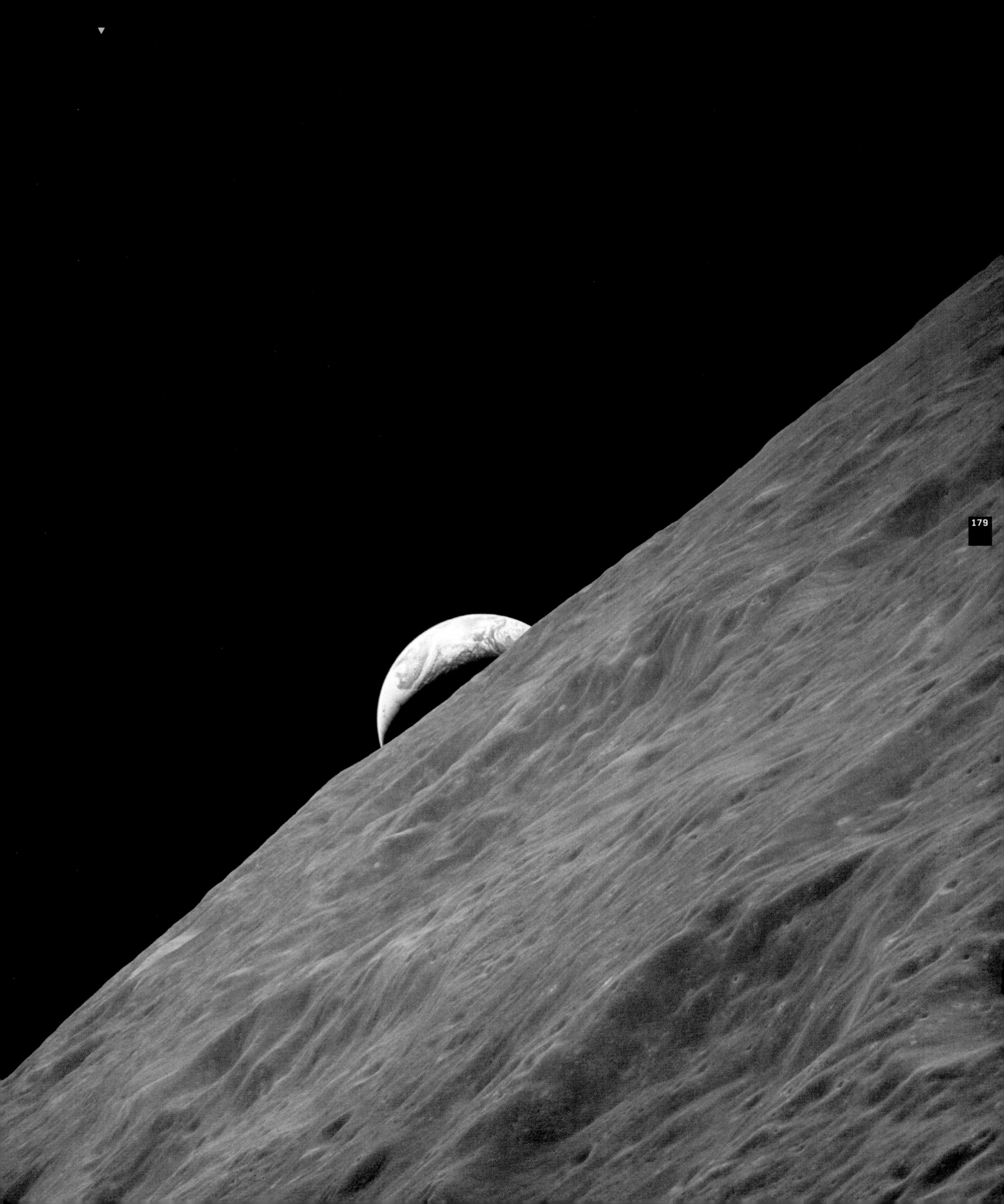

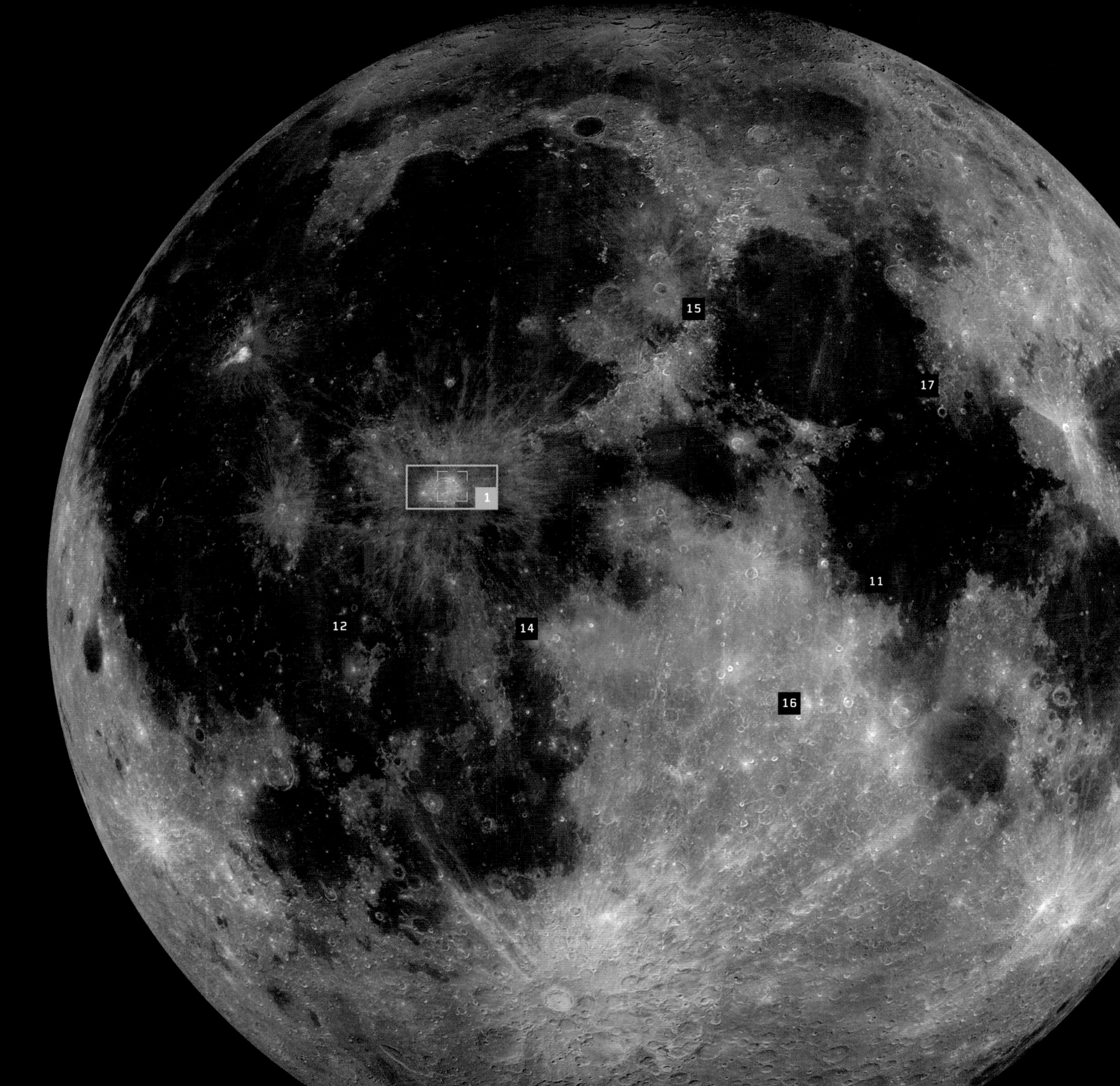

Near side

The gravity of the Earth locks the Moon into spinning just once during its 27-day orbit. This means that the Moon only ever shows one face to Earth. The lunar near side is marked out by the dark areas. These are known as the lunar maria, or the lunar seas. They were once thought to be real bodies of water on the surface of the Moon but are now known to be solidified lava plains.

[1] Copernicus Crater

Estimated to be 800 million years old, Copernicus Crater sits in the eastern region of Oceanus Procellarum, the Sea of Storms. It stretches to a diameter of 93 kilometres and sinks to a depth of 3.8 kilometres.

Landing table

[11] Apollo 11
Mare Tranquillitatis
July 20, 1969

[11] Apollo 12
Oceanus Procellarum
November 19, 1969

[14] Apollo 14
Fra Mauro
February 5, 1971

[15] Apollo 15
Hadley-Apennines
July 30, 1971

[16] Apollo 16
Descartes
April 21, 1972

[17] Apollo 17
Taurus-Littrow
December 11, 1972

Far side

The lunar far side was a total mystery until spacecraft became capable of orbiting the Moon. The pictures they returned have built up our understanding of this hidden hemisphere. Most noticeably, the lunar far side does not feature the large dark lava plains of the near side. Over 97 percent of the lunar far side is covered in impact craters, most of them preserved since the origin of the Solar System.

[2] Tsiolkovsky crater

Unusually for a crater on the far side, Tsiolkovsky has been filled with dark lava. The impact has fractured the crustal rocks, allowing the molten lava to reach the surface. 13 kilometres across, it is named after the Russian rocket pioneer.

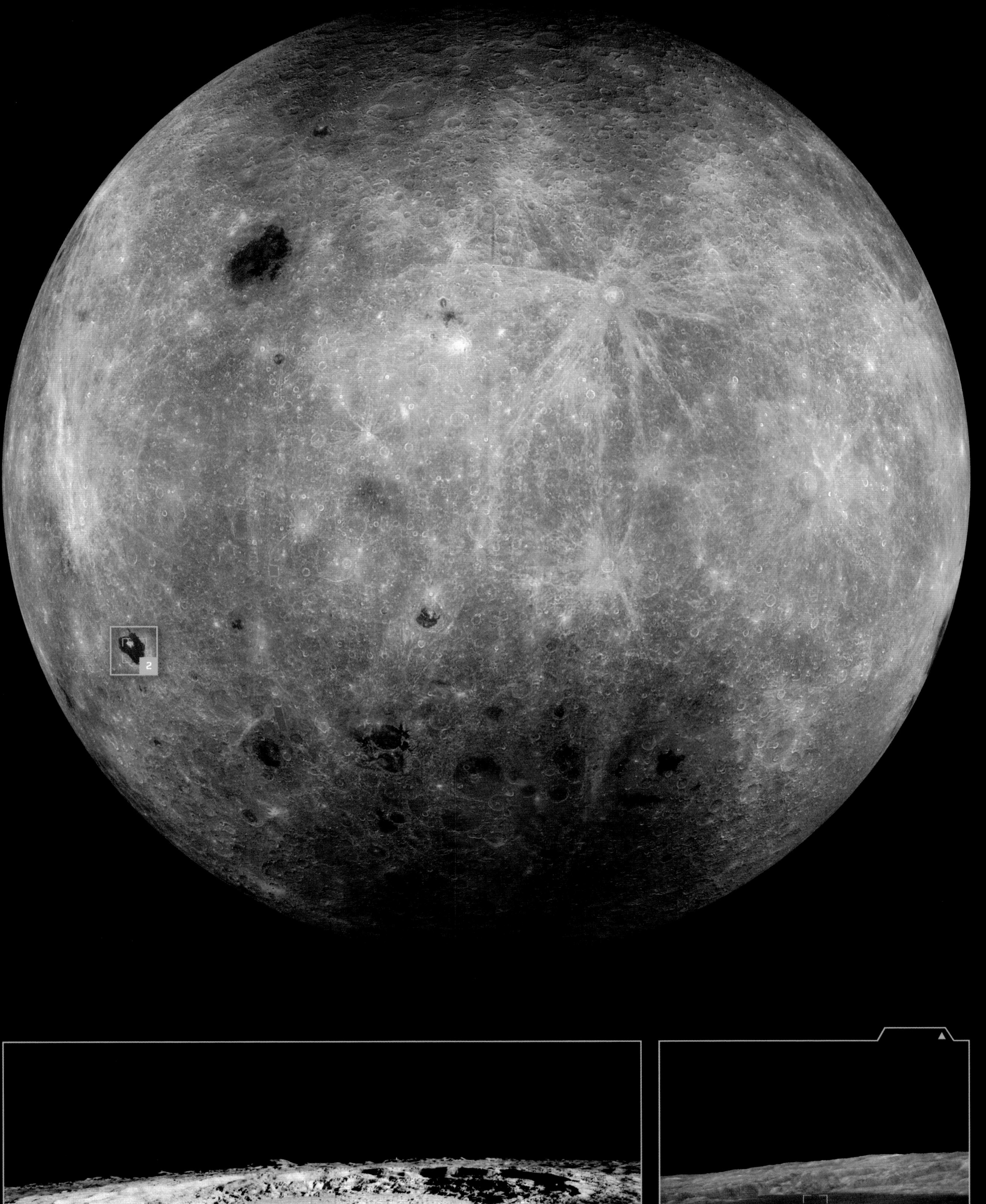
2

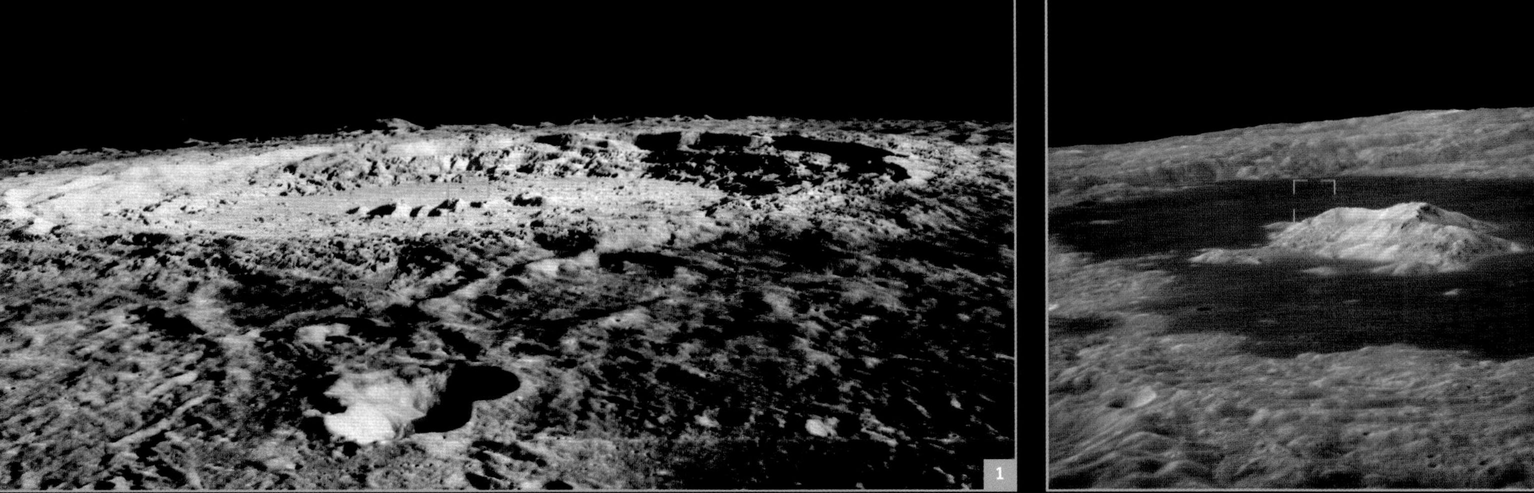
1
2

1

Human lunar exploration

The Moon is the only celestial object, other than Earth, that humans have set foot on. Between 1969 and 1972, there were six successful lunar landings. These were preceded by a plethora of unmanned probes that tested landing technology and surveyed the moon with cameras looking for safe places to land.

[1] Geologist on the Moon
Astronaut Harrison Schmidt skips across the lunar surface. Apollo astronauts quickly discovered that skipping rather than walking was the easiest method of locomotion in the weaker lunar gravity. Schmidt trained as a geologist before he became an astronaut. He spent a record-breaking 7.6 hours outside the lunar module, on the surface of the Moon. He collected rocks and drove some 23 kilometres in the lunar rover.

[2] Shorty Crater
Here, Schmidt pauses on the rim of the Shorty Crater. As well as returning rocks to the Earth for later analysis, the Apollo astronauts also deployed numerous pieces of scientific equipment on the lunar surface. These included seismometers to record the moon's meagre geological activity – slight tremors have been dubbed moonquakes. Another piece of equipment left behind was a mirror that allows a laser beam from Earth to be reflected back from the Moon. This has enabled the movement of the Moon to be so precisely measured that it is providing insight into the workings of gravity itself.

[3] Forever footprints
Taken at 02:56 GMT on 21 July 1969, Neil Armstrong's first footsetps will remain on the moon for millions of years. There is no wind on the Moon, so only the collision of particles coming from the Sun and deep space will gradually erode them.

[4] The Marsh of Decay
The Lunar Command Module 'Falcon' took Apollo 15's astronauts to an area of the Mare Imbrium known as Palus Putredinus (the Marsh of Decay). to investigate a collapsed lava tube from an ancient lunar volcano.

2

3
4

MARS_

Instantly recognisable by its red visage, Mars is approximately half the size of the Earth, and contains about one tenth of its mass. This equates to a gravitational force at the surface of Mars just over a third that of our own planet.

Mars excites our imaginations because it reminds us of Earth. It has volcanoes, polar caps, rift valleys and what appear to be dried-up riverbeds. Yet Mars has more than this. Mixed in with the familiar features are an abundance of impact craters, making the Red Planet a hybrid, something intermediate between our world and Mercury.

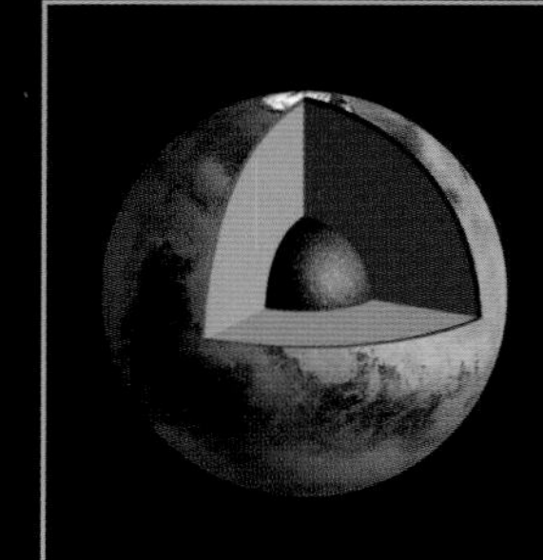

MARS'S INTERIOR
Mars is dominated by a large mantle, which surrounds a small, almost certainly solidified core. The crust of Mars is a single, solid plate covering the whole planet.

1

DISTANCE	DIAMETER	MASS	ROTATION PERIOD	ORBITAL PERIOD	MEAN SURFACE TEMPERATURE
228	6.7	0.1	24.6	687	227
MILLION KM	THOUSAND KM	EARTHS	HOURS	DAYS	KELVIN

[1] Valles Marineris region
Discovered in 1971 by NASA's Mariner 9 probe and well over 2000 kilometres long and up to 8 kilometres deep, Valles Marineris is the largest canyon in the Solar System. By comparison, the Grand Canyon in Arizona is only 446 kilometres long and 1.6 kilometres deep.

2

3

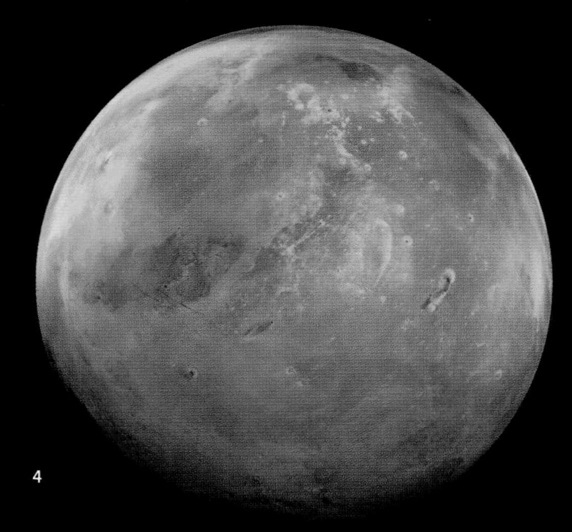
4

[2] Schiaparelli region
The 471-kilometre-wide Schiaparelli impact crater sits close to Mars's equator. It is the large circular feature in the centre of this image. The crater is named after Giovanni Schiaparelli, the pioneering astronomer who mapped Mars through a telescope during the 19th century.

The bright white areas to the south of the planet are areas covered in carbon dioxide frost. This includes the circular Hellas impact basin on the limb of the planet at lower right.

[3] Syrtis Major region
The prominent dark zone is known as Syrtis Major and was the first feature seen on Mars from Earth. The Dutch astronomer Christiaan Huygens marked it on a drawing of Mars back in 1659. It was initially assumed to be an ocean but now its dark colour is known to indicate an expanse of the volcanic rock, basalt. Syrtis Major spans an area 1500 kilometres by 1000 kilometres.

The bright cap just visible at the bottom of the planet is the permanent southern polar cap, composed of both carbon dioxide ice and water ice.

[4] Cerberus region
The Cerberus region is the dark marking to the left of centre. It does not reflect as much light as its surroundings because of differences in the composition of the rock here. The misty appearance of certain parts of this image is due to thin white clouds suspended in the planet's atmosphere.

Although difficult to see, a major geological boundary runs across the bottom third of this image. It differentiates terrains of the southern highlands from the northern plains on Mars.

Martian moons

Two moons orbit Mars. They are little more than asteroids and were probably captured by the planet when they strayed too close rather than being formed around Mars.

Phobos is the larger of the two moons [5] and has the dubious distinction of being the closest orbiting moon to any parent planet. Calculations show that it is in a gradually spiralling orbit that will eventually end with it falling to the surface and colliding with Mars. Even though it is a small body, Phobos is itself heavily cratered, indicating a violent past.

Then there is the second, even smaller, moon, Deimos [6]. It may have been in orbit around Phobos, allowing both asteroids to be captured at the same time, rather than in two separate events.

Both moons are gravitationally locked into always showing the same face to Mars. Like our own Moon, they rotate only once as they orbit their planet. Hence, their orbital periods and their rotational periods are the same.

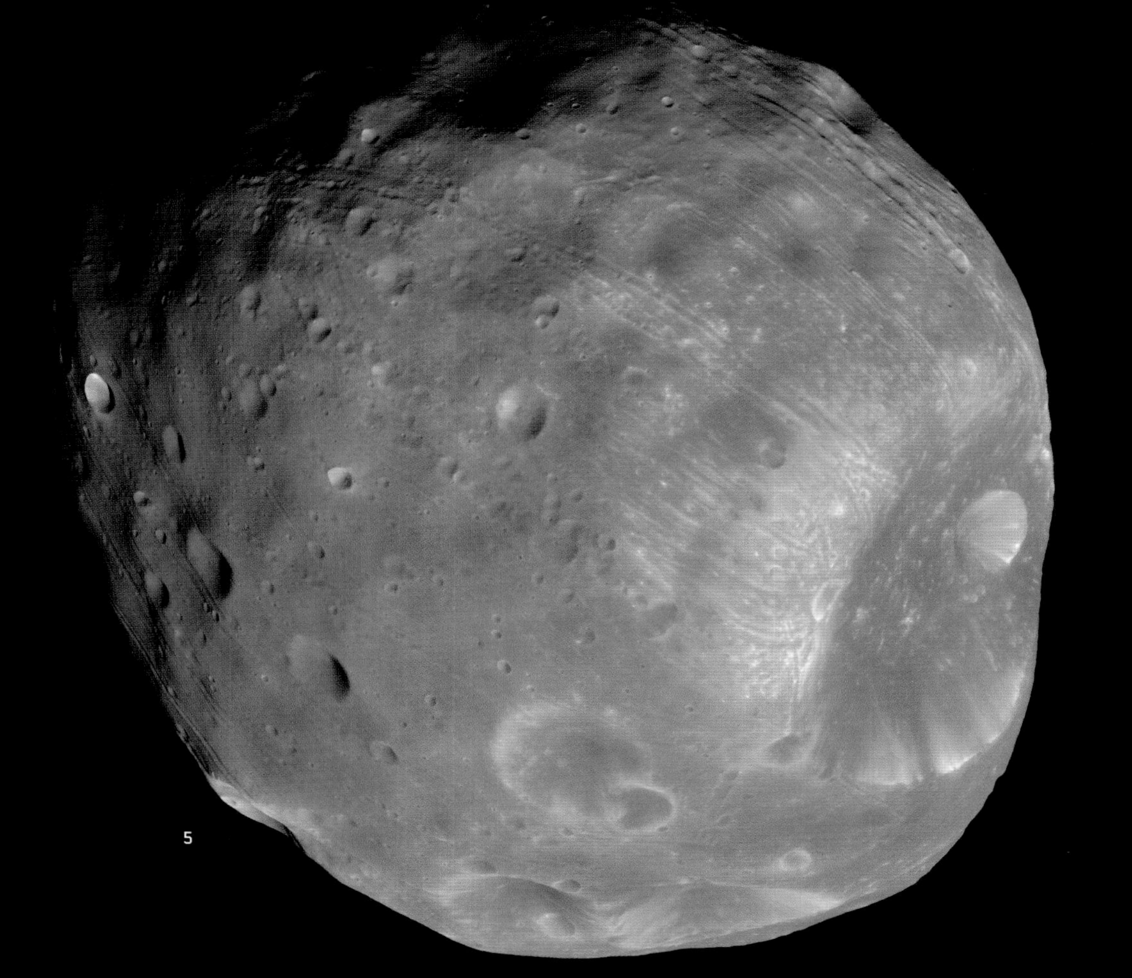
5

[5] Phobos

DISTANCE FROM MARS	DIAMETER	MASS	ROTATION PERIOD	ORBITAL PERIOD	MEAN SURFACE TEMPERATURE
9.6	22	1.8	7.7	7.7	233
THOUSAND KM	KILOMETRES	nanoEARTHS	HOURS	HOURS	KELVIN

[6] Deimos

DISTANCE FROM MARS	DIAMETER	MASS	ROTATION PERIOD	ORBITAL PERIOD	MEAN SURFACE TEMPERATURE
23.5	6.2	0.3	1.26	1.26	233
THOUSAND KM	KILOMETRES	nanoEARTHS	DAYS	DAYS	KELVIN

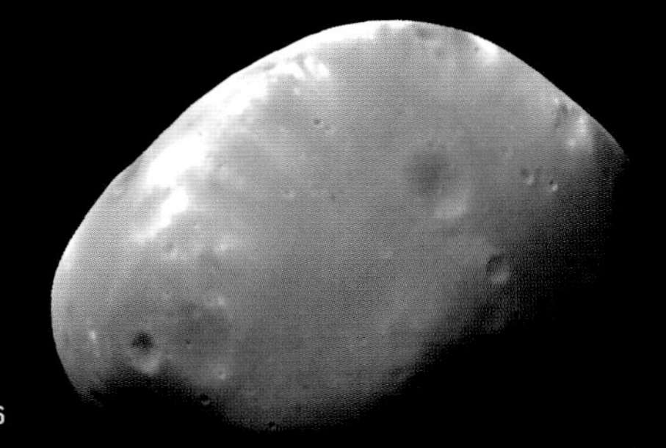
6

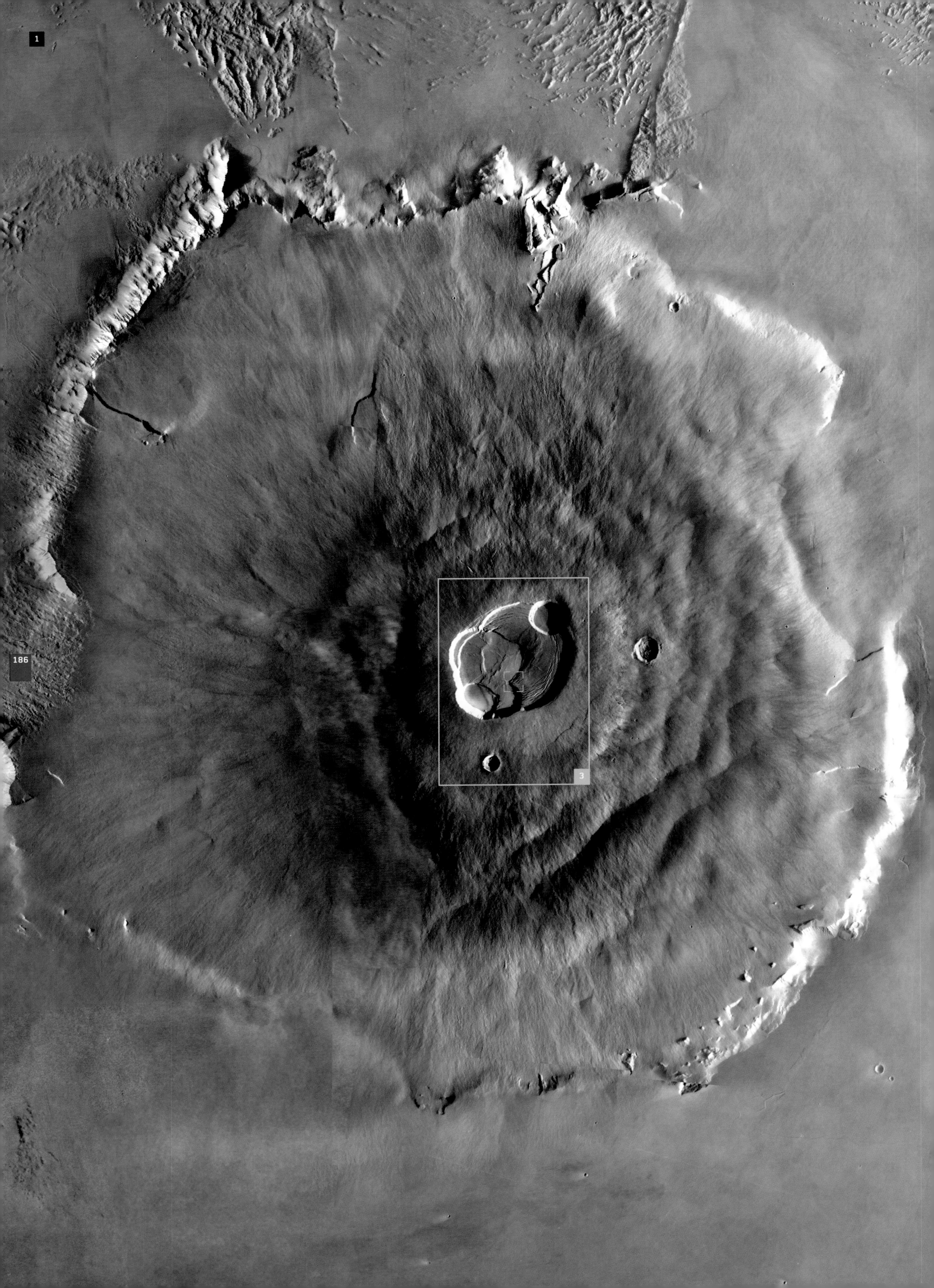
1
3

Martian volcanoes

Volcanoes dot the surface of Mars. In the weak Martian gravity, they have grown to tremendous proportions. In the past, they were the sites of extremely energetic eruptions, each time carpeting Mars with fresh flows of lava. On Earth, the volcanoes that most resemble their Martian cousins are the shield volcanoes of Hawaii.

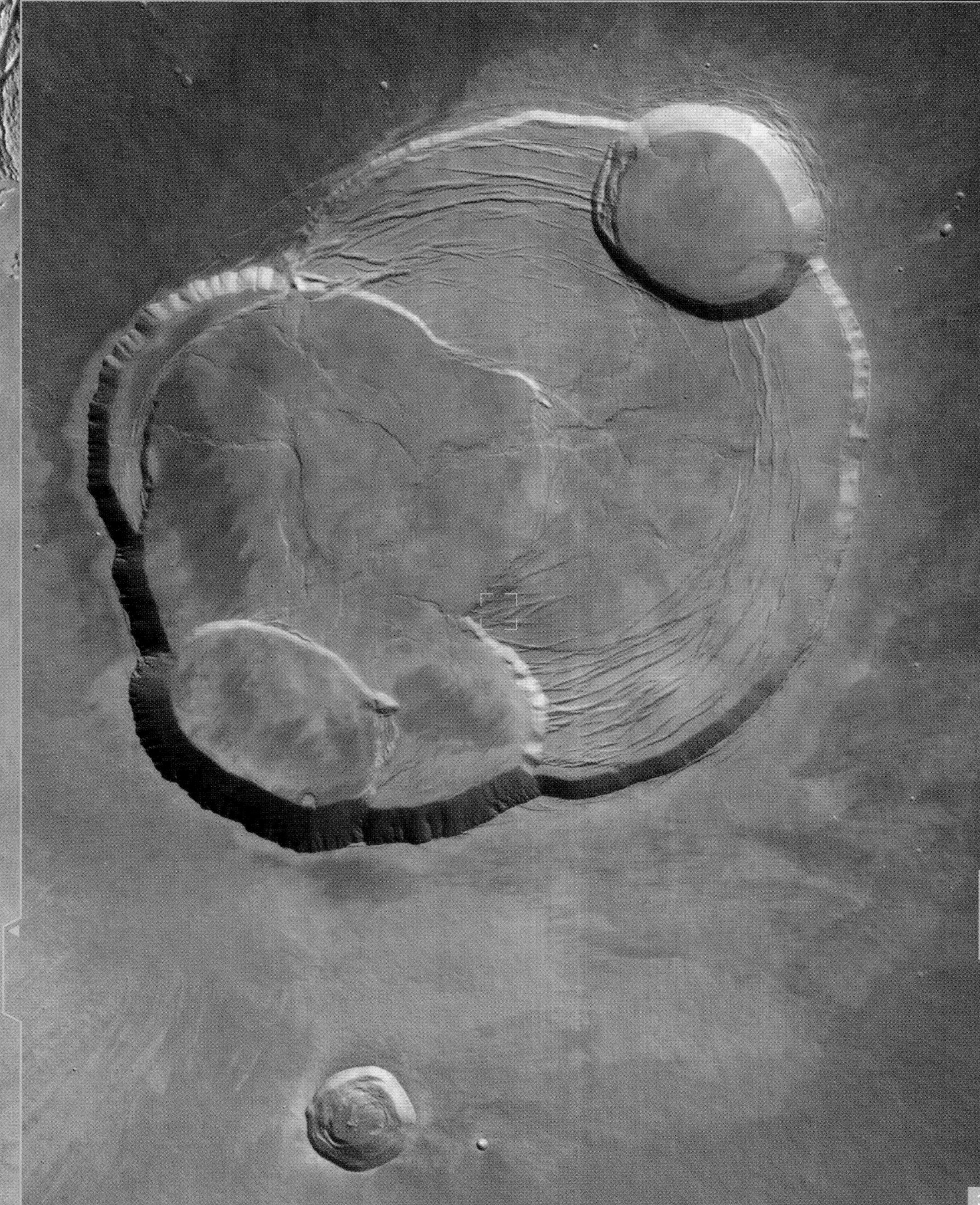

3

[1-3] Olympus Mons

Olympus Mons's [1] summit stands 27 kilometres above the average height of the Martian surface, giving it three times the elevation that Mount Everest has on Earth above sea level. The majesty of the volcano can be fully appreciated in a perspective view [2]. At the summit of the volcano lies its caldera [3], which displays a number of sub-calderas formed by successive eruptions. These have been dated and show that the last major eruption of the volcano probably took place around 150 million years ago. However, there are small lava flows on the flanks of the volcano that may be just 2.4 million years old – a blink of the eye, on astronomical scales.

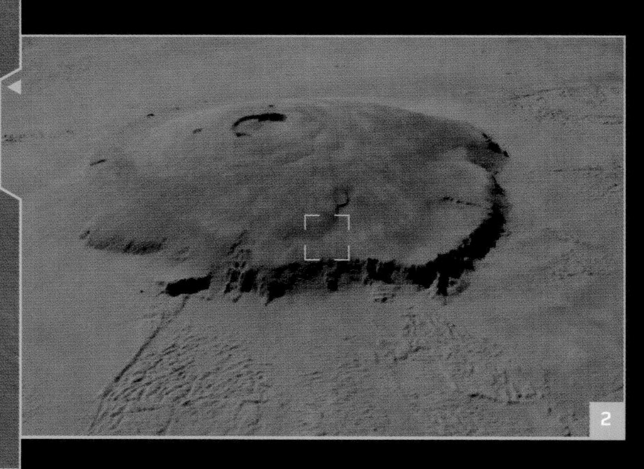

2

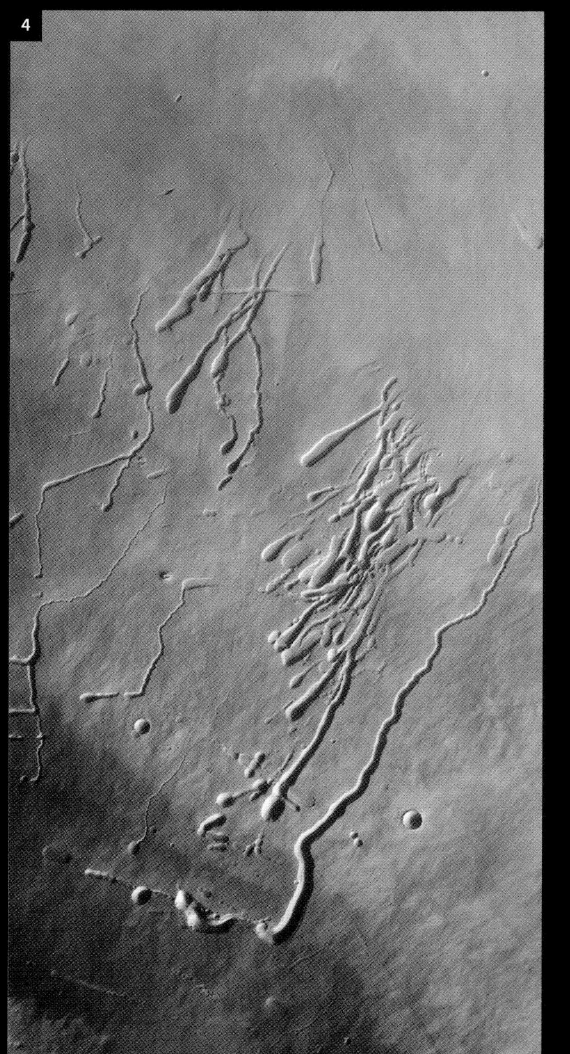

4

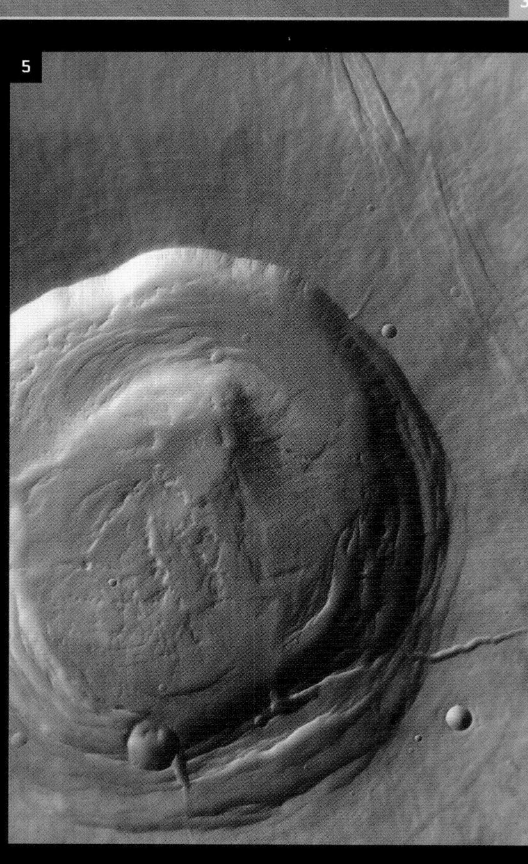

5

[4] Pavonis Mons

Although there are several volcanic regions spread across Mars, the largest volcanoes are clustered into an area known as Tharsis. Here, the crust of Mars must have been weaker than in the surrounding regions and this allowed magma from the deep interior of the planet to burst upwards and flow across the surface. Here the large Tharsis volcano Pavonis Mons displays prominent lava tubes on its flanks. Lava tubes are like the arteries of a volcano, channelling fresh lava away from the main volcano and distributing it across the surroundings. The ceilings of these lava tubes have collapsed, exposing them to view. Many more are expected to lie undiscovered, riddling the insides of the volcano.

[5] Biblis Patera

This is the caldera another large Tharsis volcano, Biblis Patera. 170 kilometres long and 100 kilometres wide, the volcano rises nearly three kilometres above its surroundings.

Valles Marineris

Planetary scientists believe that Valles Marineris began to split open across Mars about 3.5 billion years ago. The tremendous forces that cleaved the planet's surface like this were the same responsible for the growth of the giant volcanoes in nearby Tharsis region. The Valles Marineris extends for 4000 kilometres, this image shows its central 3000 kilometres.

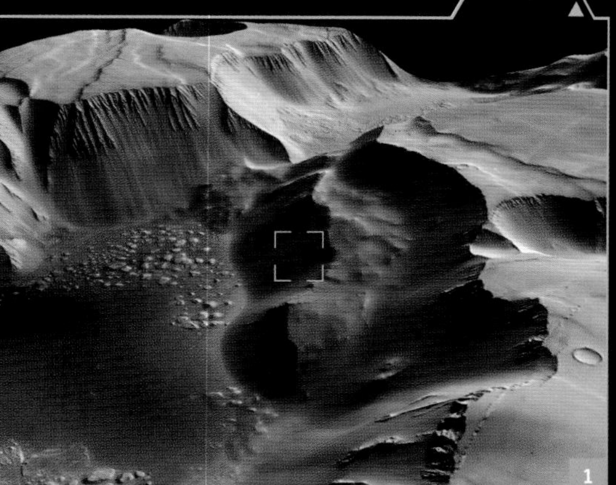
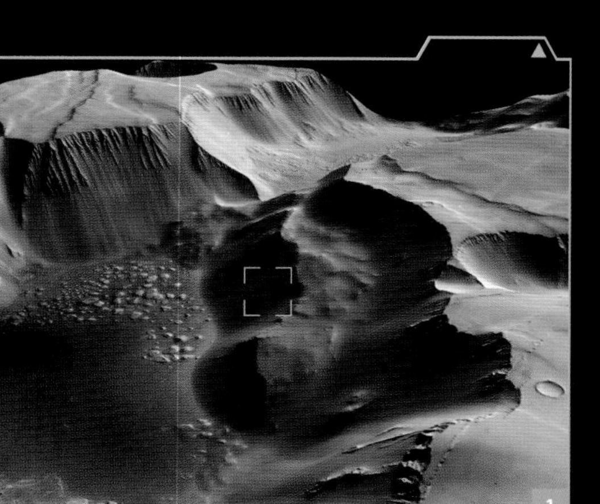

[1] Noctis Labyrinthus
At the western end of Valles Marineris lies the Noctis Labyrinthus region, a labyrinth of smaller rift valleys.

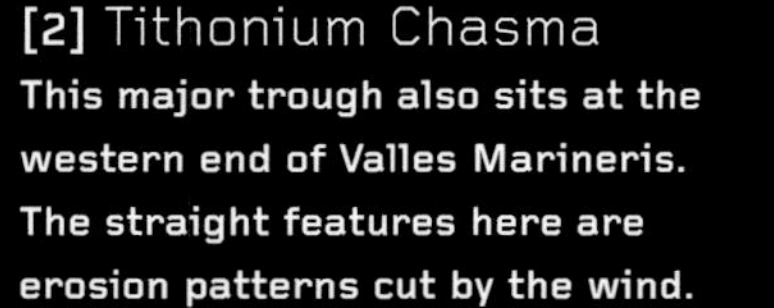

[2] Tithonium Chasma
This major trough also sits at the western end of Valles Marineris. The straight features here are erosion patterns cut by the wind.

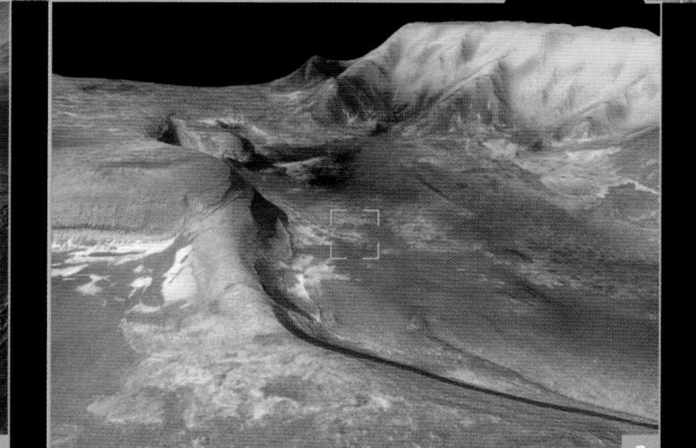

[3] Melas Chasma
This shows the southern scarp of Valles Marineris, a towering cliff almost five kilometres high.

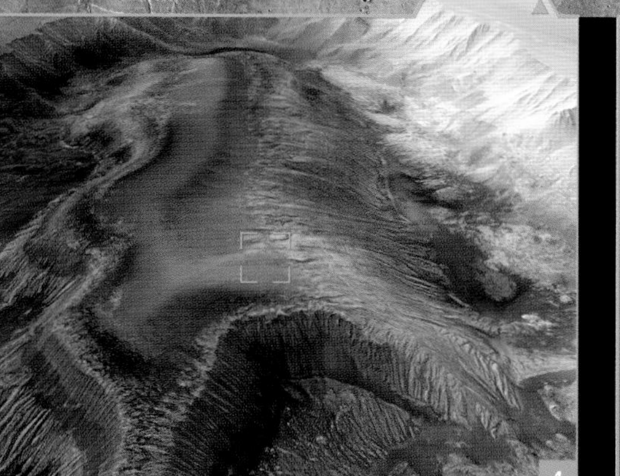

[4] Herbes Chasma

Lying to the north of Valles Marineris, Herbes Chasma is a completely enclosed depression in the Martian surface.

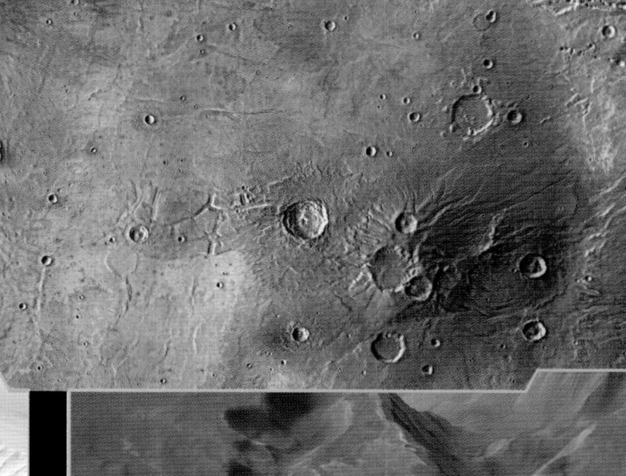

[5] Coprates Catena

This valley system to the south of Valles Marineris is a collapsed structure and may have formed as underlying water ice evaporated.

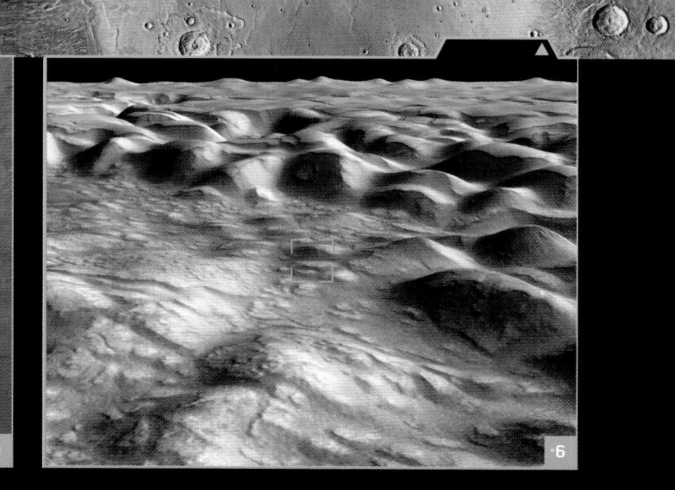

[6] Aureum Chaos

As the name suggests, this eastern region of Valles Marineris is characterized by randomly oriented blocks, each from a few to tens of kilometres wide.

2
3

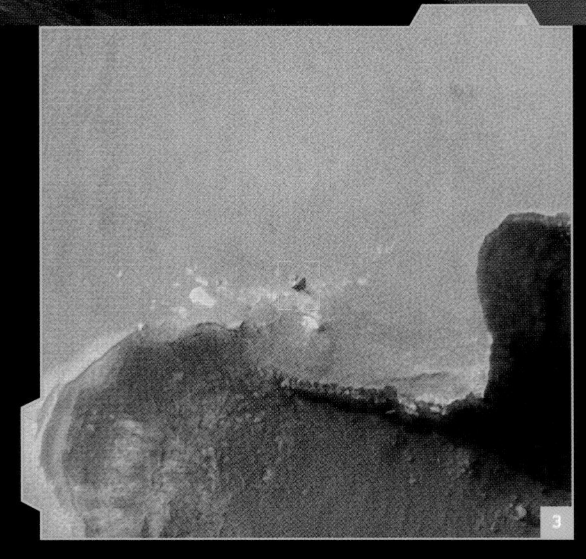

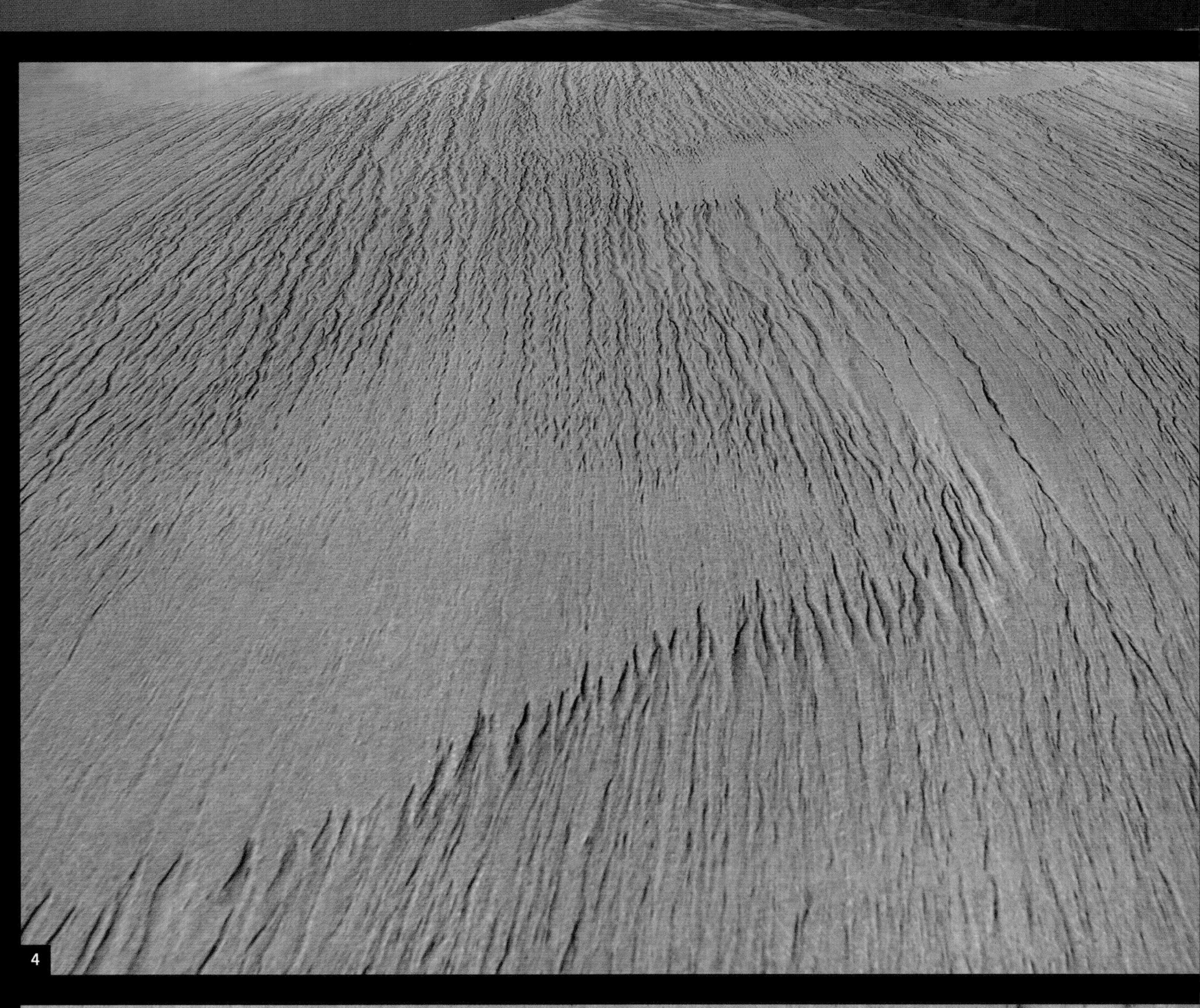

[1-3] Victoria crater
After a drive of more than nine kilometres through the Meridiani Planum region, the NASA rover Opportunity arrived at the rim of the Victoria Crater and recorded the panoramic view that greeted it [1]. Five days after the rover's arrival, the Mars Reconnaissance Orbiter swept by almost 300 kilometres overhead for a bird's eye view of the 800-metre diameter crater. Despite the satellite's altitude and the fact that Opportunity is smaller than most cars, it still managed to resolve the rover [3].

Martian weather

Even though Mars has a tenuous atmosphere, it still displays weather. This can be as subtle as the morning mists that hang in the valleys or as overwhelming as the dust storms that engulf the planet.

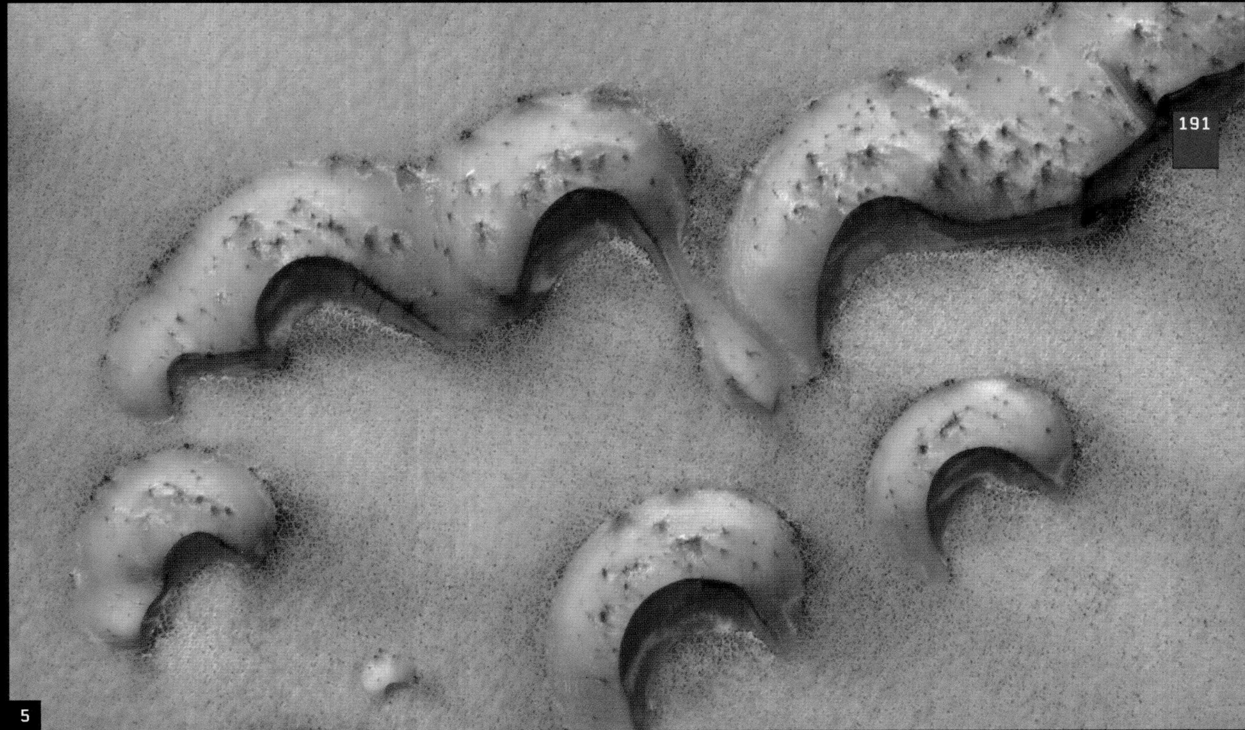

[4] Yardangs
Running for tens of kilometres, these parallel grooves near Olympus Mons are known as yardangs. A yardang is a wind-cut ridge, usually found on Earth in a desert environment. With its severe winds crossing a planet-wide desert, Mars is the perfect place to find them.

[5] Sand dunes
Sand dunes shift constantly on the Martian surface at the urging of the winds. Planetary scientists closely monitor this dune field at the extreme edge of the Martian arctic circle. They have already seen several dunes change shape and some disappear entirely.

[6, 7] The dust storms of Mars
Mars's strong winds can raise dust storms that engulf almost the entire planet. These two images show how bad the dust storms can be. On the left [6], is the view on 10 June 2001, when the planet's surface features were clearly visible. Just over six weeks later, on 31 July 2001, a raging dust storm had blocked most of the surface features from view [7]. Large dust storms can last for weeks, or even months.

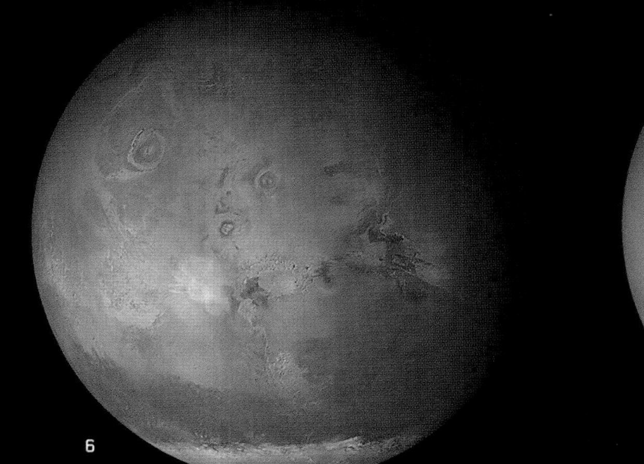

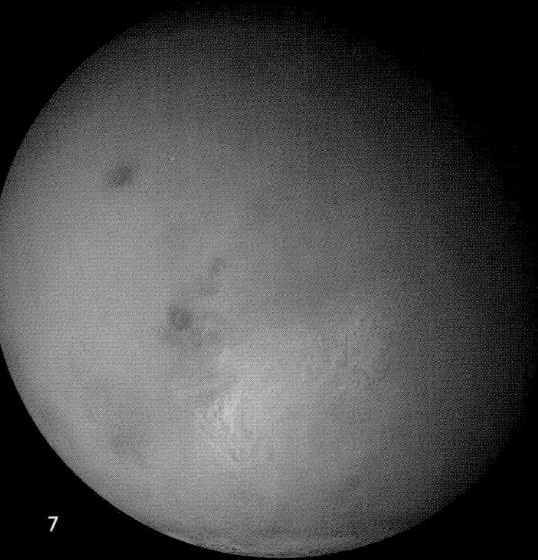

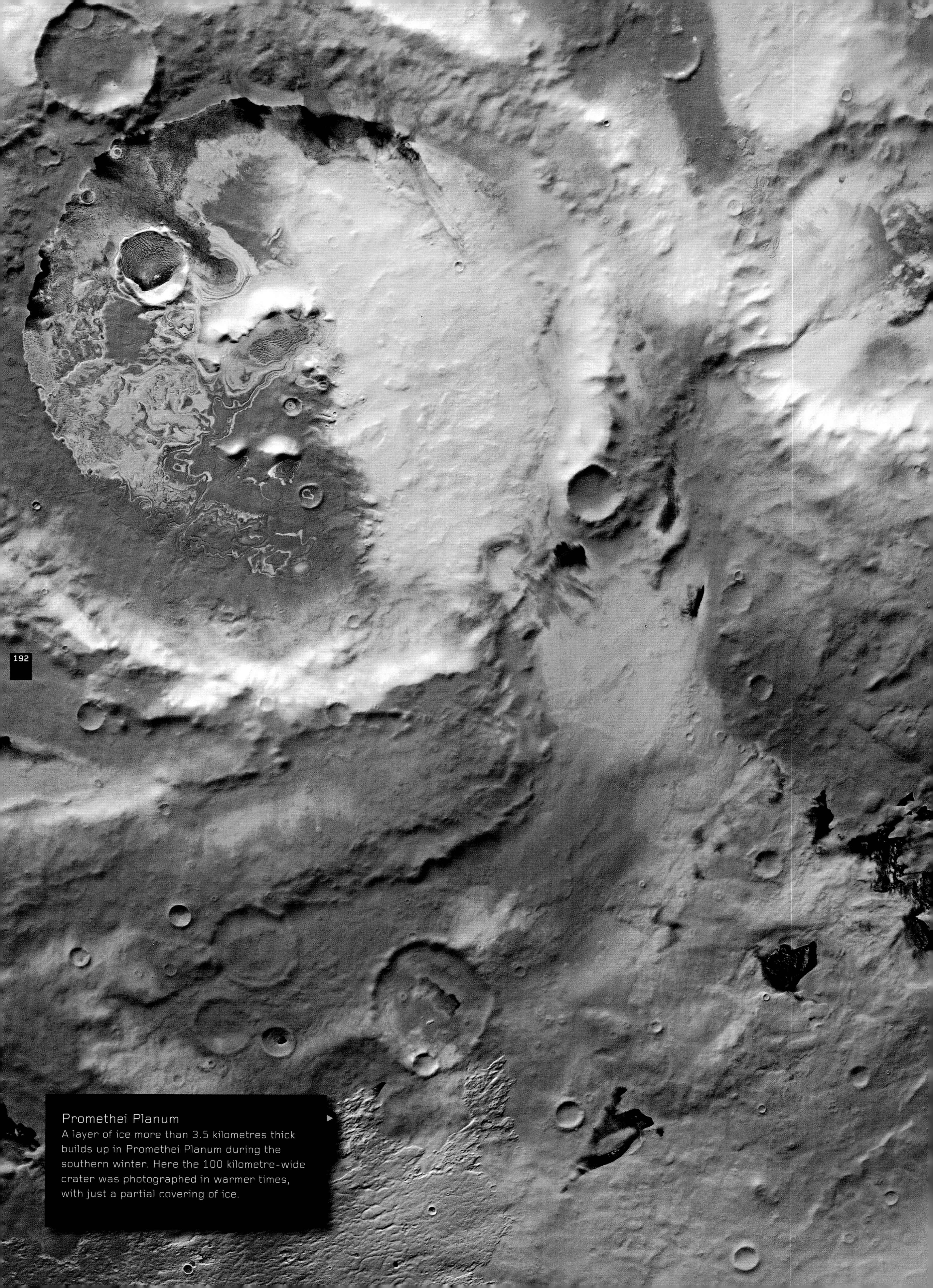

Promethei Planum

A layer of ice more than 3.5 kilometres thick builds up in Promethei Planum during the southern winter. Here the 100 kilometre-wide crater was photographed in warmer times, with just a partial covering of ice.

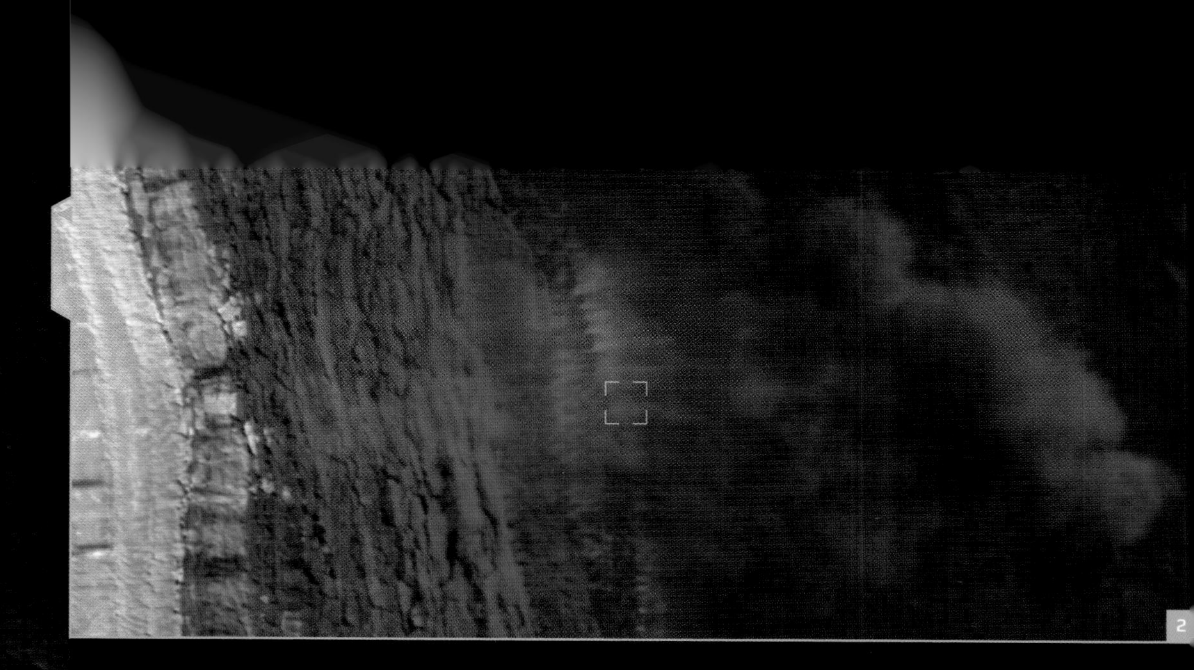

Icy plains and polar caps

Although a cold desert planet, Mars still boasts some water. Most of it is confined to ice sheets and frost, but some is found in the atmosphere, being transported around the planet as water vapour.

[1, 2] Martian avalanche

As spring progresses in the northern hemisphere of Mars, so its winter covering of carbon dioxide ice disappears back into the atmosphere. Here, weakened by rising temperatures, a section of a large shelf of carbon dioxide frost collapses and plunges down a 700 metre-high cliff [1]. Its collapse triggers an avalanche of material that sweeps down on to the plain below in a billowing cloud of dust [2].

[3-5] Martian poles

Mars's north polar cap is roughly 1100 kilometres across and is surrounded by a dark ring of sand dunes [3]. There is nearly always water ice at the poles of Mars – a crown of water ice can be seen in an unnamed crater near the northern polar region [5]. A frosting of ice also hangs onto the sides of the crater.

The south polar cap is a mixture of water ice and carbon dioxide ice. Even in summer it never shrinks below 420 kilometres across [4]. In the autumn and winter it builds up again, tripling the area of the polar cap.

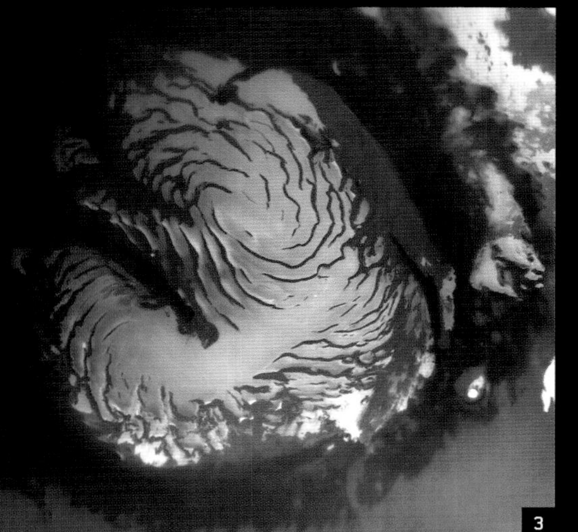

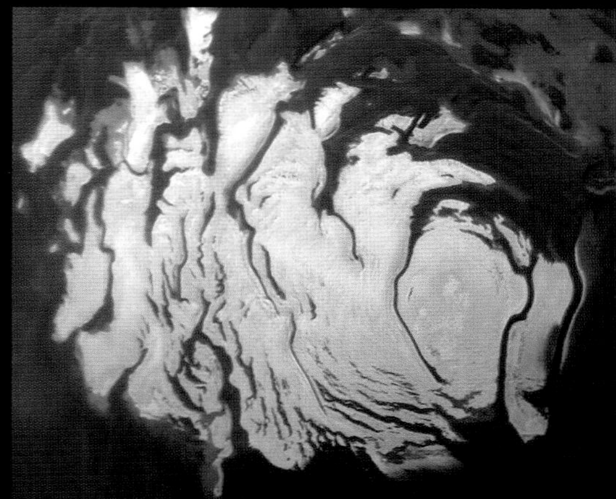

Water on Mars

There is ample evidence that water once flowed on Mars. The big question is whether there was a 'warm, wet' period when lakes and seas covered the planet. Currently, the evidence seems to be pointing towards episodes of watery conditions, each perhaps lasting a few tens to hundreds of thousands of years.

[1] Mangala Valles

This outflow channel indicates that large quantities of water, mud or possibly ice, flowed across the surface of Mars to cut these features. They might have been driven to the surface by volcanic activity. Planetary scientists are attempting to measure the amount of water beneath the surface of Mars using sounding radars on spacecraft. If there is to be any possibility of microbial life on Mars, there will have to be quantities of liquid water somewhere on the planet.

[2] Water gullies?

These sinuous gullies appear in the southern uplands of Mars and could be the result of water seeping from the side of a sunlit crater wall. Several gullies have been seen to appear on Mars over the last few years. Some planetary scientists believe that this is good evidence for water lying just below the surface; others think the gullies could be small avalanches, or the result of wind-blown activity, and therefore unrelated to flowing water.

[3] Chasma Boreale

The coming and going of the northern polar cap creates a rich sequence of layers in the terrain there. These are exposed here in a cliff at the head of Chasma Boreale, a large canyon eroded into the strata. The colours are computer generated to enhance the different layers. It appears that brighter, ice-rich tiers have been deposited between the dark dust beds. Images such as these can assist planetary scientists in understanding recent climate variations on Mars, because changes in the swirling wind conditions are likely to be recorded in these layered deposits.

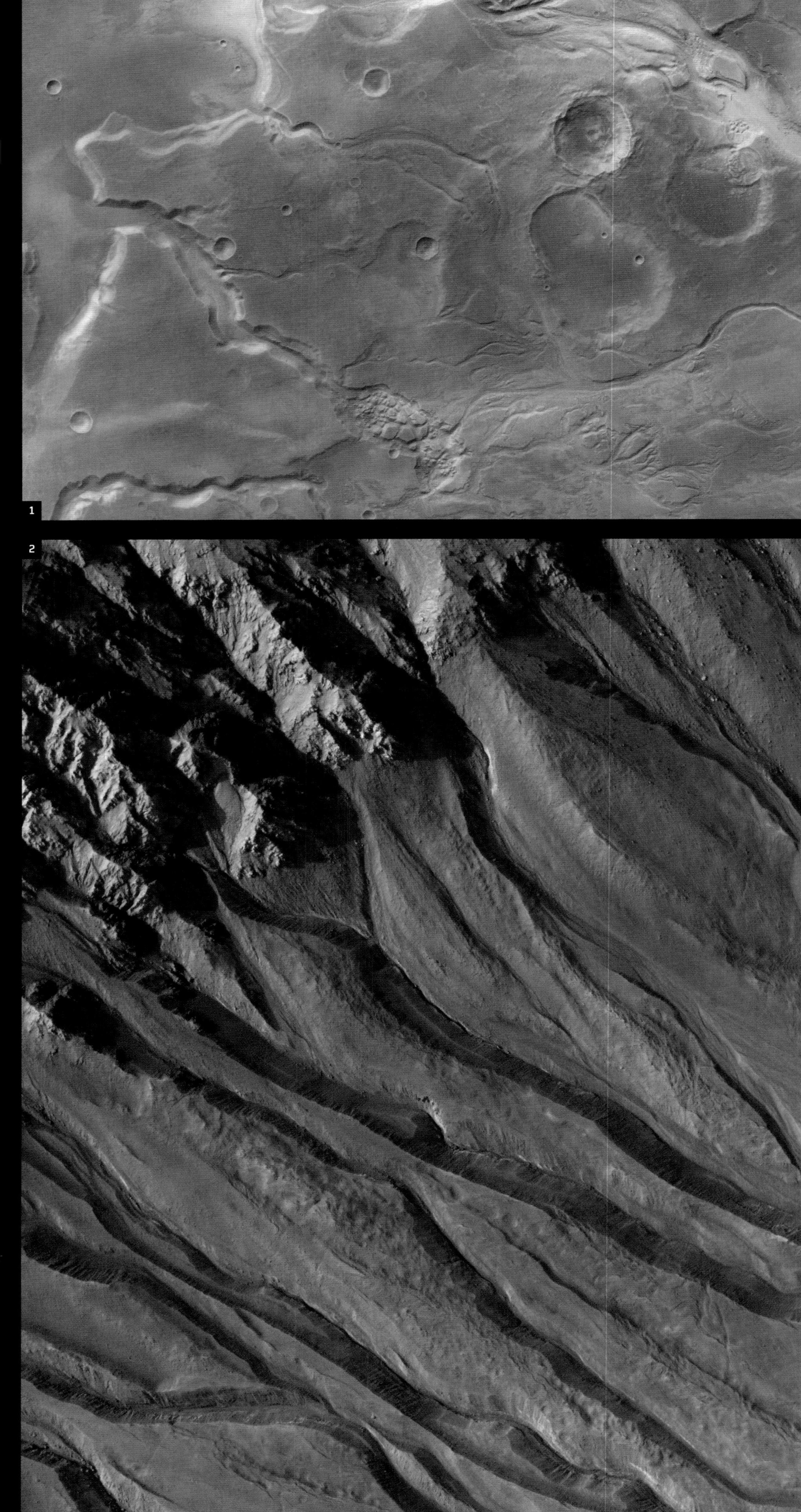

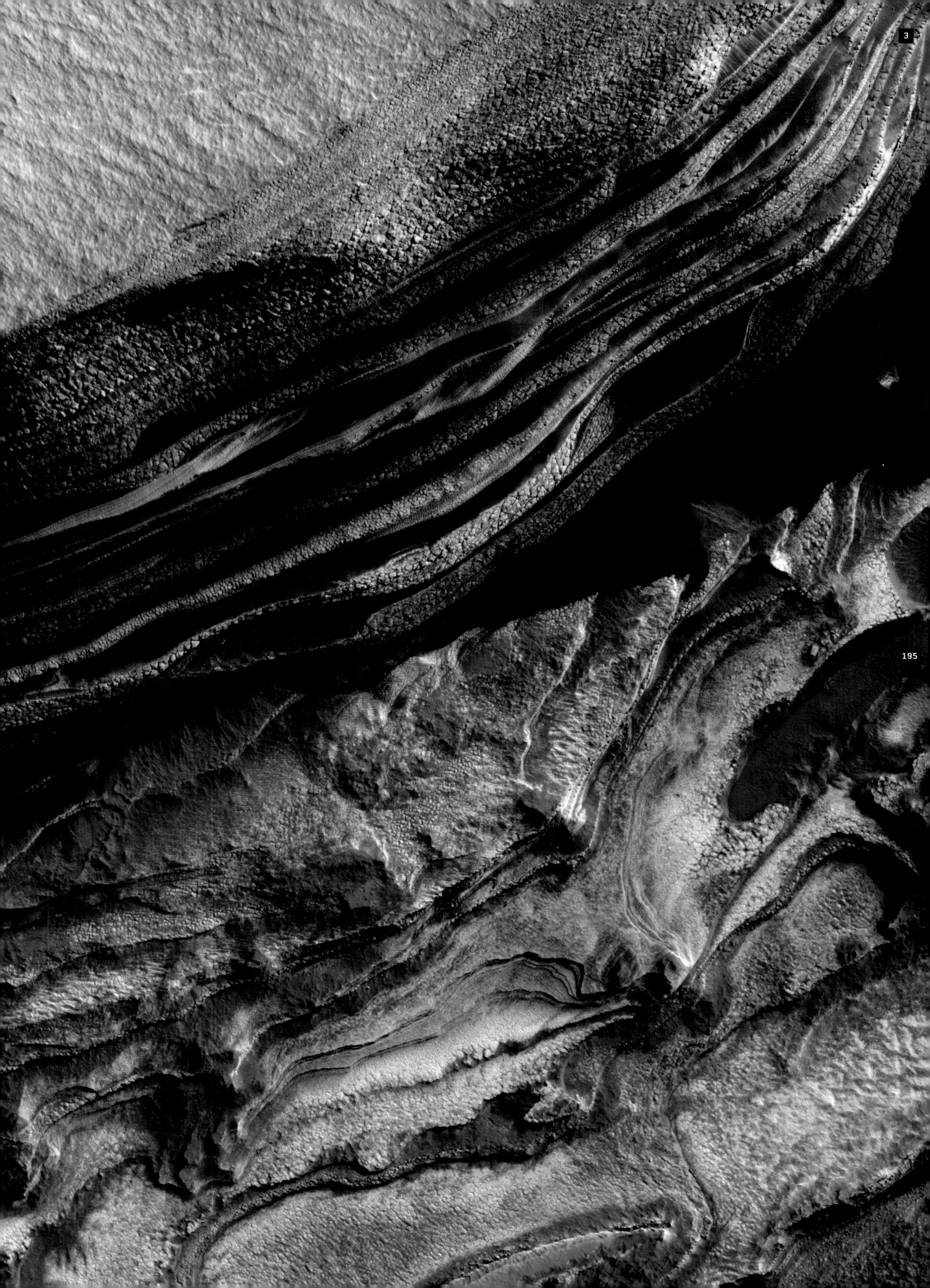

3

THE ASTEROID BELT

Between Mars and Jupiter is a wide expanse of space populated not by planets but by a multitude of space rocks called asteroids. The largest asteroid is Ceres at around 950 kilometres in diameter but most are mountain-sized lumps of rock or smaller.

Astronomers estimate that there are hundreds of millions of asteroids, most of them smaller than 1 kilometre in diameter. Robotic telescopes keep track of them and scan the night sky for ever-smaller members. Most of them stay within the main belt but a sub-population can orbit near Earth. Each asteroid is known by a number, which denotes the order in which it was discovered, followed by an approved name. Juno was the third asteroid to be discovered, so is known as 3 Juno.

There are three broad compositions of asteroid: silicate, metal and carbonaceous. The silicate-rich asteroids tend to be found toward the inner region of the belt, within 2.5 times the Earth's orbital radius from the Sun. Towards the centre of the belt, the metal dominated asteroids reach their peak and account for around 10 percent of the entire asteroid population. Then, in the belt's outermost regions, the dominant asteroid composition is carbon-rich. As yet, the reason for this compositional segregation is unknown.

The first asteroids were identified during the early 19th century and were immediately assumed to be the remains of a planet that had fragmented. Now, however, it is widely thought that the asteroids are the building blocks of a planet that was prevented from forming by the gravitational influence of the nearby giant planet Jupiter. Some asteroids do appear to be fragmented objects but these are thought to the result of collisions between asteroids.

[1] 1 CERES
Ceres

In 1801, Ceres became the first asteroid discovered by astronomers. Italian Giuseppe Piazzi beat a consortium of other European sky-watchers to make the discovery on 1 January. The astronomers of the time had all felt that another planet should exist in the apparently empty region of space between Mars and Jupiter.

Soon after they discovered Ceres, it became obvious that the little world was not large enough to be considered a true planet, as it is less than a quarter the size of Mercury. Nevertheless, Ceres and the next three largest asteroids, 4 Vesta, 2 Pallas, and 10 Hygiea, collectively contain more than half the mass of the main asteroid belt.

These Hubble Space Telescope images show that it is a round object, rather than an irregularly shaped lump of rock. It is probably the 'seed' of a planet that Jupiter's gravity prevented from growing into a bona fide one.

According to the conventions passed by the International Astronomical Union in 1999, Ceres is large enough to be classified as a dwarf planet. This sequence shows the different faces of Ceres as it rotates.

DISTANCE FROM SUN	DIAMETER	MASS	ROTATION PERIOD	ORBITAL PERIOD	MEAN SURFACE TEMPERATURE
415 MILLION KM	0.95 THOUSAND KM	0.2 milliEARTHS	9.5 HOURS	4.6 YEARS	167 KELVIN

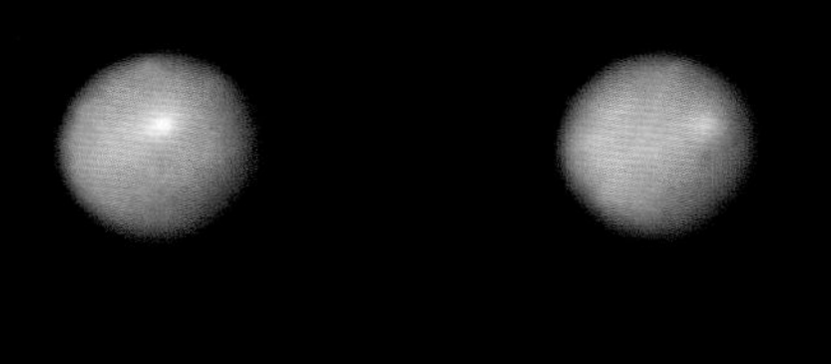

1

[2, 3] 433 EROS
Eros

Eros was the 433rd asteroid discovered but importantly it was the first near-Earth asteroid to be found by astronomers. On their journeys around the Sun, the near-Earth asteroids leave the main belt, cross Mars's orbit and swing close to Earth's orbit, before completing their path back to the asteroid belt. Astronomers know of around 5400 near-Earth asteroids, with Eros being the second largest.

The peanut-shaped Eros is a primitive body that dates from the formation of the planets, some 4.5 billion years ago. Since that time, the asteroid has changed little. The only processes that have modified it are the occasional impact of much smaller space rocks. These have left a number of scars in the form of craters across its battered body [2].

The gravitational field of Eros is less than one thousandth that of Earth. It would be impossible to walk on its surface and if an astronaut tripped over, it would take hours to fall to the floor. Nevertheless, it is susceptible to the pull of gravity from the Earth and Mars. Simulations suggest that Eros may begin to cross the Earth's orbit during the next 2 million years. This would mean it became a danger to Earth as it could possibly collide with our planet.

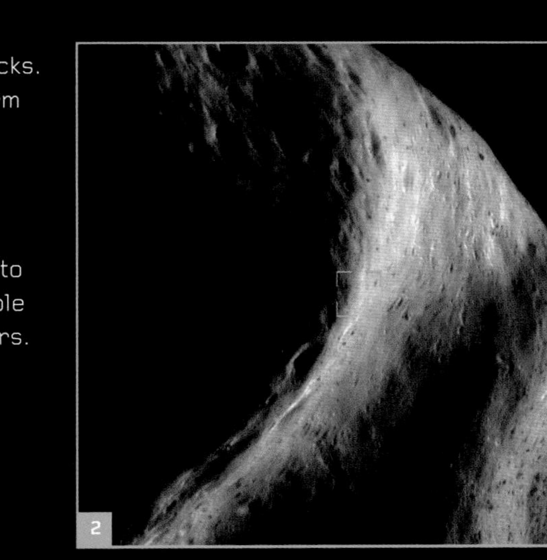

2

DISTANCE FROM SUN	LENGTH	MASS	ROTATION PERIOD	ORBITAL PERIOD	MEAN SURFACE TEMPERATURE
218	33	1.2	5.3	643	227

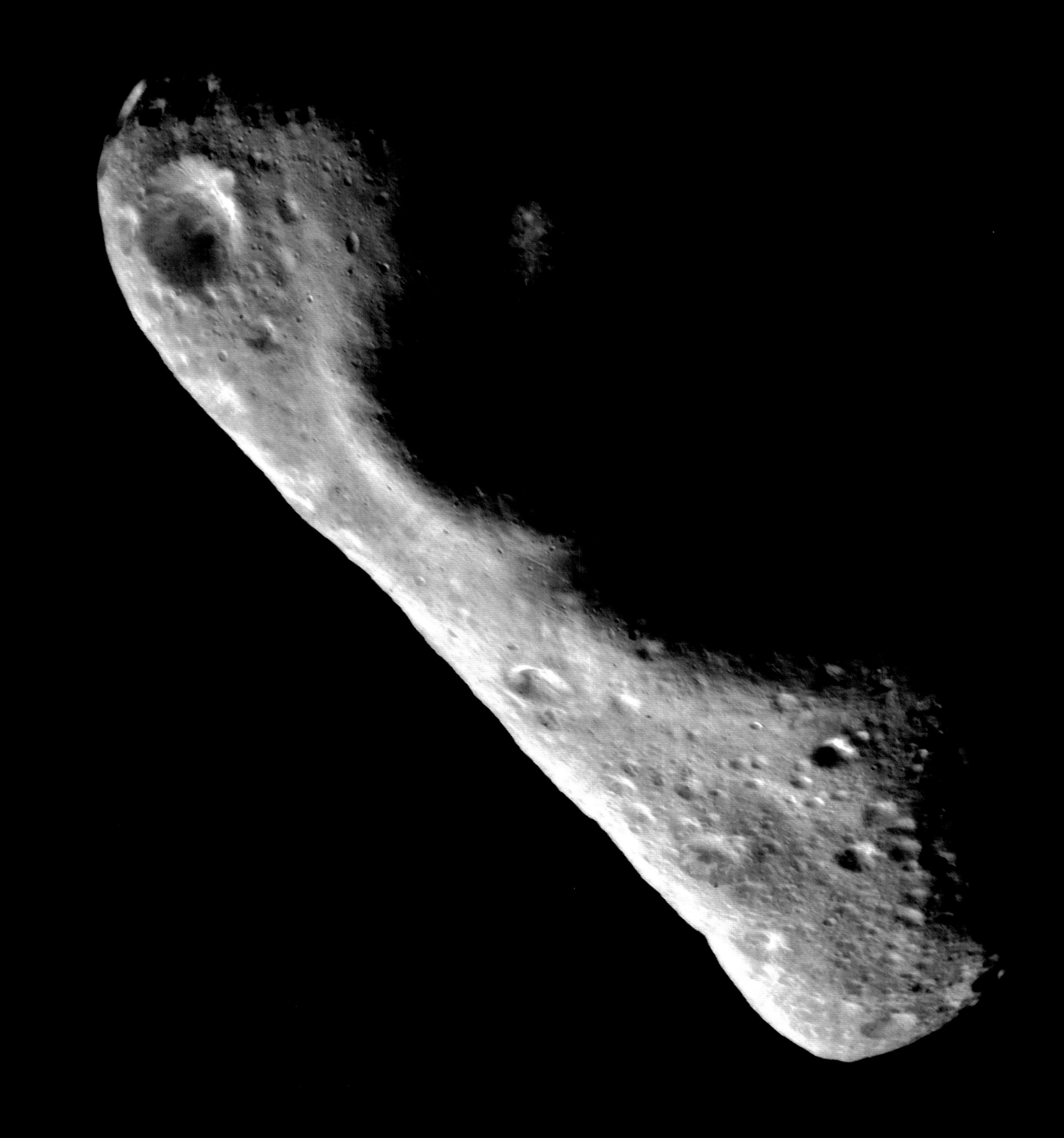

[1] Vesta

Analysis of the light reflected by Vesta shows that it is composed of the same minerals as a class of meteorites that have fallen to Earth. Astronomers therefore believe that these meteorites are fragments of Vesta ejected in a giant impact that took place less than a billion years ago and which flattened the southern end of the asteroid.

DISTANCE	DIAMETER	MASS	ROTATION PERIOD	ORBITAL PERIOD	MEAN SURFACE TEMPERATURE
353	560	0.05	5.4	3.6	170
MILLION KM	KILOMETRES	milliEARTHS	HOURS	YEARS	KELVIN

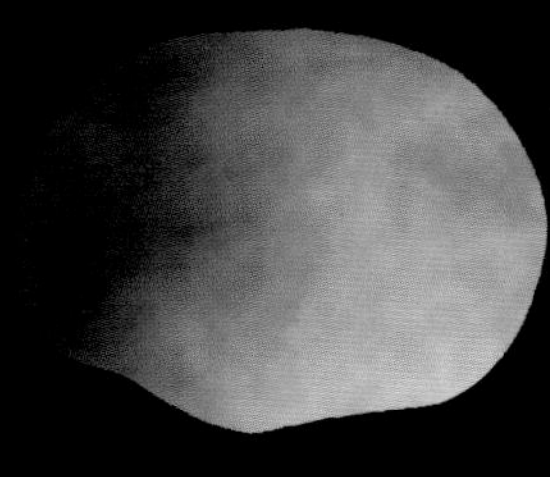

1

[2, 3] Ida

The irregularly shaped stony asteroid Ida was discovered to have a moon, Dactyl [4], in 1993. At the time, asteroids were thought to be single objects. Now astronomers know of several other asteroids with moons. As with all irregularly shaped objects, Ida looks strikingly different depending upon the viewing angle [3]. It is a silicate-rich asteroid.

DISTANCE	LENGTH	MASS	ROTATION PERIOD	ORBITAL PERIOD	MEAN SURFACE TEMPERATURE
408	53	7	4.6	4.8	158
MILLION KM	KILOMETRES	nanoEARTHS	HOURS	YEARS	KELVIN

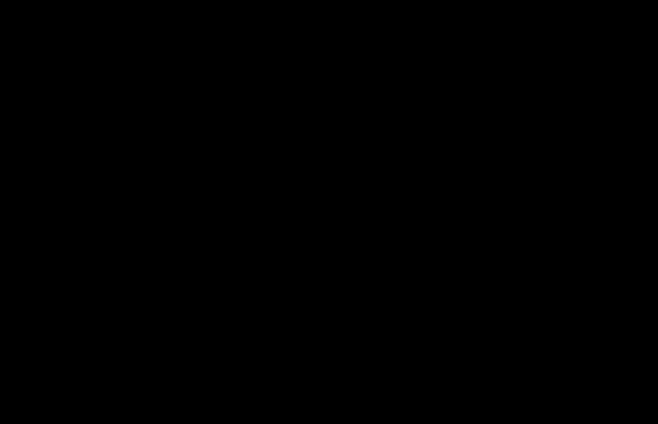

[4] Dactyl

DISTANCE FROM IDA	DIAMETER	MASS	ROTATION PERIOD	ORBITAL PERIOD	MEAN SURFACE TEMPERATURE
108	1.4	~	~	1.56	158
KM	KILOMETRES	EARTHS	HOURS	YEARS	KELVIN

[5] Gaspra

Another silicate-rich asteroid, Gaspra tumbles end-over-end through space as it orbits the Sun. Its lack of large craters suggests that it is a fragment of a larger body that split apart in a collision around 200 million years ago and this has not been long enough for Gaspra to suffer any large impacts.

DISTANCE	LENGTH	MASS	ROTATION PERIOD	ORBITAL PERIOD	MEAN SURFACE TEMPERATURE
331	18	4.1	7	3.3	181
MILLION KM	KILOMETRES	nanoEARTHS	HOURS	YEARS	KELVIN

[6] Mathilde

Mathilde is a carbonaceous asteroid that is literally not all it seems. Instead of a solid object as it appears to be, astronomers think that Mathilde is a honeycomb built from a fragile collection of loosely bound rocks. Such objects are called 'rubble-pile' asteroids. They can rotate only slowly; otherwise they would fly apart.

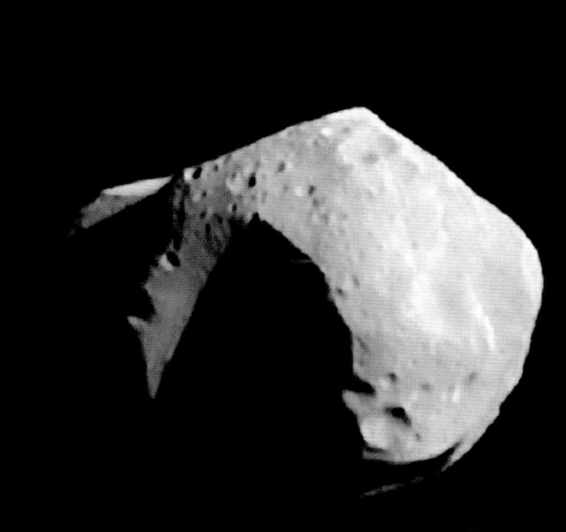

6

DISTANCE	DIAMETER	MASS	ROTATION PERIOD	ORBITAL PERIOD	MEAN SURFACE TEMPERATURE
396	60	17	17.4	4.3	174
MILLION KM	KILOMETRES	nanoEARTHS	HOURS	YEARS	KELVIN

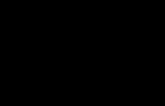

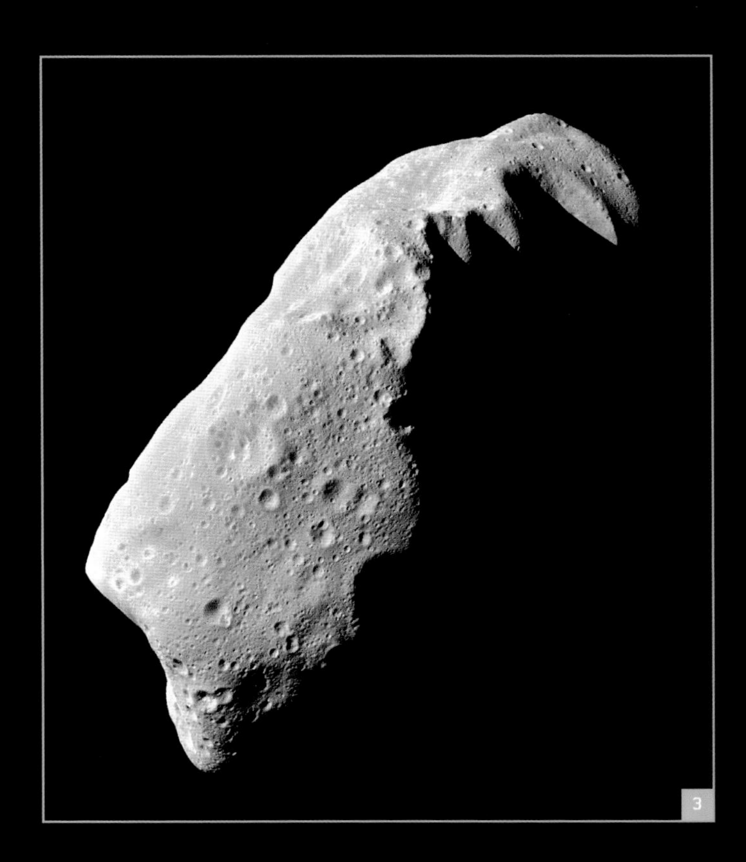
3

2
4
5

GAS GIANTS_

Out beyond the asteroid belt is the realm of the gas giant planets. These are fundamentally different from the rocky worlds of the inner solar system. The most obvious contrast is size: they are much larger. Jupiter is the hugest and stretches over 11 times the diameter of Earth. Neptune is the smallest but is still almost four times the Earth's diameter. These giant planets all have extraordinarily thick atmospheres of gas, mostly made up of the two lightest elements: hydrogen and helium. Jupiter and Saturn share the same chemical composition as the Sun, with 98 percent of their bulk being composed of these two gases. Yet they do not shine like the Sun because they are not large enough to compress their interiors to the density required to ignite nuclear fusion.

The term gas giant was not coined by an astronomer but by the science fiction author James Blish in a version of his story 'Solar Plexus' published in 1952.

Whereas Jupiter and Saturn, along with the rocky planets, are visible to the unaided eye and so have been known since antiquity, telescopes are required to see Uranus and Neptune reliably. Uranus was actually first seen by the British astronomer John Flamsteed in 1690 but he mistakenly thought it was a star and labelled it 34 Tauri. It was not until William Herschel saw it through a much better telescope in 1781, that its actual status was recognised. As a result, Herschel is credited with the discovery.

Formation

The gas giants are thought to exist in the outer Solar System for two reasons. Firstly, at this distance from the Sun the so called astronomical ices – water, ammonia and methane – can begin to condense into solid lumps, bolstering the amount of planet-forming material available. Secondly, the orbits are larger and so naturally contain more material from which a forming planet can feed. Jupiter and Saturn appear to have condensed in a 'sweet spot' where this confluence of factors built planetary cores large enough to pull vast quantities of hydrogen and helium out of the surrounding nebula.

Uranus and Neptune can be thought of as a sub-class of gas giant, called ice giants. This is because their composition is not so dominated by hydrogen and helium. Instead, they also contain significant quantities of astronomical ices. About half the size of Jupiter and Saturn, the ice giants of our Solar System are smaller than their nearest neighbours too. This probably indicates that the disc of matter from which all the planets formed was thinning a little this far out from the Sun.

Three out of the four gas giants have strong weather patterns in their atmosphere. Unlike the weather in the atmospheres of the rocky planets, which are closer to the Sun, this dynamic behaviour is probably not driven by the Sun's heat. Five times further from the Sun than is the Earth, Jupiter receives only one twenty-fifth as much light. At Saturn, this fraction drops dramatically to just one hundredth of Earth's illumination. Instead, the energy to drive the weather comes from heat released by the planets themselves.

This probably indicates that the insides of the gas giants have yet to settle completely into their final stable configurations. Of the four, only Uranus does not release much extra energy, and its atmosphere is a serene, featureless ball. Why should Uranus have reached this equilibrium but the other gas giants have not? As yet, no one knows.

Internal conditions

Although astronomers often talk about the gas giants having thick atmospheres and rocky-metallic cores, this can give a false impression

A map of Jupiter
This is how Jupiter looked on 11 and 12 December 2000. Clearly visible are Jupiter's characteristic bands of light and dark coloured clouds, and the Great Red Spot storm system. Many clouds appear stretched because of Jupiter's winds and turbulence. Small bright spots within the orange band north of the equator are thunderstorms.

about the planets, leading to the idea that the gas giants are large rocky planets with extraordinarily deep atmospheres. This is incorrect because, in reality, the planet's atmosphere must become denser and denser, the deeper into the planet one goes. It is a much more extreme example of the way an Earthly ocean becomes denser and denser, the deeper a diver swims.

At some level the density must make the gas behave more like a liquid. Then this liquid itself is squeezed tighter and tighter by the weight of the layers above. Eventually the hydrogen and helium atoms are compressed so much that some of their constituent particles, known as electrons, begin to flow freely between the atomic nuclei. This behaviour mimics the effect of an electrically conducting metal.

Whilst it is true that the denser material, such as the rocky and metallic substances, will sink to the centre of the planet, it does not create a solid planetary core, as we would usually think of it in the inner planets. This is because the pressure at these depths creates tremendous heat. The interior of Jupiter is estimated to be 30,000 Kelvin. This is more

All of the gas giants generate strong magnetic fields although Jupiter and Saturn's generating mechanism is almost certainly different from Neptune and Uranus's. In the first two worlds, the rapid rotation of their liquid metallic layers is thought to be responsible for generating the field. The ice giants, lacking the liquid metallic hydrogen, rely on swirling motions within layers of water–ammonia mixture to generate their magnetic fields.

Jupiter has the largest planetary magnetic field in the Solar System. At the giant planet's cloud tops it is over ten times the strength of Earth's at our world's surface. The main region extends for 7 million kilometres into space and traps electrically charged particles to create a searingly radioactive zone around the planet. The moons Amalthea, Io, Europa, and Ganymede all orbit within the region.

Most of the particles found trapped in Jupiter's magnetic field come from the Sun, although Io is a significant contributor as well, casting out atoms and particles into space from the active volcanoes on its surface. If the solar activity is strong, it can compress

Jupiter's magnetic field funnels particles into the atmosphere of the planet and causes aurorae, just like Earth's. Highlighting Io's contribution to this process, volcanic activity on the moon has been observed to precede the appearance of aurorae on Jupiter.

Gas giants around other stars

Of the gas giants that have been found around other stars, perhaps the most staggering detail is how close most of them are to the parent star. A close orbit dramatically shortens the length of their year. In our Solar System, Jupiter takes nearly 12 earth-years to orbit the Sun and it is the fastest of the giants. Neptune, the outermost gas giant, has an enormous orbit to follow and so takes nearly 165 earth-years to complete its lap.

Around other stars, some gas giants are in such tight orbits that their year lasts just a few days. Another factor that distinguishes these gas giants from our own is size. Some extrasolar giants appear to be considerably larger than their solar cousins. This is thought to be a consequence of the extra heating they receive due to their proximity to their star.

JUPITER_

At two and a half times the mass of all the other planets in our Solar System combined, Jupiter is the king of the planets. Its most obvious features are the cloud bands that run parallel to the planet's equator and each other. Most of the planet's atmosphere is composed of the transparent gases hydrogen and helium. The colours come from clouds formed by other molecules, rather like the white water-vapour clouds in Earth's otherwise transparent atmosphere.

The lighter bands are known as belts. They are generally found at higher altitudes and consist of ammonia crystals. The darker bands are called zones. They are high-pressure systems that push away the higher, lighter clouds opening our view to the darker clouds beneath. These are dominated by the more complicated molecule, ammonium hydrosulphide that gives them their colour.

Jupiter rotates quickly, completing one whole revolution in just less than 10 hours. This rapid movement helps to 'stir' the atmosphere, contributing to the dynamic weather patterns seen on this giant world.

[1] Jupiter's northern lights

As happens around Earth, Jupiter's magnetic field snags particles from the Sun and guides them into the planet's polar atmosphere. Around Jupiter, the field also catches electrically charged particles of sulphur given off by the volcanic moon, Io, and channels them pole-ward, too. When the particles hit the atmosphere they make it glow, giving off an aurora just like the northern and southern lights seen on Earth. Jupiter's southern lights can just be glimpsed at the bottom of the planet.

[2] Jupiter's methane

This image of Jupiter was taken at an infrared wavelength just beyond visible light. This particular wavelength, 1.69 micrometres, is strongly absorbed by methane molecules. So this image can be thought of as a map of the methane in Jupiter's upper atmosphere. Dark areas show strong absorption of the infrared light and so indicate where there are large concentrations of methane. The bright areas, including the circle of the Great Red Spot, illustrate areas where high ammonia clouds reflect the infrared light back into space before it can be absorbed by the lower lying methane banks. The white circle near the right edge of Jupiter's bright equatorial belt is the volcanic moon Io.

[3] Jupiter's rings

Jupiter is banded by a thin ring system, mostly composed of dust grains. It is so faint that it can only be seen when the sunlight scatters through the dust particles, rather than reflects off them. The ring system is about 7000 kilometres in diameter but only 30 kilometres deep.

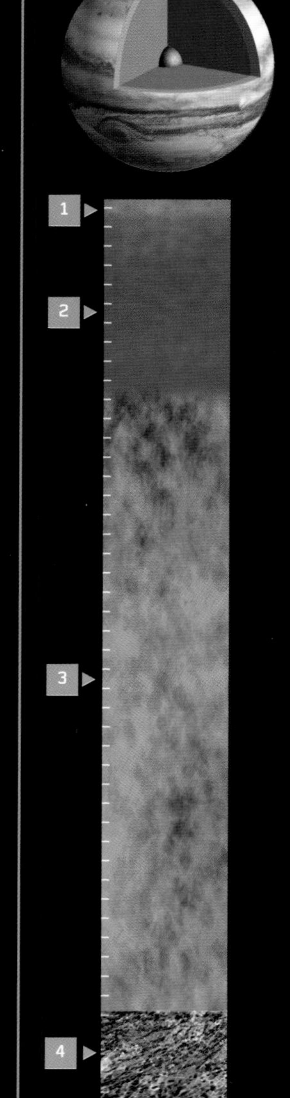

JUPITER'S INTERIOR
A core of churning rocks and metal sits at the centre of the planet. It contains some ten times the mass of the Earth and forms the foundation for the atmosphere and cloud layers. These are mostly made of hydrogen and helium and change from a liquid metal, to a liquid to the normal gaseous state in ascending order.

[1] The cloud colours are determined by the chemicals that can condense in these chilly regions of the planet's atmosphere.

[2] The pressure on the hydrogen and helium gas that dominates the atmosphere, makes it behave like a liquid.

[3] The pressure is now so extreme, that the hydrogen and helium behave like a liquid metal.

[4] At the very centre of the planet is an incredibly dense mass of rocky and metallic chemicals.

DISTANCE	DIAMETER	MASS	ROTATION PERIOD	ORBITAL PERIOD	MEAN CLOUD TOP TEMPERATURE
779	143	318	9.9	11.9	165
MILLION KM	THOUSAND KM	EARTHS	HOURS	YEARS	KELVIN

1 2 3

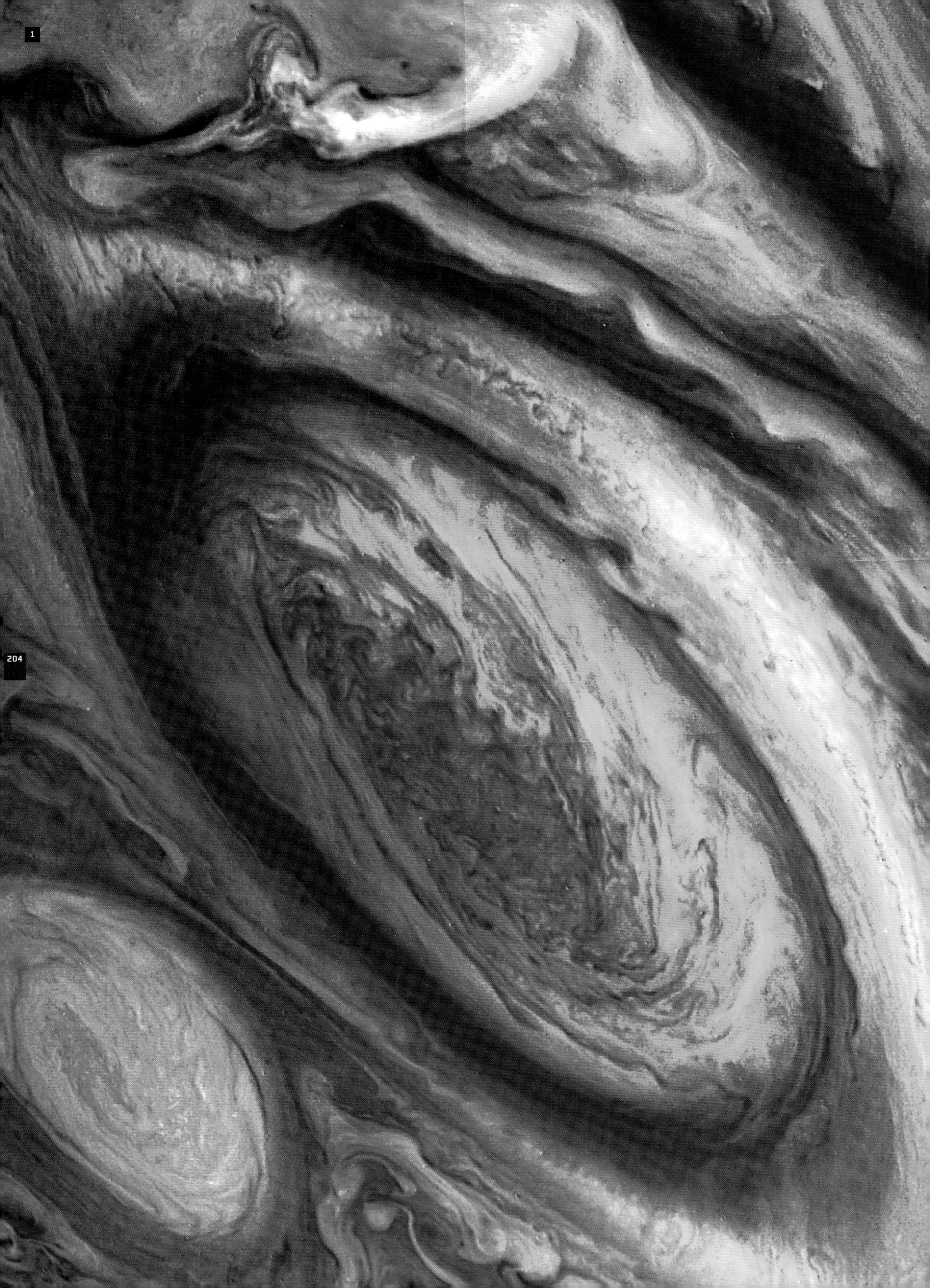
1

The Jovian atmosphere

upiter's atmosphere is vast in scale, with weather systems to match. Huge yclonic storms last for centuries and planetary scientists on Earth watch new veather systems develop over months and even years. Vast sheets of lightning, arger than Earth in size, crack through the atmosphere.

1, 2] The Great Red Spot

he Great Red Spot [1] is a persistent nticyclonic storm on Jupiter that is about he same size as the entire Earth. It was irst reliably recorded in observations by talian astronomer Giovanni Domenico Cassini round 1665 and has persisted in the Jovian tmosphere since.

Although known as the Great Red Spot, t has not been constantly red throughout

years with the middle one forming in 1939. They are white because rising gases in the centre of each storm contain ammonia. When the ammonia arrives in the chillier reaches of the upper atmosphere, it condenses into bright white clouds.

[3] Red Spot Junior

Late in 2005, Jupiter grew another red spot. It was the result of a merger between three

[4] Impact scars

Jupiter's gravitational field gives it a strong influence over passing comets. In 1994, around 20 large fragments of comet Shoemaker-Levy 9 collided with Jupiter. The impacts took place between July 16 and July 22 producing spectacular explosions that left the planet temporarily 'scarred'. The black smudges in this image are those impact scars and are typically clouds of dark material, each

The moons of Jupiter

Jupiter holds court over a large number of moons. Following the discovery of the four largest in 1610, astronomers found no more until 1892. In the 20th century, photography and direct exploration by spacecraft accelerated the discovery rate. Almost five times as many moons have been discovered in the last 30 years as were discovered during the previous 300 years. The total currently stands at more than 60.

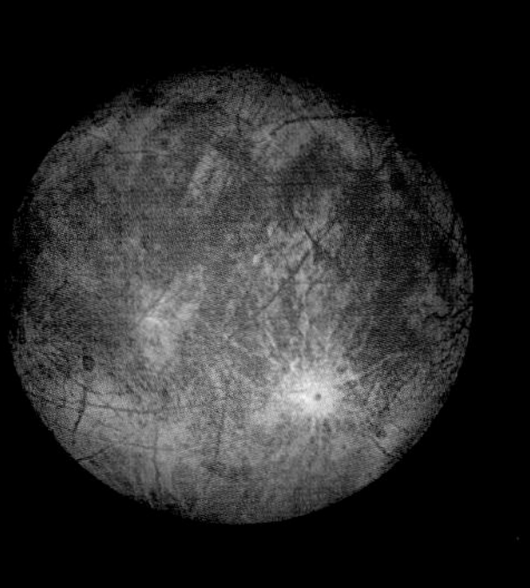

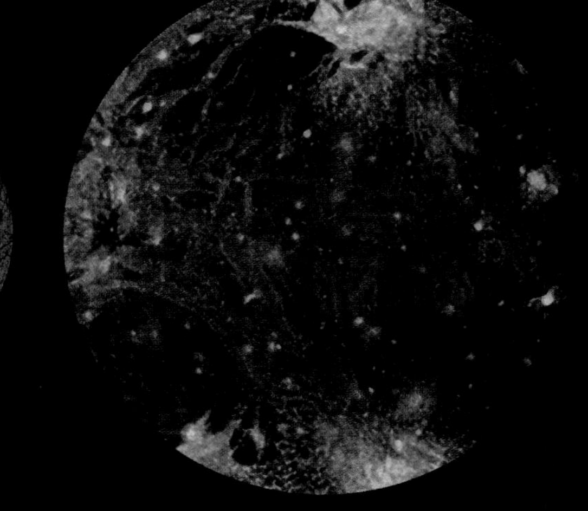

The four satellites of Jupiter that were discovered by the Italian astronomer Galileo Galilei in 1610 represent an important mini-system in their own right. Historically, they are important because they proved conclusively that not everything in the Universe revolved around the Earth, as was originally thought. This paved the way towards our modern understanding of the Sun as the centre of the Solar System.

With the advent of powerful telescopes and spacecraft that can resolve the surfaces of these celestial objects, the moons have become fascinating in themselves. Each Galilean moon is a world in its own right, striking for its similarities with, as well as its contrasts to, its siblings. For example, whereas Io has the youngest surface in the Solar System because of the way its volcanic activity is constantly spewing lava onto its surface, Callisto has one of the oldest exteriors. Virtually unchanged for 4.6 billion years, all Callisto has done is sit in space and suffer the occasional meteorite strike.

Although the large Galilean satellites dominate the Jovian moon system, there are many other smaller moons, too. To date, some 59 other moons have been identified. They are all smaller balls of rock and ice, most of them formed in-situ, but some are almost certainly captured asteroids. This corresponds almost perfectly with the groupings that astronomers use, dividing the moons into the regular satellites and the irregular satellites.

The regular satellites are the Galilean moons and the so-called Amalthea group [1]. The latter are the innermost moons of Jupiter and consist of four, smaller worlds made of rocks and ice. All of these are thought to have formed in position as Jupiter was forming.

The irregular satellites are found in more distant orbits. They are all smaller objects than the regular satellites and often their orbits are highly inclined to the plane of the regular satellites. Many of these outer moons travel around their orbits in the opposite direction to Jupiter's spin, an almost certain indication that they did not form there but have been captured as they drifted by.

One group in particular, called the Carme group, was probably once a single object captured by Jupiter and then subsequently broken apart by a large impact. There are 13 key members of this group, each moving in a similar orbit to the others and each counted as a separate moon of Jupiter.

1
Themisto
Lysithea
Himalia Elara
Leda
S/2000 J11
S/2003 J3
Carpo
S/2003 J12
Euporie
2
S/2003 J14
S/2003 J2
0 200,000 400,000 600,000 800,000 1,000,000 1,200,000 1,400,000 1,600,000 1,800,000 2,000,000 2,200,000 2,400,000 2,600,000 2,800,000 3,000,000

1
Metis
Adrastea
Amalthea
Thebe
Io
Europa
Ganymede
Callisto
0 20,000 40,000 60,000 80,000 100,000 120,000 140,000 160,000 180,000

2
Harpalyke
Mneme
Thelxinoe
S/2003 J18
Orthosie
Thyone
Ananke
Ionaste
Helike
Euanthe
S/2003 J16
Hermippe
Praxidike
S/2003 J17
S/2003 J15
S/2003 J9
Eurydome
S/2003 J19
Arche
Aitne
Chaldene
Isonoe
Kale
Carme
Taygete
Sponde
Kalyke
Kallichore
S/2003 J23
Aoede
Megaclite
S/2003 J10
Cyllene
Autonoe
Pasithee
S/2003 J4
Erinome
Pasiphae
Eukelade
Hegemone
Sinope
S/2003 J5
Callirrhoe
20,500,000 21,000,000 21,500,000 22,000,000 22,500,000 23,000,000 23,500,000 24,000,000

▲

Jupiter and Io

Io, the innermost large moon can often be observed drifting across the face of Jupiter, as it take less than two days to complete one orbit. Astronomers term such passages transits.

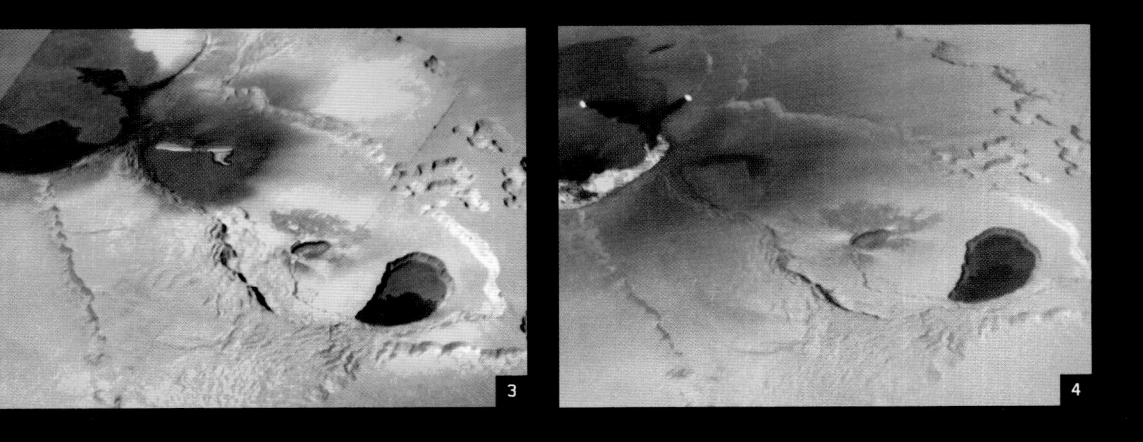

Io

The innermost Galilean moon, Io, is the most volcanically active body in the Solar System. Much more active than the Earth – some estimates place the activity at 100 times more – there is never a time when Io is not in a state of catastrophic eruption and the entire surface of Io can be covered with volcanic debris over the course of a century or two.

Io's lava flows are not silicate-based as they are on Earth, instead they are derived from sulphur. Io owes its dramatic surface colouring to compounds of sulphur.

The moon is driven to these extremes by the gravitational force of Jupiter that is squeezing it like a vice as Io travels around its orbit.

[1, 2] Pillan Patera

This eruption of Io's Pillan Patera volcano [1] has shot a plume of sulphur to an altitude of 140 kilometres. In Io's weak gravitational field, not all of this gas will fall back to the surface. Some will escape into space creating an exhaust of sulphur that trails behind Io in its orbit. Towards the centre of Io's disc, another erupting volcano, Prometheus [2], can be seen. The shadow of its plume is visible as a dark smudge below the volcano.

[3, 4] Tvashtar Patera

Here, the dark markings are a chain of calderas in the Tvashtar Patera region of Io. The image [3] was taken in November 1999 and shows an eruption taking place. By February 2000 [4], the eruption was still ongoing but had moved to another caldera.

[5] Tupan Patera

The volcanic caldera named Tupan Patera shimmers with exotic colours derived from sulphur. The dark colour is probably still warm lava, whilst the red deposits are sulphurous 'ash' condensed from the volcanic gases. The caldera itself is 75 kilometres across, surrounded by cliffs about 900 metres tall.

DISTANCE FROM JUPITER	DIAMETER	MASS	ROTATION PERIOD	ORBITAL PERIOD	MEAN SURFACE TEMPERATURE
422	3.6	0.01	1.8	1.8	130
THOUSAND KM	THOUSAND KM	EARTHS	DAYS	DAYS	KELVIN

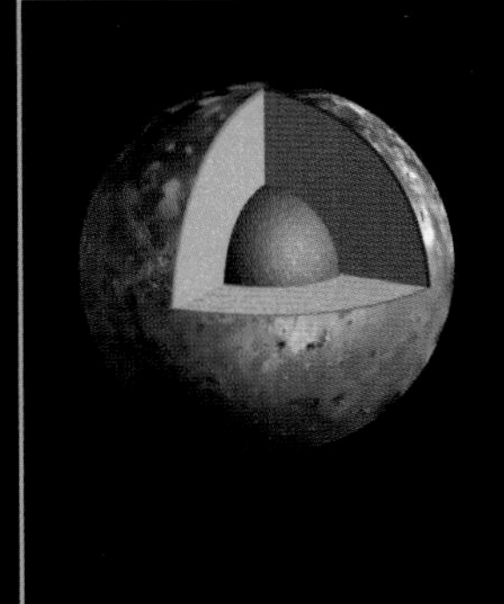

IO'S INTERIOR

Io's core is a mixture of iron and iron sulphide, extending almost halfway through its interior. Its mantle is a cauldron of molten sulphur and silicate compounds and its solid surface is a churning mix of lava flows.

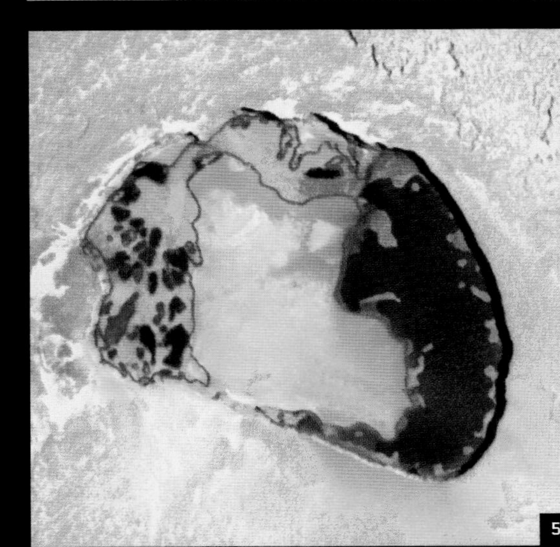

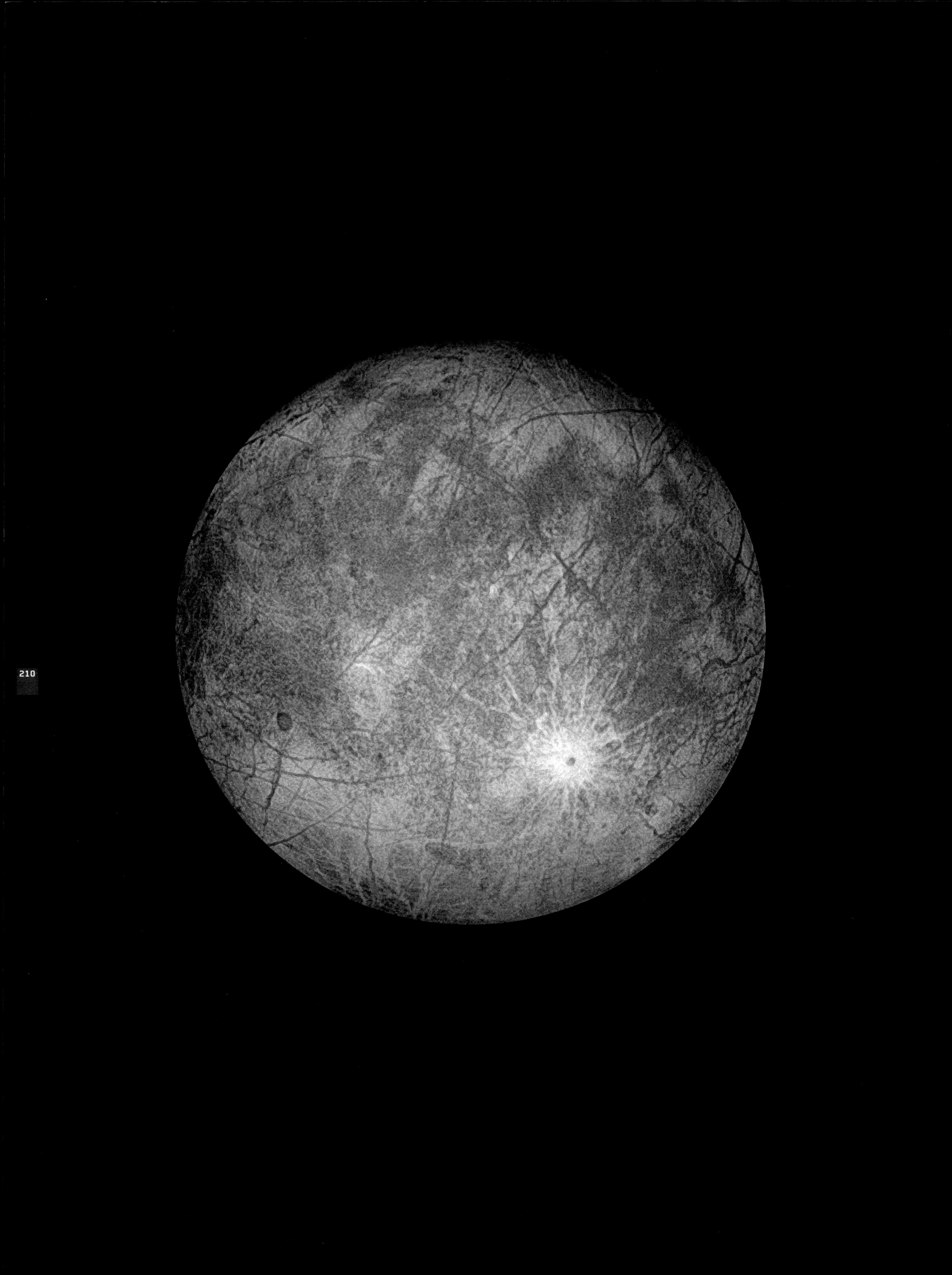

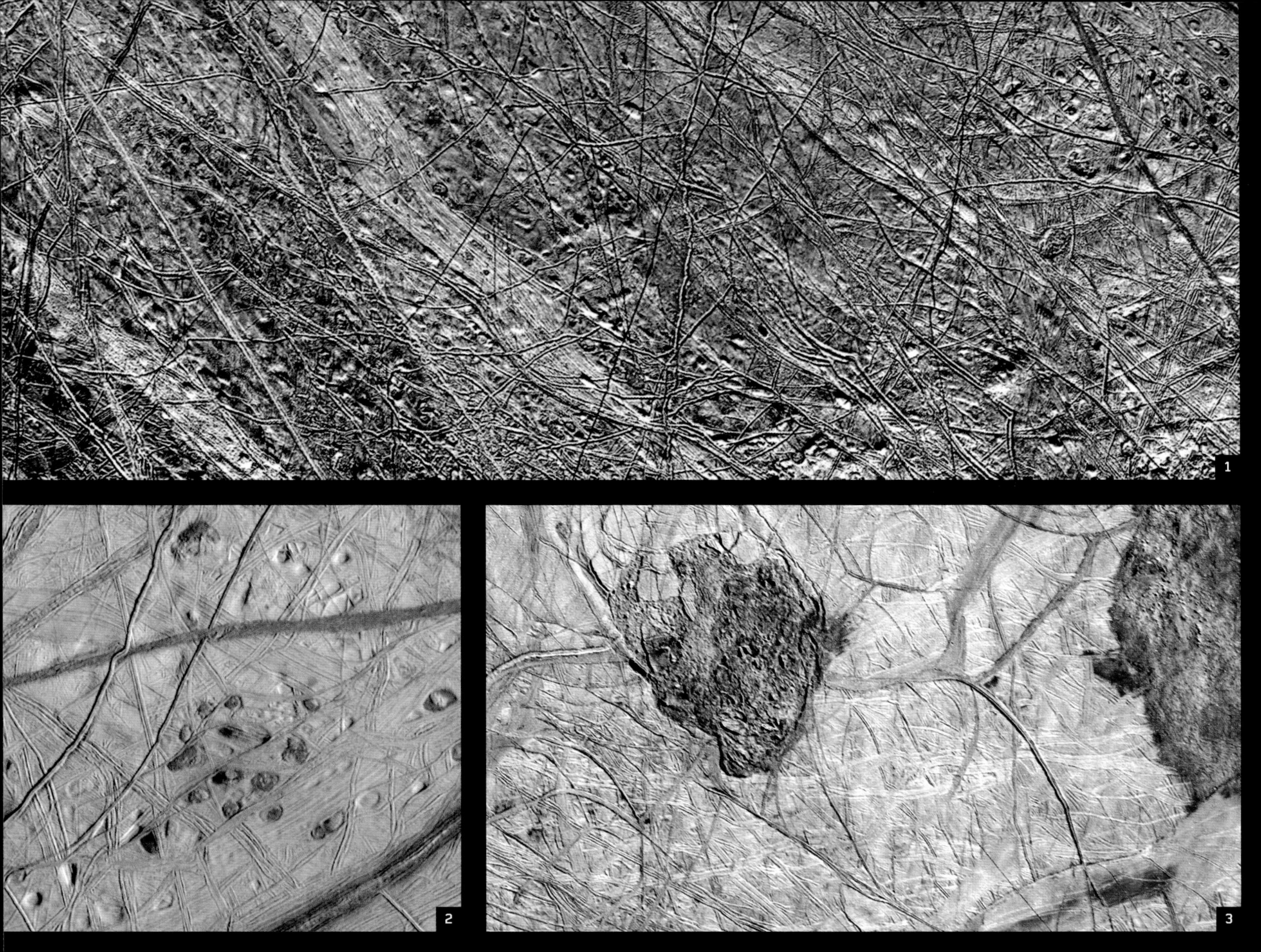

1

2

3

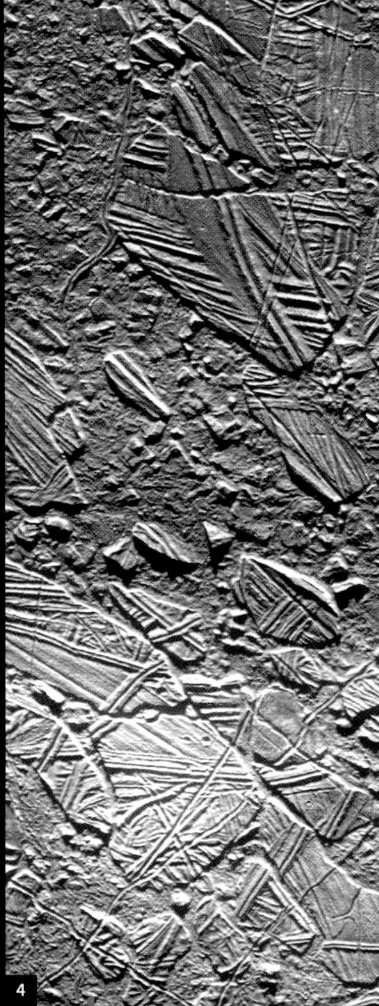

4

Europa

The smallest Galilean satellite is arguably the most interesting. The same gravitational forces that squeeze Io compress Europa, but, because Europa is further from Jupiter, the heating effects are not as intense. This has resulted in the interior of the planet being hot enough and volcanic enough to melt ice, but not so hot as to drive that water off into space or to expose Europa to the runaway volcanism that afflicts Io.

So, astronomers believe that a global ocean of water sits between Europa's icy crust and its rocky layers. Some have even wondered whether microbial life could exist in this ocean.

[3] Thera and Thrace

These two ruddy regions sit in the older, ridged plains of Jupiter's moon Europa. Thera (left) is about 70 x 85 kilometres and appears to be a depression, whereas Thrace (right) is longer and appears to stand just proud of the surrounding plains. Thrace abuts the grey band Libya Linea to the south and appears to darken Libya. Some planetary scientists believe that these regions were created in a 'melt-through' of Europa's icy crust, which exposed the ocean below, or that warm ice welled up from below and caused the partial melting of the surface. Either way,

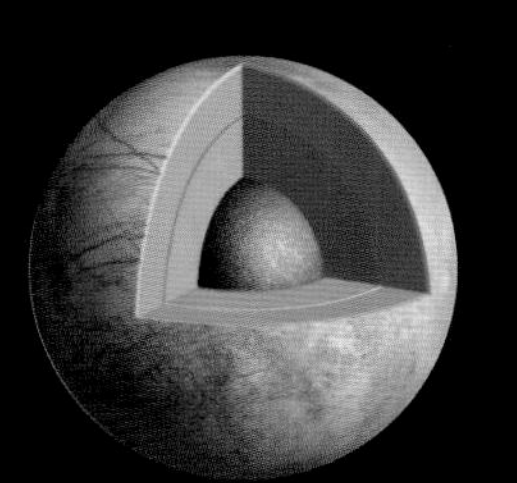

EUROPA'S INTERIOR

Metallic compounds dominate Europa's deep core and, surrounding this, is a mantle of rocky material. These interior regions are probably not completely solid but partially molten, which maintains a global ocean of water some 10–100 kilometres thick. The top-most layer is a solid crust of ice.

Ganymede

Ganymede is the largest moon in the Solar System, beating Saturn's Titan by a mere 100 kilometres in diameter. It is just 400 or so kilometres bigger than Callisto, the next largest Galilean satellite; yet it has managed to experience a completely different history. Ganymede's surface is split almost equally into two different terrain types. One is an ancient surface that resembles the frigid mask of Callisto; the other is a dynamic face that bears the marks of large-scale re-surfacing.

Something appears to have happened to Ganymede around a billion years ago that created this dichotomy, setting in motion a chain of world-altering events that are only dying out today. It may be that gravitational forces from the other Galilean satellites distorted Ganymede's orbit into an elliptical shape. With Jupiter's gravitational force no longer equal at all points of the moon's orbit, Ganymede would have experienced enough stresses to melt its interior, allowing warmer ices to well up to the surface and push apart older terrain blocks to create distinct fresh ridges.

The same tidal heating effect could also have melted sufficient water to create a global ocean, which may still exist underneath the surface of the moon.

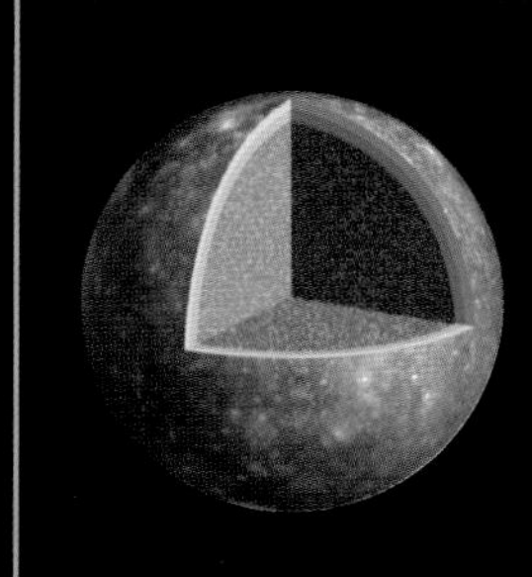

GANYMEDE'S INTERIOR
A metal core and a rocky mantle could lie underneath a global ocean of salty water. Overlying all of this is a thick crust of solid ice.

DISTANCE FROM JUPITER	DIAMETER	MASS	ROTATION PERIOD	ORBITAL PERIOD	MEAN SURFACE TEMPERATURE
1	5.2	0.03	7.15	7.15	110
MILLION KM	THOUSAND KM	EARTHS	DAYS	DAYS	KELVIN

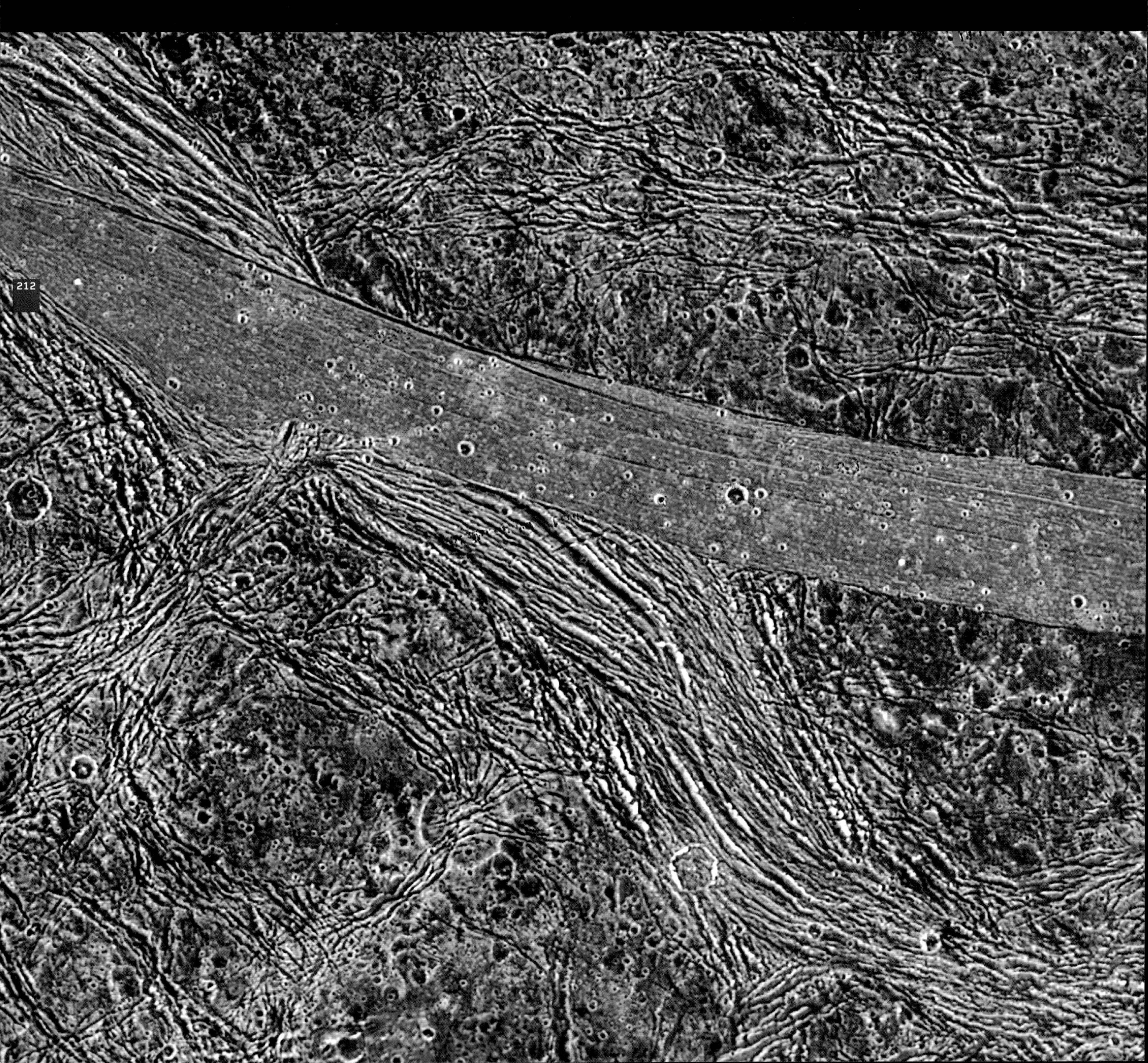

Callisto

Callisto is the odd-one-out of the Galilean satellites. Unlike the others, it is heavily pockmarked with craters. This indicates the great age of its surface and the fact that the moon has remained largely unchanged since its formation. As the outermost Galilean satellite, Callisto escapes the full force of Jupiter's gravitational grip and as a result has does not have a molten interior like its sisters.

The comparative lack of Jupiter's gravitional molestation has another consequence. The interior of Callisto has probably not settled into onion-like layers of metallic core, silicate mantle and crust, but may remain an undifferentiated mixture.

Callisto is dominated by the Valhalla Crater. At 600 kilometres across the crater is large, but more impressive than its size are the shock waves from the calamity that have raised a series of concentric ripples that extend almost a quarter of the way around the moon.

There is one overwhelming mystery about Callisto: unexpectedly, it has a weak magnetic field. The lack of metallic core, and the apparent absence of internal heat, would usually preclude a magnetic field, yet spacecraft data show it to be present. Some astronomers have hypothesized a thin ocean beneath the ancient crust might be responsible – but if that's the case, what is keeping it warm? As yet, astronomers have few clues.

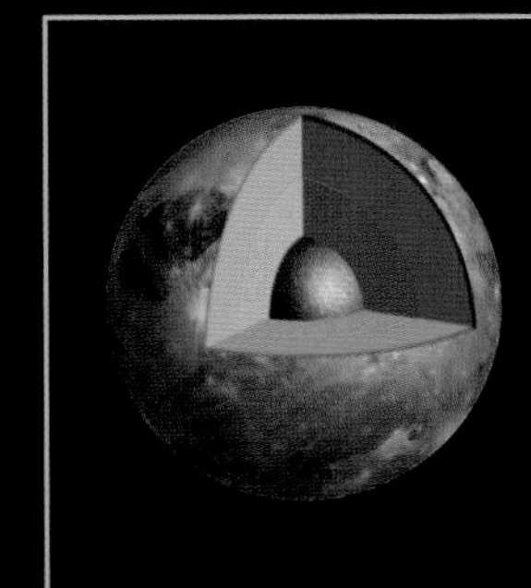

CALLISTO'S INTERIOR
A mass of largely undifferentiated rocks and metals lie inside Callisto. There is a small chance that a shallow ocean sits between this and the ancient icy crust.

DISTANCE FROM JUPITER	DIAMETER	MASS	ROTATION PERIOD	ORBITAL PERIOD	MEAN SURFACE TEMPERATURE
1.9	4.8	0.02	16.7	16.7	134
MILLION KM	THOUSAND KM	EARTHS	DAYS	DAYS	KELVIN

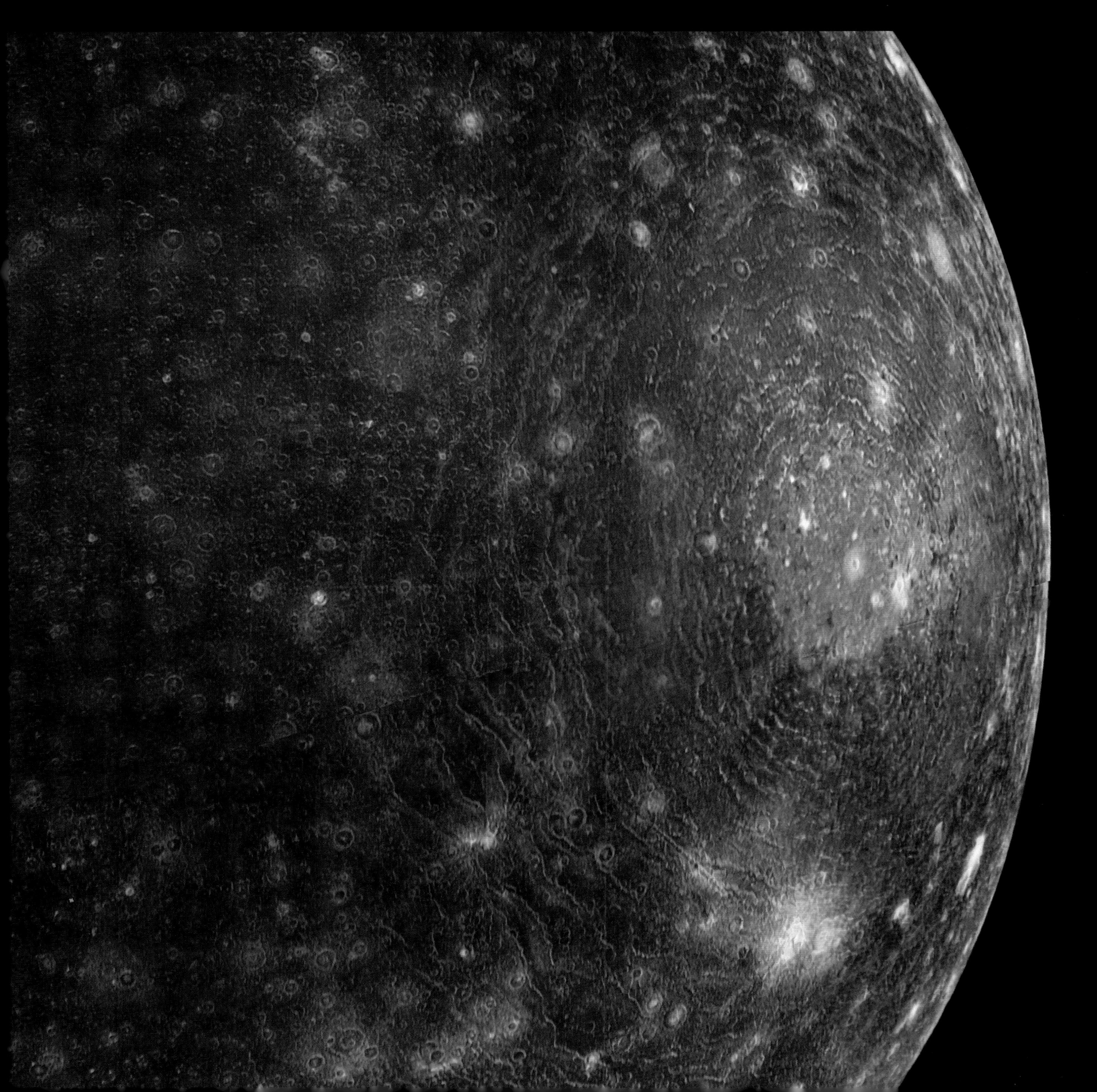

SATURN_

In comparison with Jupiter's turbulent visage, Saturn appears serene because, despite their similar sizes, Saturn does not seem to possess such strong cloud features. That is not to say that storm features cannot appear. Indeed, one southern latitude of Saturn has been dubbed storm alley, because of the large number of storms seen in this region.

[1] Saturn's aurora

Saturn's auroral lights are seen here in ultraviolet wavelengths, superimposed upon a visible light image. They are driven by the pressure of particles given out by the Sun slamming into the atmosphere of Saturn. The planet's magnetic field guides them to specific locations and they appear as a ring, because this is where the field dives into the planet. Whilst on Earth a typical auroral display lasts for some ten minutes, on Saturn it can last for days.

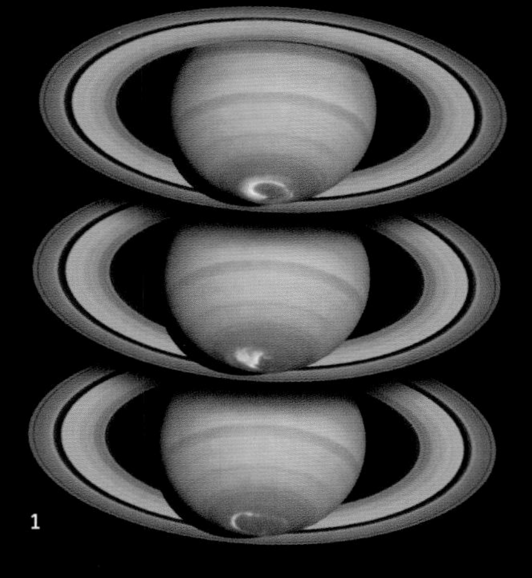

1

DISTANCE	DIAMETER	MASS	ROTATION PERIOD	ORBITAL PERIOD	MEAN SURFACE TEMPERATURE
1.4	121	95	10.6	29.7	134
MILLION KM	THOUSAND KM	EARTHS	HOURS	YEARS	KELVIN

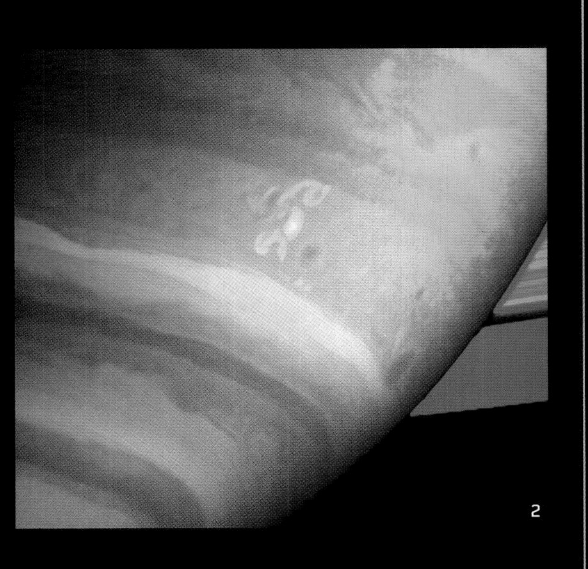

2

[2] The Dragon Storm

The Dragon Storm appeared in storm alley during 2004. This image was taken in infrared light that senses different amounts of methane gas, revealing the depth of Saturn's clouds. Deep clouds, seen through layers of methane show up as red, and brown indicates clouds at intermediate altitudes. High clouds show up as grey. The rings are bright blue because there is no methane between them.

The Dragon Storm's arrival coincided with bursts of radio waves, indicating that it was was generating lightning. However, the most interesting aspect of the Dragon Storm is that it appeared in the same location as a number of previous storms. This suggests that a lot of Saturn's weather could be taking place well below the visible cloud decks and only occasionally manages to break through into the upper layers.

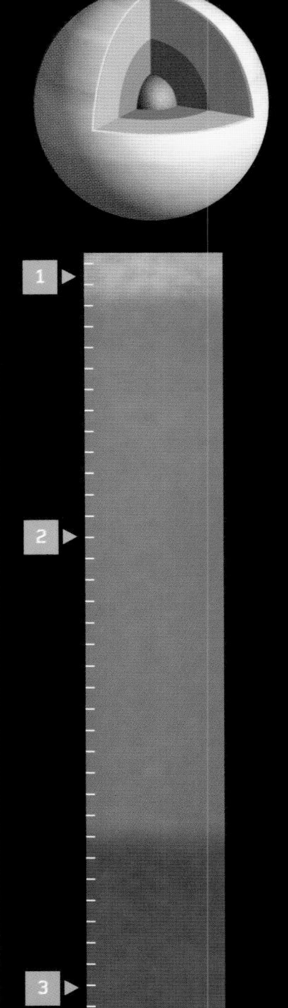

SATURN'S INTERIOR
Saturn's rocky, metallic core contains 10–20 times the mass of the Earth. Surrounding the core lies a zone of liquid metallic hydrogen and helium – shallower than Jupiter's – itself surrounded by a large expanse of liquid and gaseous hydrogen and helium. In this region, it can rain helium. Above this are the cloud tops and then a layer of ammonia haze.

[1] Saturn's pale clouds are mostly hazes of ammonia, formed in the cold upper reaches of the planet's atmosphere.

[2] Increasing pressure forces Saturn's helium and hydrogen to behave like liquids. This happens to the helium first, causing it to 'rain' through the hydrogen.

[3] Extreme pressure fores hydrogen and helium to behave like liquid metals.

[4] At the centre of Saturn sits an incredibly dense core of rocky and metallic chemicals.

Saturn's rings

Undoubtedly Saturn's most recognizable feature is its magnificent ring system. In 1610, Galileo Galilei was the first person to notice that Saturn through a telescope was no longer a single point of light.

[1] Saturn Eclipse
We had to wait until the arrival of the Cassini probe in July 2004 to see the full extent of Saturn's rings. Taken as Saturn eclipsed the Sun, this image shows the rings stretching from 6700 kilometres above Saturn's cloud tops to the diffuse fringes of the E ring, 480,000 kilometres away.

[2] Rings
Detailed study reveals that the rings are almost exclusively made of bright particles of water ice. This suggests that they are astronomically young, maybe only a few hundred million years old, as they should discolour with age. It is possible that they are the fragments of a moon that was shattered in an asteroid collision.

The gaps between the rings are each caused by a gravitational resonance with one of Saturn's many moons. Any ring particle that finds itself in these gaps would fall into synchrony with a moon and be gradually nudged into a different orbit by the moon's gravity. The most obvious gap is known as the Cassini Division.

[3] Saturnian Seasons
The rings change from our perspective on Earth because Saturn is tilted on its rotation axis. As Saturn makes its 29-year journey around the Sun, so the angle at which we see the rings changes. Because they are only 10 metres thick, when we see them edge-on, they appear to disappear. Then, they gradually open up again. This sequence shows four years' worth of variation.

1

2

3
Cassini Division
A Ring
Encke Division

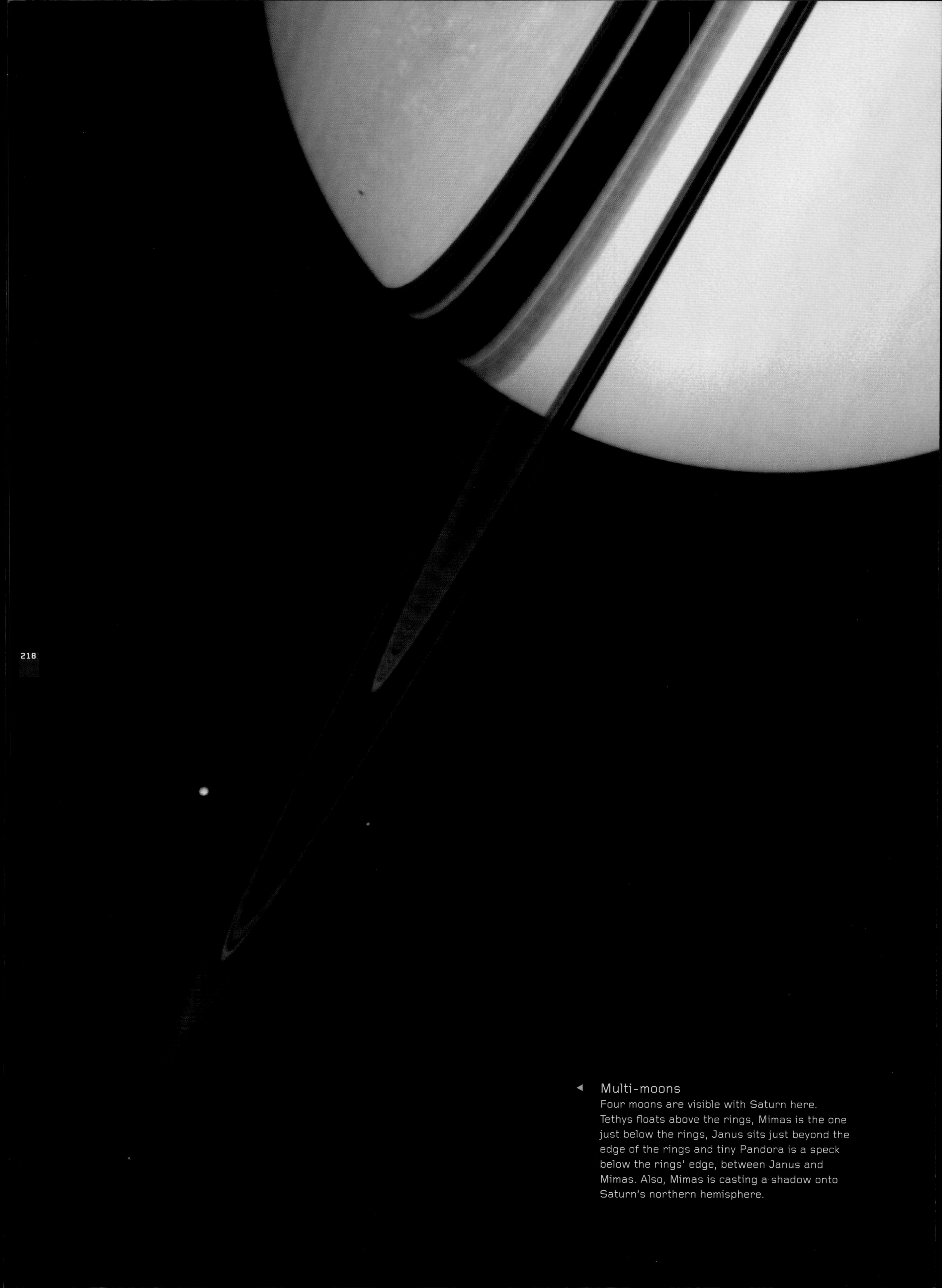

◀ Multi-moons
Four moons are visible with Saturn here. Tethys floats above the rings, Mimas is the one just below the rings, Janus sits just beyond the edge of the rings and tiny Pandora is a speck below the rings' edge, between Janus and Mimas. Also, Mimas is casting a shadow onto Saturn's northern hemisphere.

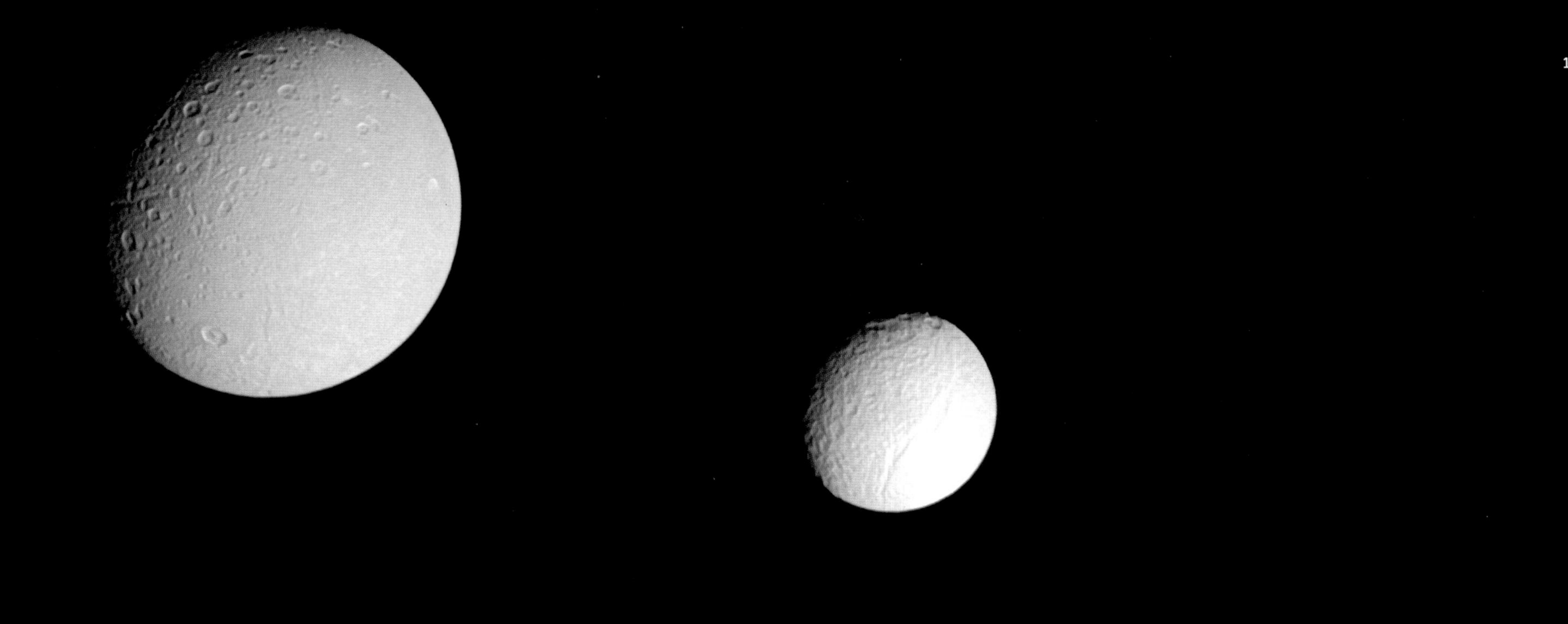

The moons of Saturn

In keeping with Jupiter, Saturn also has a large collection of moons. These can also be split into those that formed around the planet naturally and those that were captured later by its gravity. The gravity of some of the moons helps to shape Saturn's ring system.

In 1997, there were 18 known moons. Now there are over 60 and the total keeps on climbing. Saturn's moon system is astonishingly varied in shape, size, age and origin. Some are rocky, whilst others are icy. Many have ancient surfaces whilst some show evidence of internal heating and consequent re-surfacing activity. Some appear to have formed with Saturn, billions of years ago, while others seem to be pieces of a once larger world that has since fragmented. Then there is Titan, Saturn's largest moon and the only moon in the Solar System to have a thick atmosphere.

In the above picture [1], the moons Dione, Tethys and Pandora are caught near the rings. Dione (left) and Pandora (in front of the rings, right) are on the near side of the ring system. Tethys (middle) is on the far side of the rings.

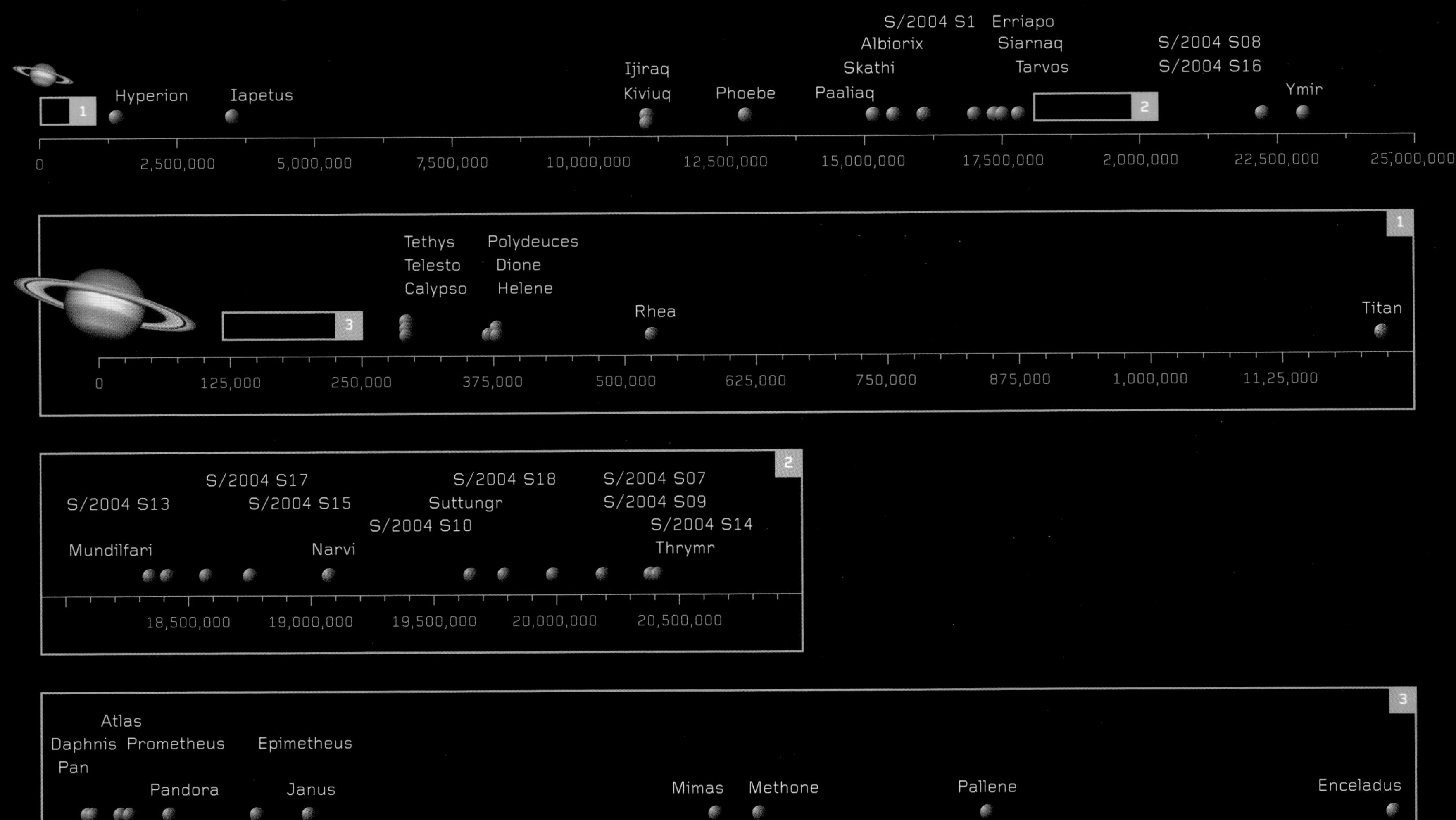

Mimas and Saturn's ring shadows

When this image was taken, Saturn's northern hemisphere was relatively free of the clouds that usually give the planet its yellow colour. So, just like on a clear day on Earth, the scattered sunlight appears blue. The dark bands that run across the image are the shadows of the rings and sitting in front of this pastel scene is the moon Mimas.

[1] Pandora

This small irregular moon is a shepherd moon to one of Saturn's rings. That means its gravity helps define the ring's extent. In Pandora's case, it shepherds the faint outer ring, called the F ring and is helped in this task by another small moon, Prometheus.

DISTANCE FROM SATURN	DIAMETER	MASS	ROTATION PERIOD	ORBITAL PERIOD	MEAN SURFACE TEMPERATURE
142	80	0.3	0.63	0.63	78
THOUSAND KM	KILOMETRES	nanoEARTHS	DAYS	DAYS	KELVIN

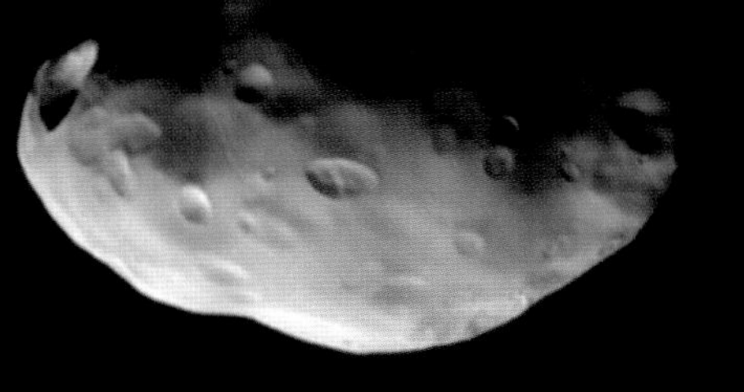

1

[2] Epimetheus

This dark, forbidding worldlet virtually shares an orbit with another small moon, Janus. It is thought that Epimetheus and Janus are fragments of a once single object that has since broken apart. Every four years the pair, which are travelling in the same direction, draw so close that a collision looks inevitable. Then, at the last moment they shift their orbits slightly and drift apart again.

DISTANCE FROM SATURN	DIAMETER	MASS	ROTATION PERIOD	ORBITAL PERIOD	MEAN SURFACE TEMPERATURE
151	114	0.9	0.69	0.69	78
THOUSAND KM	KILOMETRES	nanoEARTHS	DAYS	DAYS	KELVIN

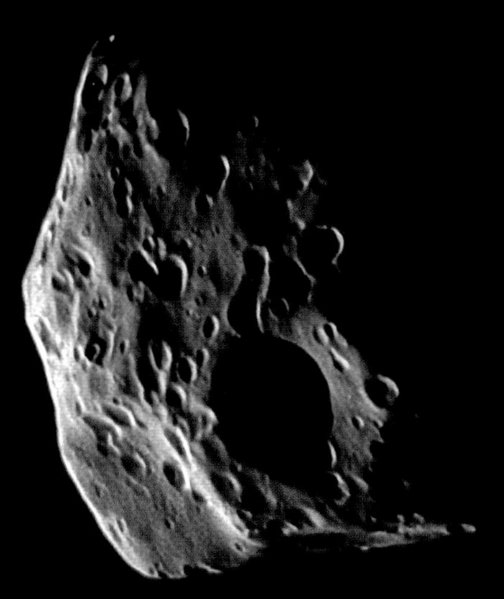

2

[3] Mimas

This moon is little more than a ball of ice in space, yet its gravity is responsible for clearing out the Cassini Division in Saturn's rings. The most prominent feature on Mimas is the colossal Herschel Crater, an impact scar that stretches 140 kilometres wide, with walls that rise some 5 kilometres above the surface.

DISTANCE FROM SATURN	DIAMETER	MASS	ROTATION PERIOD	ORBITAL PERIOD	MEAN SURFACE TEMPERATURE
186	397	5	0.94	0.94	64
THOUSAND KM	KILOMETRES	microEARTHS	DAYS	DAYS	KELVIN

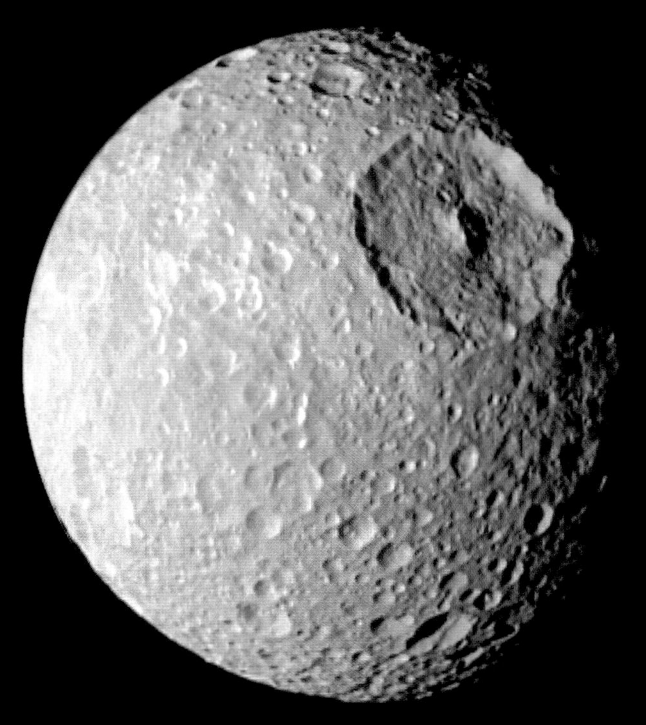

3

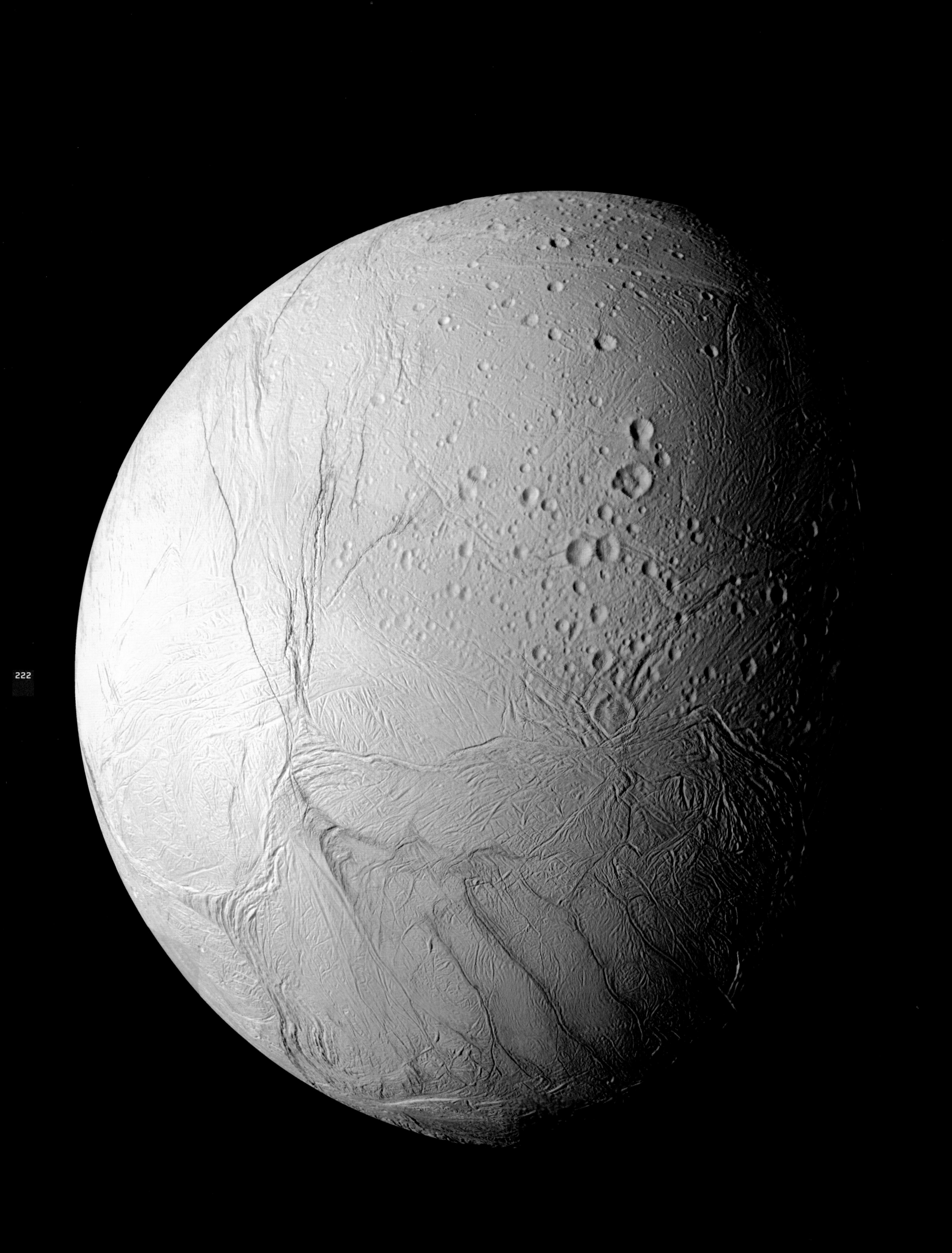

222

1

Enceladus

Little more than a dot against the giant face of Saturn and its rings [1], Enceladus was once believed to be an inert ball of ice. In the 1980s however, astronomers began to suspect there was more to the tiny moon than first met the eye because of its relatively young surface.

The Cassini probe's arrival in orbit around Saturn in 2004 revealed Enceladus to be a vibrant, volcanic world. At first, it appeared that the moon had a faint atmosphere of carbon dioxide, methane and water vapour. However, when Cassini trained its cameras back on the moon a few months later, it saw tremendous plumes of ice crystals jetting upwards from the surface [2].

Debris clouds from such eruptions were giving the impression of an atmosphere when in reality they were volcanic plumes. This makes Enceladus one of only three moons where active eruptions of material have been seen – Jupiter's Io and Neptune's Triton are the other two.

Investigations have shown that the plumes jet into space from regions near the south pole called 'tiger stripes'. Tinted blue in the image opposite, tiger stripes are warmer than their surroundings and are believed to form as internally heated ice becomes buoyant enough to force its way through cracks and fractures in the surrounding solid layer. Transformed into water, it erupts into space where the frigid temperatures immediately force it to re-crystallize. Such eruptions of water are known as cryovolcanism.

Density measurements suggest that Enceladus contains more rock than a typical icy moon, so it may have a greater reserve of radioactive materials to draw heat from. However, the primary mechanism responsible for its internal heat source is believed to be the tidal forces Enceladus experiences, caught as it is in a gravitational tug of war between Saturn and several of the larger, outer satellites.

DISTANCE FROM SATURN	DIAMETER	MASS	ROTATION PERIOD	ORBITAL PERIOD	MEAN SURFACE TEMPERATURE
238	504	20	1.37	1.37	75
THOUSAND KM	KILOMETRES	milliEARTHS	DAYS	DAYS	KELVIN

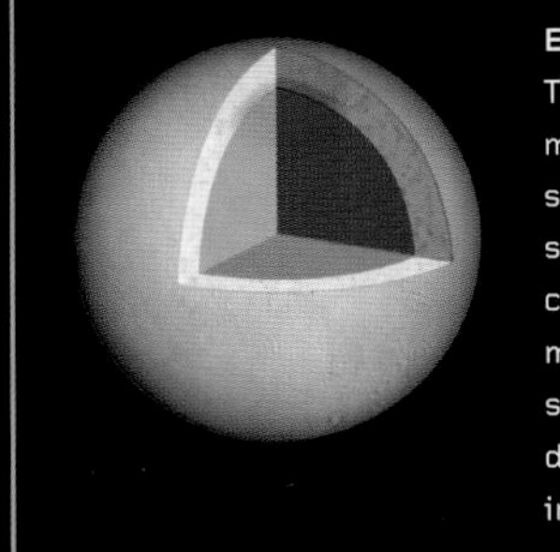

ENCELADUS'S INTERIOR
The large core is mostly composed of silicate material, with a smattering of metallic compounds. The ice-rich mantle sits on top. At the south pole, warm ice is driven outwards to erupt into space.

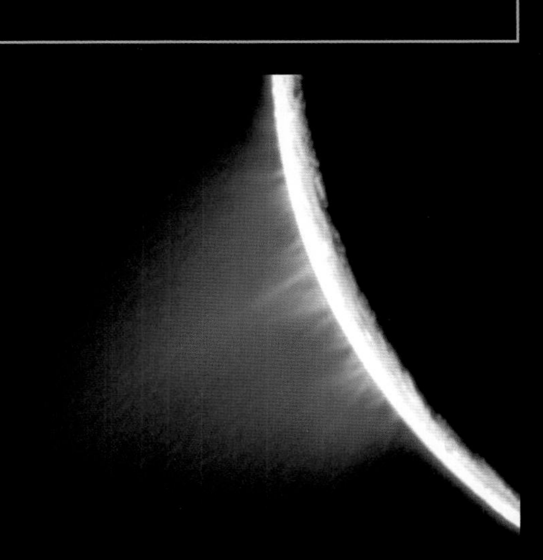

2

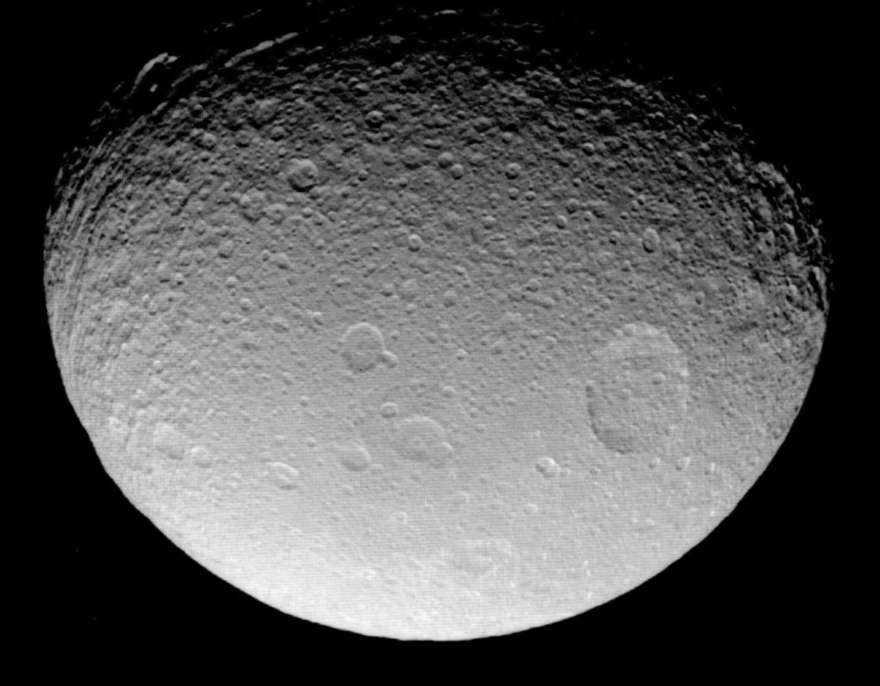

1

[1-3] Tethys

Tethys is a battered ancient moon with crater upon crater upon crater. The density of Tethys is so close to water ice that planetary scientists believe it is nothing but a giant snow ball orbiting Saturn. It displays a number of interesting features, including an excellent example of a large impact crater, the vast Odysseus basin [2].

Stretching over 450 kilometres across, Odysseus's outer ring is defined by steep, cliff-like walls. The inner ring is 140 kilometres across and is composed of a circular band of icy mountains. Such giant impacts are only possible in the early Solar System and mark the last phases of planet and moon formation. The fact that Odysseus survives so well today clearly indicates that not much has happened on Tethys since its formation. Even Ithaca Chasma [3], a deep groove system that cuts the surface of the world, is pockmarked with craters, indicating that it, too, is an ancient feature.

DISTANCE FROM SATURN	DIAMETER	MASS	ROTATION PERIOD	ORBITAL PERIOD	MEAN SURFACE TEMPERATURE
295	1.06	0.1	1.89	1.89	86
THOUSAND KM	THOUSAND KM	milliEARTHS	DAYS	DAYS	KELVIN

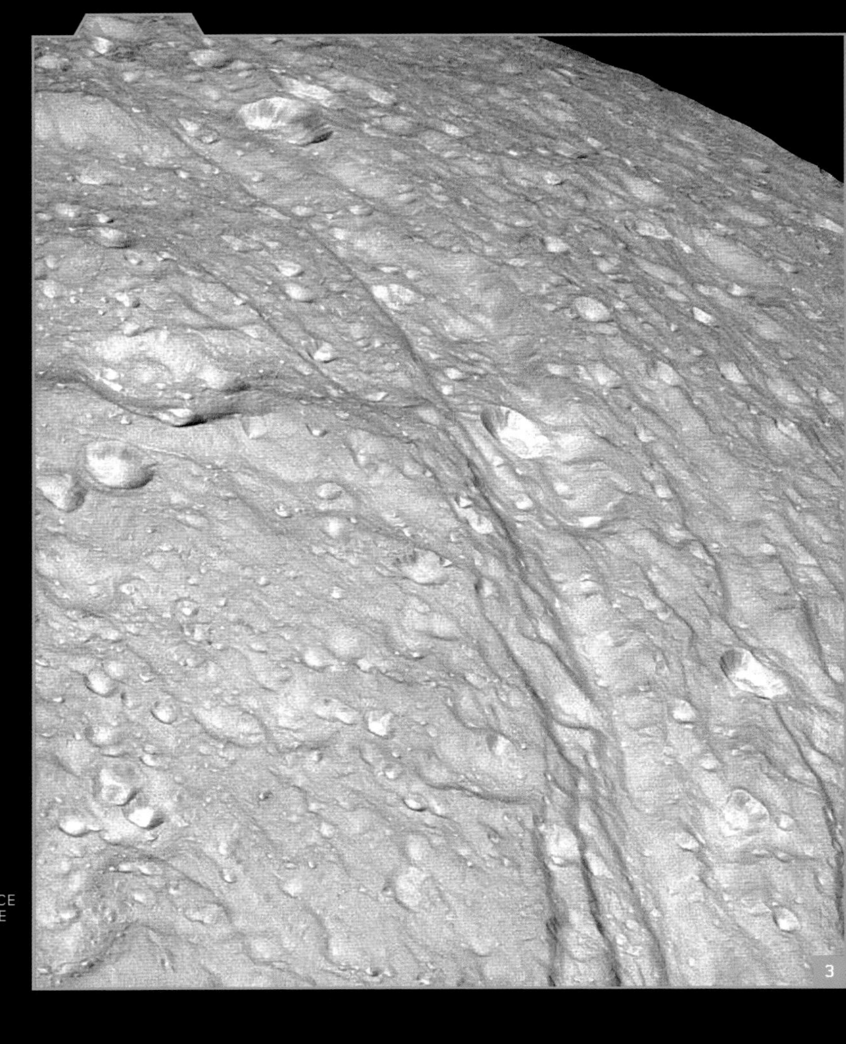

[4] Telesto

The predominantly smooth surface of the small Saturnian moon Telesto indicates that it is probably covered in fine ice grains. These have smothered the smaller craters thought to exist here. Telesto is trapped by the gravity of Tethys and is literally pushed around Saturn in the same orbit as the larger moon.

DISTANCE FROM SATURN	DIAMETER	MASS	ROTATION PERIOD	ORBITAL PERIOD	MEAN SURFACE TEMPERATURE
2.9	12	~	1.89	1.89	83
MILLION KM	KILOMETRES	EARTHS	DAYS	DAYS	KELVIN

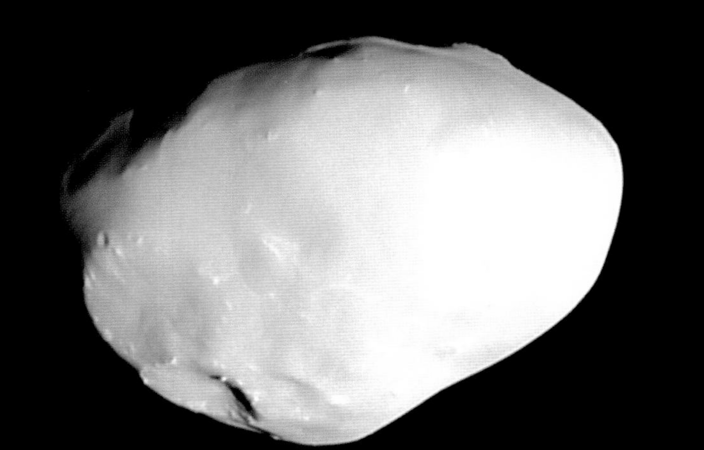

Dione passing by

Hovering above Saturn's rings, the icy moon Dione transits across the planet's face. The line across the image reveals just how narrow the rings truly are – a mere 10 metres on average. Above Dione, the blue shadow of the rings falls across Saturn's northern hemisphere.

226

Rhea and Saturn

Orbiting half a million kilometres in front of Saturn, Rhea is dwarfed by the giant planet. It is a mostly icy world, with only about a quarter of its mass coming from rocks and metals.

[1, 2] Dione

Although composed mostly of water ice, Dione's density indicates that it does have a proportion of heavier, rockier material inside. Its surface is not all heavily cratered; indicating that subsequent modification to the original ancient crust must have taken place. This has led to cracks and ridges appearing as the crust has moved over time. The bright streaks in the close up image [2] are huge, almost vertical ice cliffs catching the sunlight.

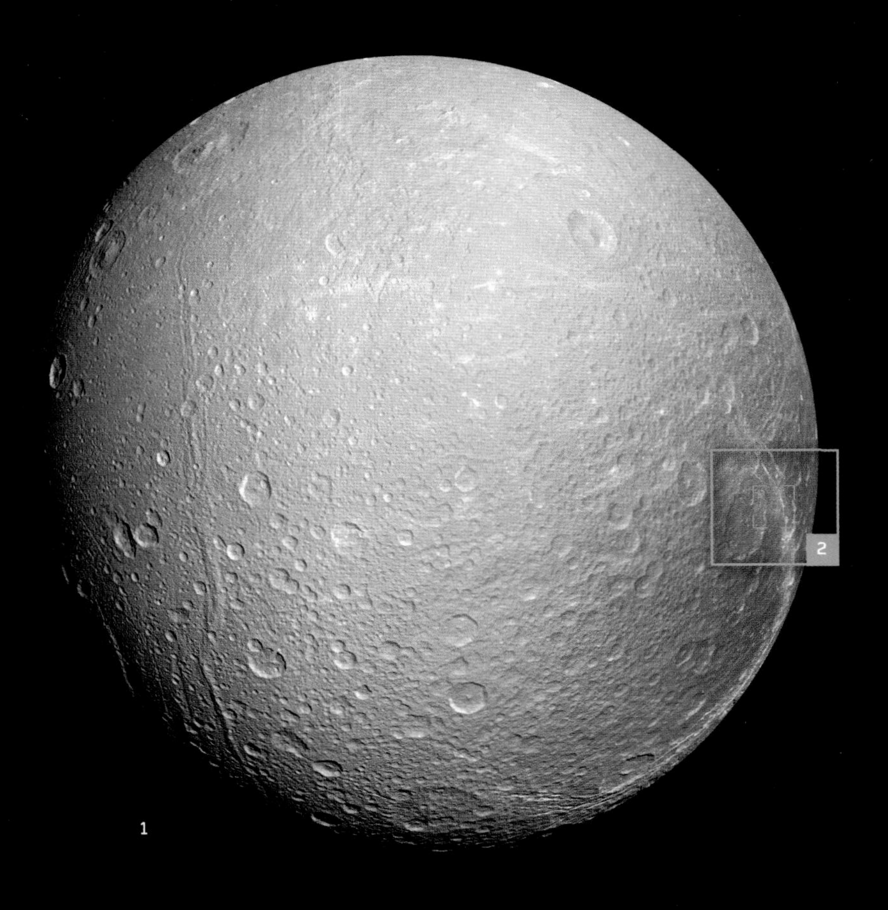
1

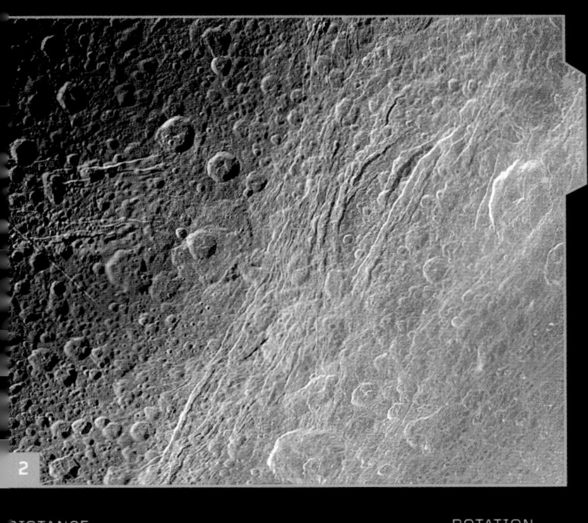
2

DISTANCE FROM SATURN	DIAMETER	MASS	ROTATION PERIOD	ORBITAL PERIOD	MEAN SURFACE TEMPERATURE
377	1.1	0.2	2.73	2.73	87
THOUSAND KM	THOUSAND KM	milliEARTHS	DAYS	DAYS	KELVIN

[3-5] Rhea

The second largest of Saturn's moons, Rhea has little in common with its cloud-shrouded big brother, Titan. Rather, it more closely resembles the smaller icy satellites. The surface of Rhea is a tapestry of craters, including two overlapping impact basins that have in turn been pounded by smaller impacts.

A close-up of part of a crater 90 kilometres wide [4], shows how the moon has been repeatedly pounded by innumerable smaller asteroids and meteorites. The surface of Rhea is now probably a pummelled mass of small icy fragments.

When computers are used to colour-code the extremely subtle variations in contrast across Rhea's surface [5], a difference can be seen. This may be down to variations in the surface composition or the size of the icy grains.

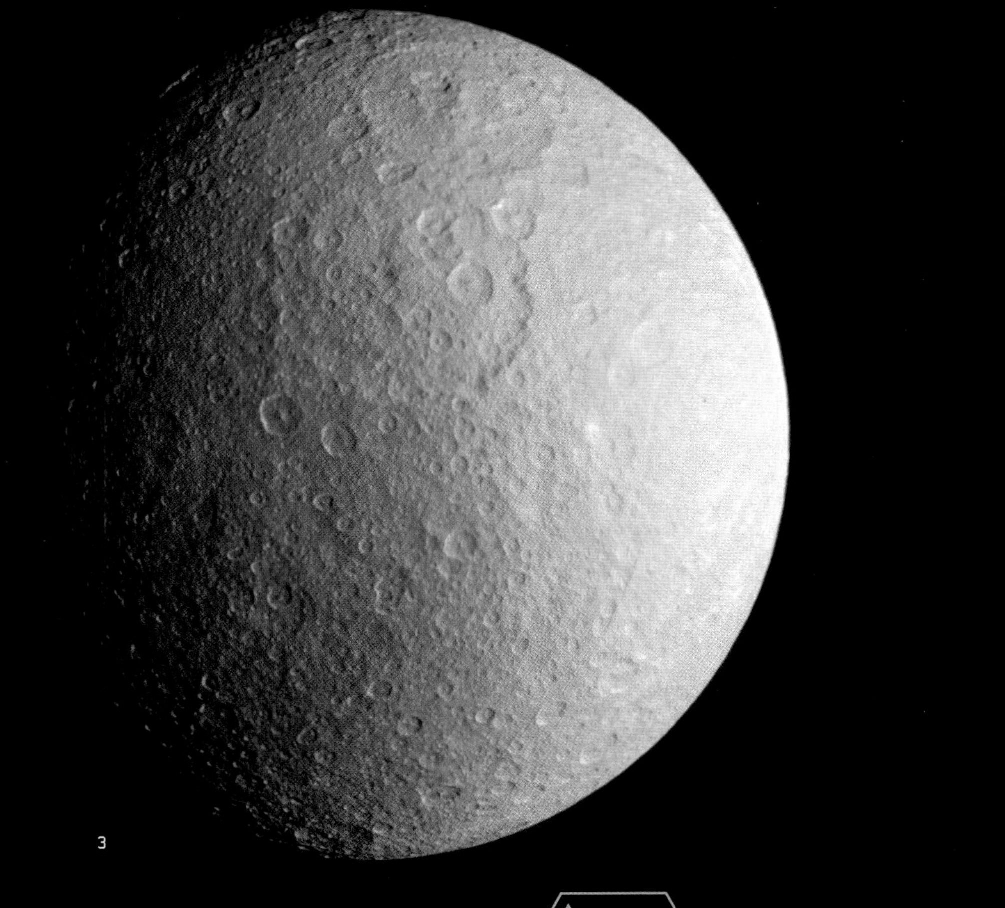
3

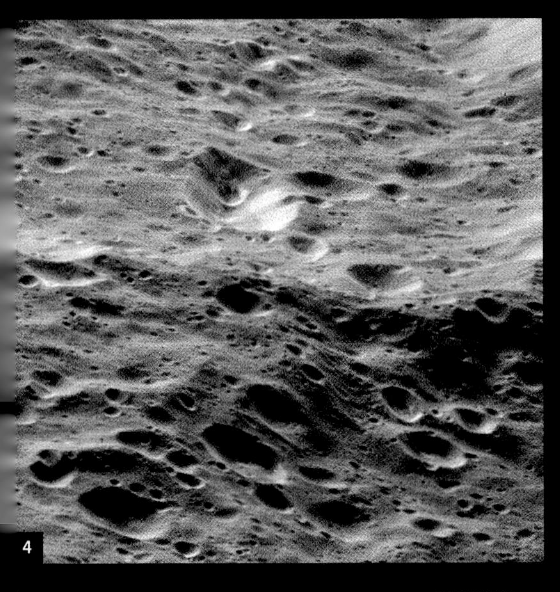
4

5

DISTANCE FROM SATURN	DIAMETER	MASS	ROTATION PERIOD	ORBITAL PERIOD	MEAN SURFACE TEMPERATURE
527	1.5	0.3	4.51	4.51	76
THOUSAND KM	THOUSAND KM	milliEARTHS	DAYS	DAYS	KELVIN

Titan

With its dense atmosphere and complex meteorology, Titan, although a moon, can vie with most planets for complexity – indeed, it is larger than the smallest planet, Mercury. The only reason Titan is still thought of as a moon is because it orbits a planet rather than the Sun.

Titan's dominating feature is its atmosphere. It is distended because of the moon's relative lack of gravity, just 0.14 that of Earth's. Principally composed of transparent nitrogen gas, there is also a small percentage of methane, which serves the same role on Titan as water vapour does on Earth. Titan's clouds are coloured orange due to their methane content which can condense and fall as rain across the moon's surface.

The most tenuous upper hazes of Titan can only be seen by the amount of ultraviolet light they scatter from the Sun. They have been included, on the otherwise visible-wavelength image opposite, as a purple hue.

[1] Radar lakes

This radar image of the surface shows dark spots from which there are no reflections. Planetary scientists believe that they are lakes of liquid methane, which would absorb the energy of the radar beams instead of reflecting them.

[2] A cryovolcano?

Guabonito is the name of the circular structure at the centre of this image. It is 90 kilometres wide and could be either an impact crater or possibly a volcanic caldera. Planetary scientists are combing the data looking for confirmation.

[3] Titan touchdown

The permanent twilight of Titan can be seen in this image taken on the moon's surface by the European spacecraft Huygens in 2005. The 'rocks' in the foreground of the image are actually little more than pebbles just 15 centimetres or less in size. Huygens landed in a dried-up outflow channel.

[4] Infrared Titan

These computer-coloured images are infrared views of Titan. The infrared wavelengths penetrate the clouds and see the surface of the moon. The top and bottom globes are the same hemisphere, viewed in October 2005 and then again in January 2006. Just south of the equator is Tui Regio, a bright infrared region nicknamed the 'chevron' for obvious regions. It is thought to be an icy deposit of water or carbon dioxide, probably of volcanic origin.

The middle globe was taken in December 2005 and shows the opposite hemisphere of Titan. Here a bright polar hood of gases can be seen but, as yet, the composition of this material is unknown.

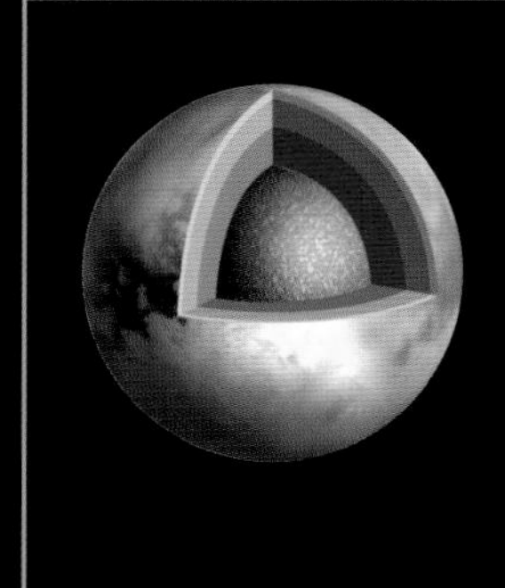

TITAN'S INTERIOR
Titan's mantle of rocks and ice sits on a core of metallic compounds. Above the mantle lies a mushy ocean of ammonia and water. This could drive cryovolcanism. The surface is covered with solid geological ice features.

DISTANCE FROM SATURN	DIAMETER	MASS	ROTATION PERIOD	ORBITAL PERIOD	MEAN SURFACE TEMPERATURE
1.2	5.2	0.02	16	16	94
MILLION KM	THOUSAND KM	EARTHS	DAYS	DAYS	KELVIN

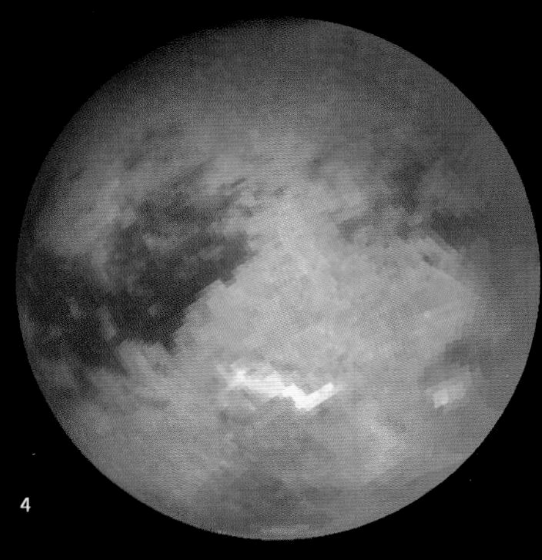

4

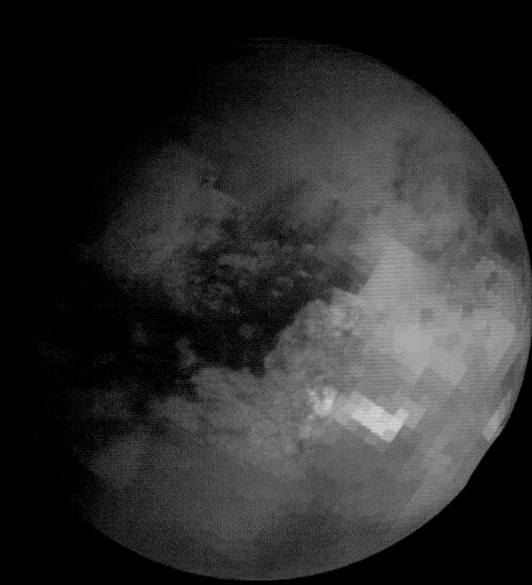

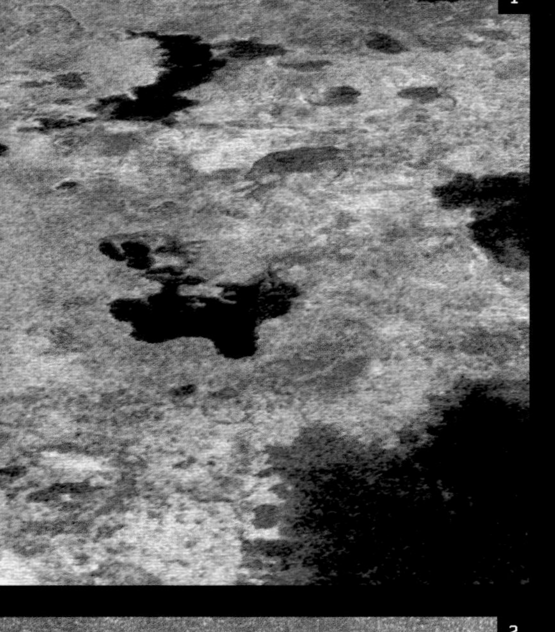

1

3

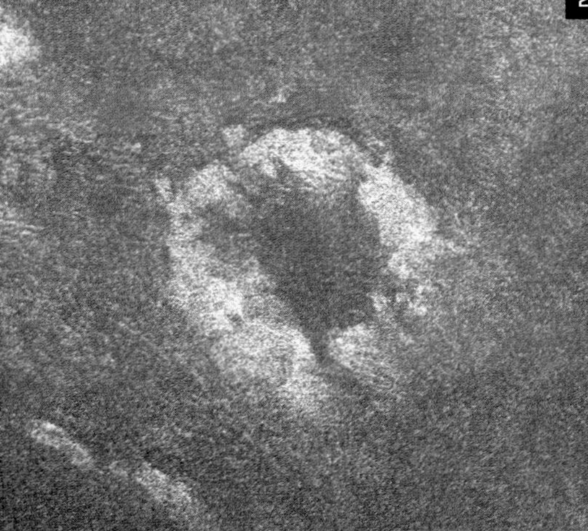

2

Hyperion

Looking like a cosmic bath sponge, Hyperion is a peculiar little world. It chaotically tumbles through its orbit around Saturn. The sponge analogy may be strangely apt since astronomers think that it is a porous moon, possibly with large caves inside it. A particularly large crater stretches over most of this face of Hyperion, with walls reaching higher than 10 kilometres.

To the unaided eye, Hyperion would appear reddish. This view is a combination of infrared, visible and ultraviolet images. The red colour has been toned down to show the subtle markings across the surface.

DISTANCE FROM SATURN	DIAMETER	MASS	ROTATION PERIOD	ORBITAL PERIOD	MEAN SURFACE TEMPERATURE
1.5	360	0.09	~	21.3	83
MILLION KM	KILOMETRES	nanoEARTHS	DAYS	DAYS	KELVIN

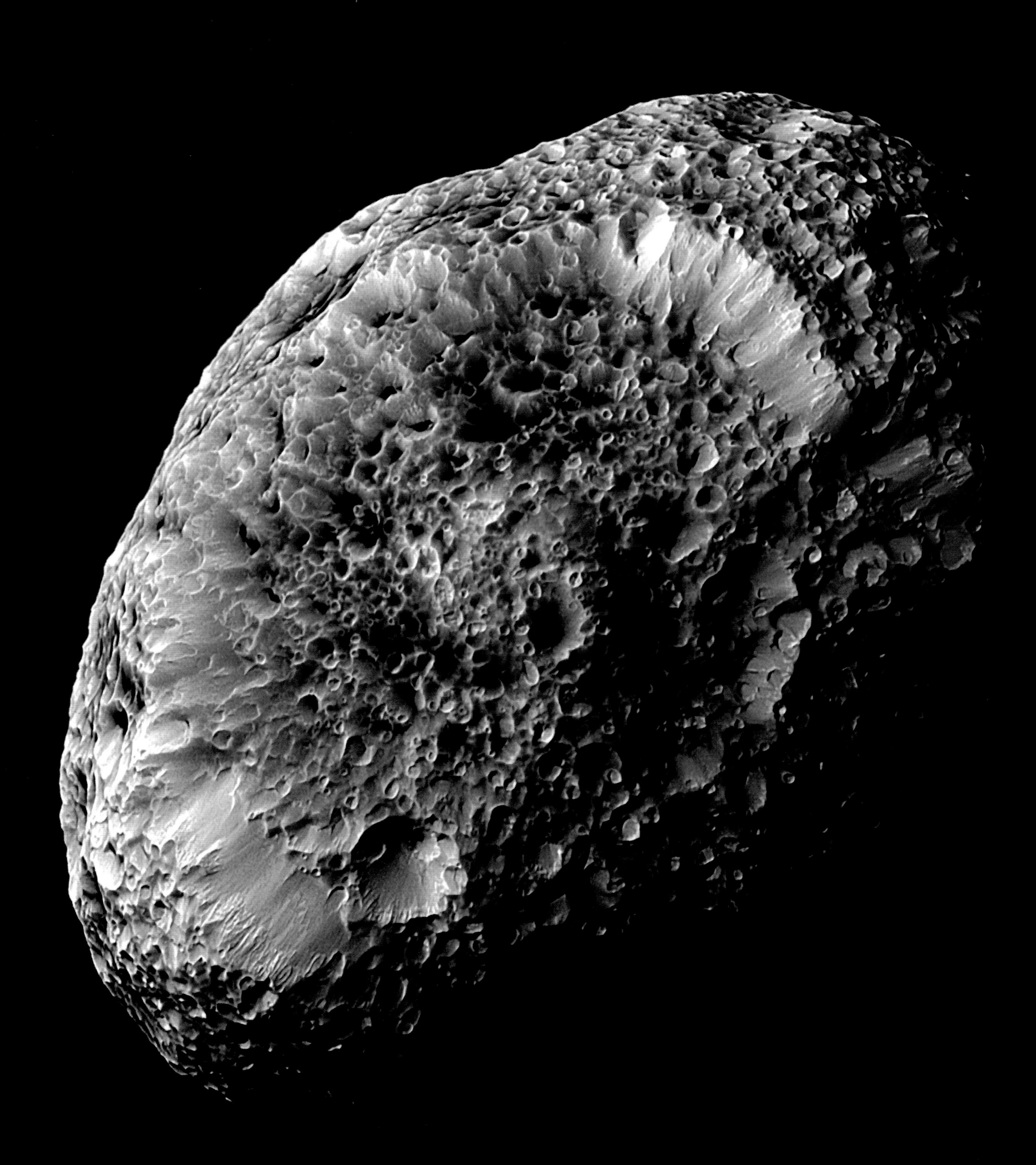

Iapetus

A number of Saturn's moons appear to have differently coloured hemispheres but Iapetus takes this to the extreme. This view shows the complicated transition region between the dark, leading hemisphere and the bright, trailing hemisphere. The dark material is believed to have come from beyond Iapetus, coating the moon as it travelled through space. It is composed of carbonaceous compounds that are commonly found in primitive meteorites.

Another puzzling feature of the moon is the equatorial ridge [1] that runs for 1300 kilometres across the Cassini Regio area of the moon. In parts it rises in height to 10 kilometres but as yet there is no truly convincing explanation for it.

DISTANCE FROM SATURN	DIAMETER	MASS	ROTATION PERIOD	ORBITAL PERIOD	MEAN SURFACE TEMPERATURE
3.6	1.4	0.3	79	79	83
MILLION KM	THOUSAND KM	milliEARTHS	DAYS	DAYS	KELVIN

URANUS_

Although you would never know it from the bland face it displays, Uranus is tipped onto its side and receives more sunlight through its polar regions than its equator. Astronomers think that this peculiar orientation has been caused by a collision with a large asteroid or small planet at some time in the distant past.

As it moves around its 84-year-long orbit, the northern hemisphere spends approximately a quarter of that time bathed in perpetual sunlight whilst the south is completely dark. Following a more normal day and night period for the next quarter of the orbit, the attitude is reversed and the south experiences a 21-year-long day. Then another day-night section occurs and the cycle starts again.

Uranus was the second gas giant discovered to have rings. Unlike Saturn's, Uranus's rings are composed of faint bands of dark rocks.

[1] Infrared Uranus

At infrared wavelengths, Uranus shows many more atmospheric details. The colours indicate altitude with green and blue regions showing where the atmosphere is clear and sunlight can penetrate deeply. Yellow and grey regions illustrate where sunlight is reflecting from a higher haze or cloud layer. Finally, orange and red denote the highest clouds, similar to cirrus clouds on Earth. At infrared wavelengths, the ring system also becomes visible. The bright dots surrounding the planet are its moons.

DISTANCE	DIAMETER	MASS	ROTATION PERIOD	ORBITAL PERIOD	MEAN CLOUD TOP TEMPERATURE
2.7	51	14.5	17	84.3	53
BILLION KM	THOUSAND KM	EARTHS	HOURS	YEARS	KELVIN

1

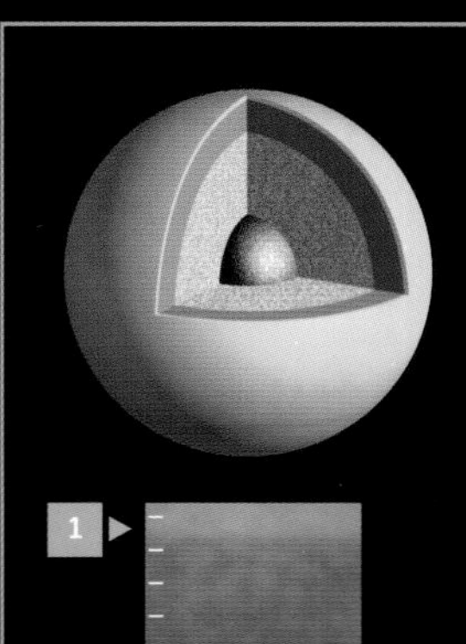

URANUS'S INTERIOR
From the central dense core of rocks and ices, Uranus is dominated by a mantle made up of a strongly compressed 'ocean' of liquid gases. This gives way to a dense, ice-rich atmosphere and finally the cloud tops.

[1] Cloud layer, containing methane.

[2] Pressure in the lower atmosphere builds, turning the gases liquid. This includes hydrogen and helium.

[3] The planet's mantle contains a mixture of liquid gases including ammonia, methane and water.

[4] At the centre of the planet is a dense mass of rocky and icy chemicals, some metals too.

1

[1] Ariel

Ariel is an icy ball that is covered in long canyons and ancient craters. The giant cracks in the moon's surface may have formed long ago when it expanded as it froze.

DISTANCE FROM URANUS	DIAMETER	MASS	ROTATION PERIOD	ORBITAL PERIOD	MEAN CLOUD TOP TEMPERATURE
191	1.2	0.23	2.52	2.52	58
THOUSAND KM	THOUSAND KM	milliEARTHS	DAYS	DAYS	KELVIN

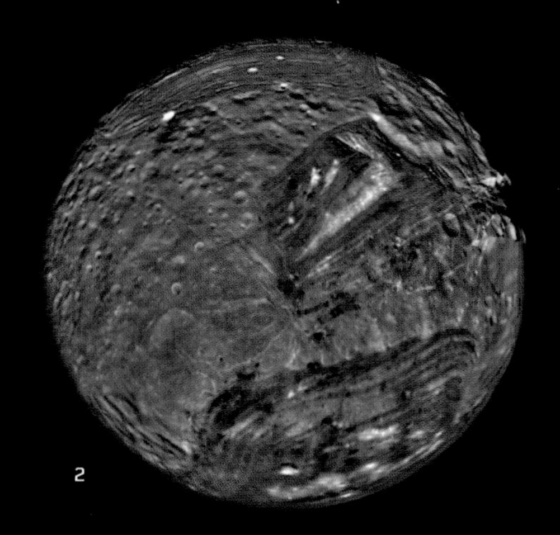

2

[2] Miranda

Miranda is a patchwork moon of contrasting terrain types, from heavily cratered zones to smoother, almost rectangular patches. Miranda's interior may once have been warm enough to melt large parts of its surface, which then re-froze into the jumble of terrains seen today.

DISTANCE FROM URANUS	DIAMETER	MASS	ROTATION PERIOD	ORBITAL PERIOD	MEAN SURFACE TEMPERATURE
129	480	0.01	1.41	1.41	59
THOUSAND KM	KILOMETRES	milliEARTHS	DAYS	DAYS	KELVIN

[3] Umbriel

Dark Umbriel only reflects around 16 percent of the sunlight that strikes its surface. The brightest area is a round marking of unknown origin close to the equator (seen at the top of this image). It could be frost lying in a crater.

DISTANCE FROM URANUS	DIAMETER	MASS	ROTATION PERIOD	ORBITAL PERIOD	MEAN SURFACE TEMPERATURE
266	1.2	0.2	4.14	4.14	60
THOUSAND KM	THOUSAND KM	milliEARTHS	DAYS	DAYS	KELVIN

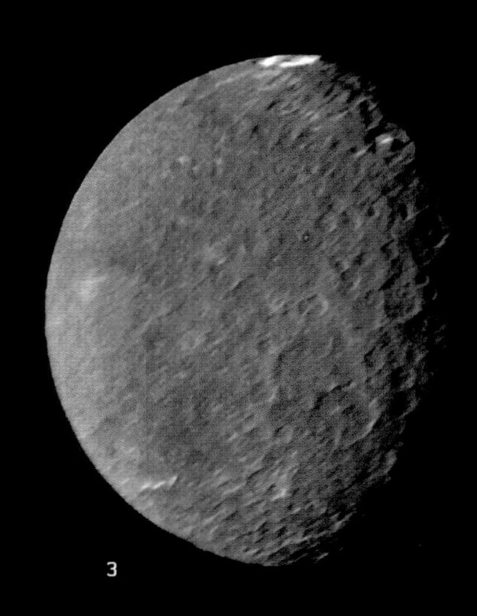

3

The moons of Uranus

Although not as grand as Jupiter's or Saturn's families, Uranus still has a credible 27 moons. Many of them are crowded just beyond the planet's ring system and computer simulations show their orbits to be unstable. This is because they gravitationally interfere with each other, distorting one another's orbits. It is possible that some will collide during the next 100 million years, creating fragments that will become a new generation of Uranian moons.

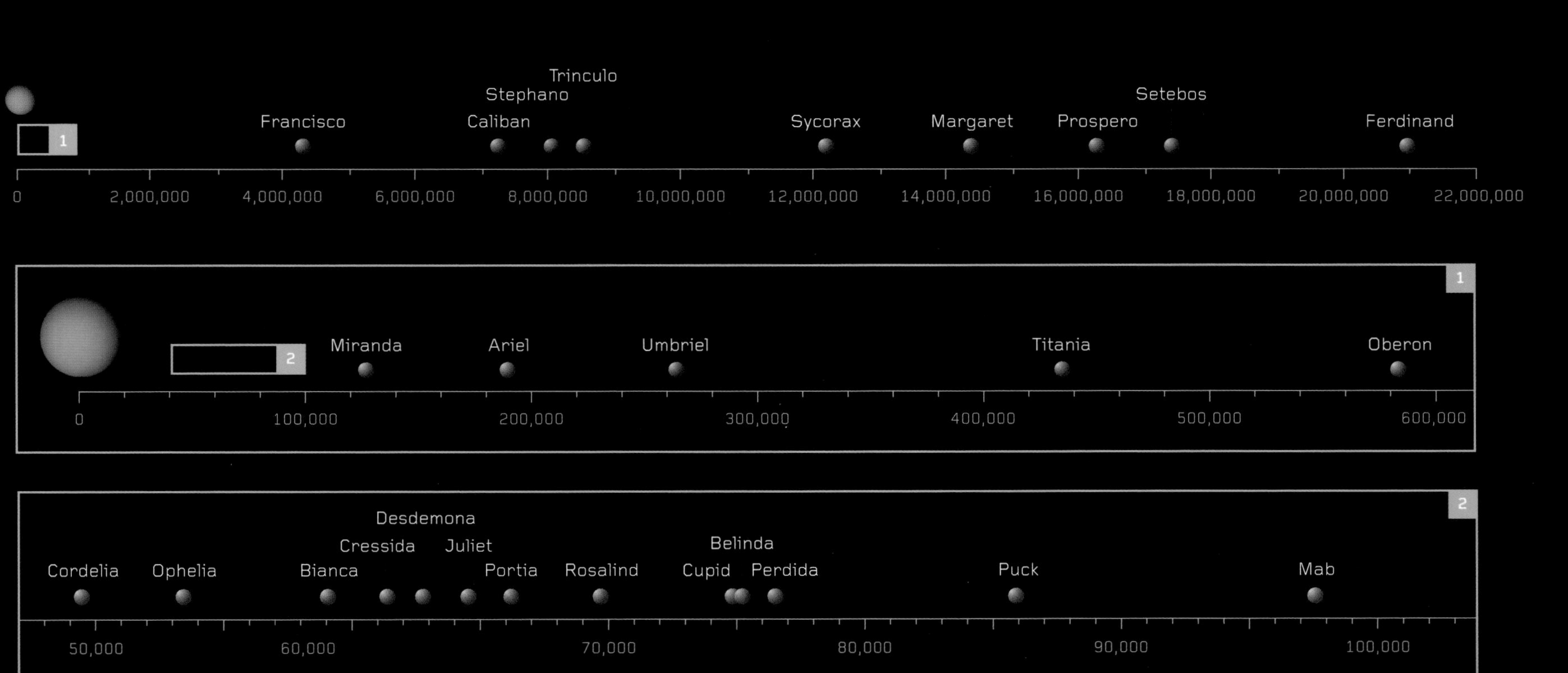

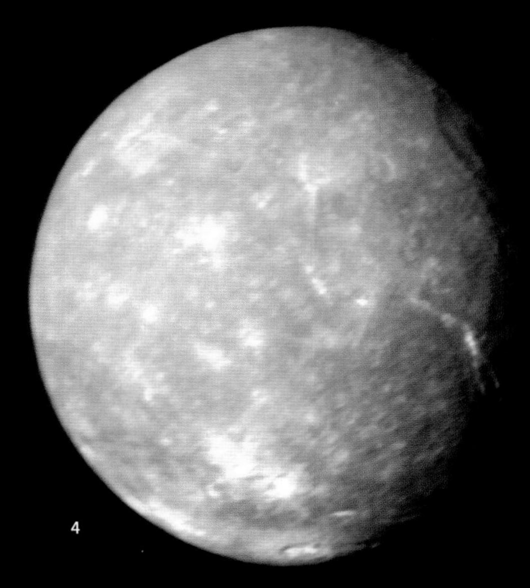

4

[4] Titania

Composed of one-half ice, one-third rock and the rest methane-rich compounds, Titania shows the signs of once being geologically active. Messin Chasma, a large canyon to rival Earth's Grand Canyon stretches across the moon (lower right).

DISTANCE FROM URANUS	DIAMETER	MASS	ROTATION PERIOD	ORBITAL PERIOD	MEAN SURFACE TEMPERATURE
435 THOUSAND KM	1.6 THOUSAND KM	0.6 milliEARTHS	8.71 DAYS	8.71 DAYS	60 KELVIN

[5] Oberon

As well as the usual craters, Oberon also has mountains, one of which is six kilometres high and can be seen on the lower left edge of the moon. The dark floors of some of the craters suggest that the impact punctured the crust and revealed the moon's mantle.

DISTANCE FROM URANUS	DIAMETER	MASS	ROTATION PERIOD	ORBITAL PERIOD	MEAN SURFACE TEMPERATURE
584 THOUSAND KM	1.5 THOUSAND KM	0.5 milliEARTHS	13.5 DAYS	13.5 DAYS	61 KELVIN

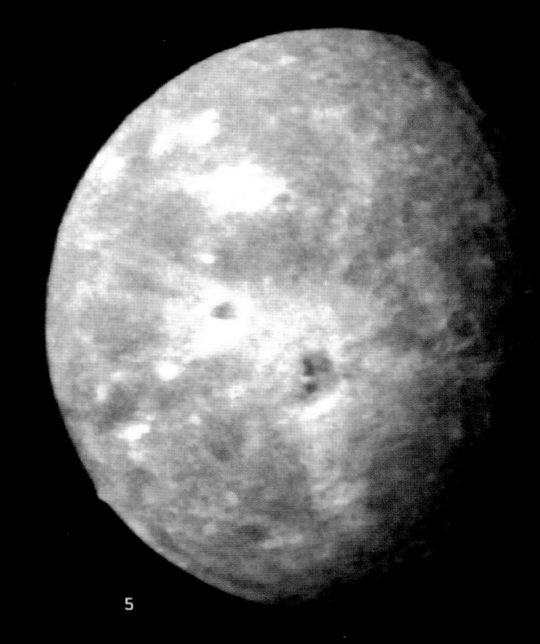

5

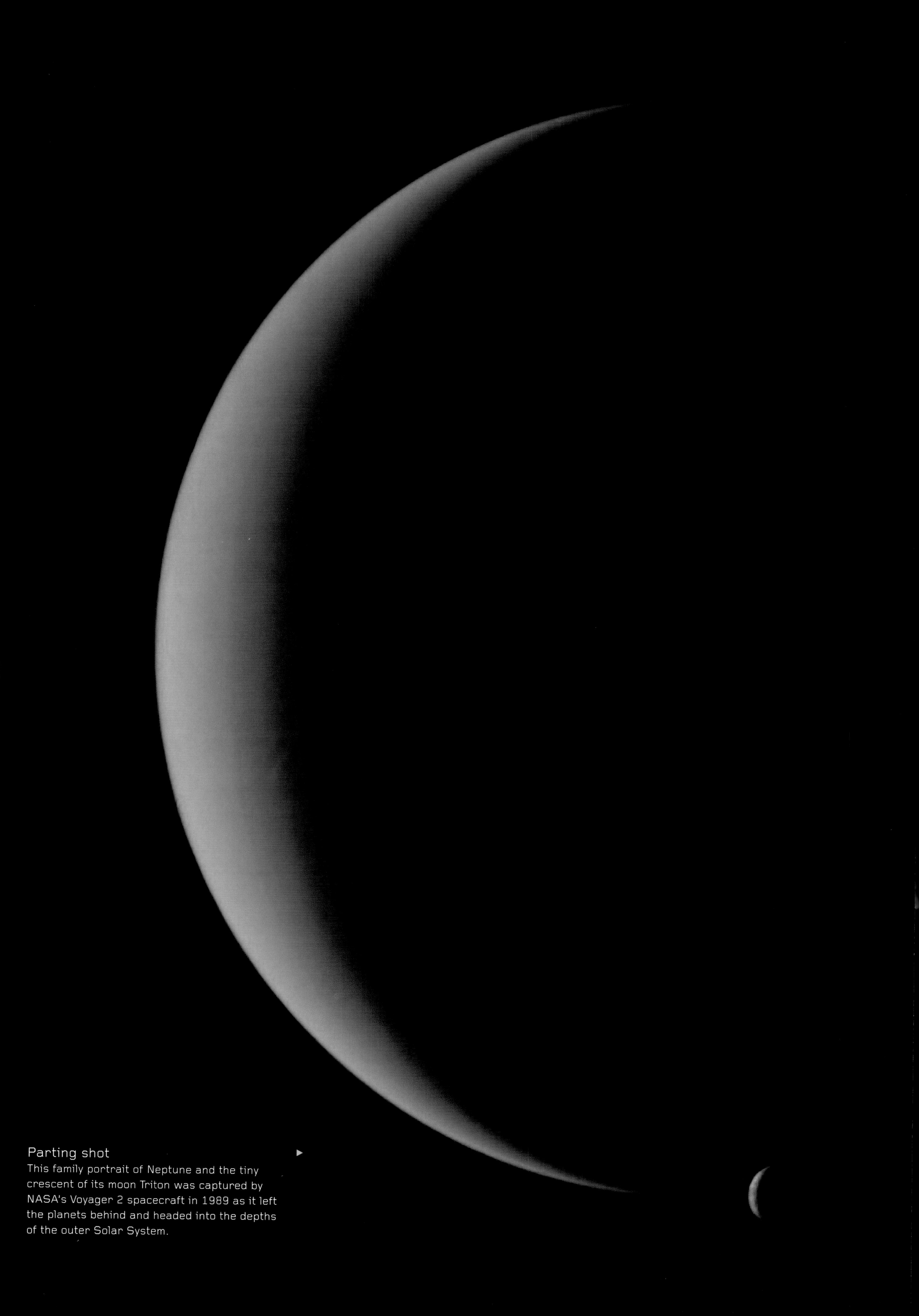

Parting shot

This family portrait of Neptune and the tiny crescent of its moon Triton was captured by NASA's Voyager 2 spacecraft in 1989 as it left the planets behind and headed into the depths of the outer Solar System.

NEPTUNE_

The final planet in the Solar System, Neptune is a more active world than Uranus. It generates over one and a half times the amount of heat it receives from the Sun by an as yet unknown internal mechanism. This may be radioactivity, or the product of chemical reactions involving methane at great pressure.

[1-3] Neptune's weather

The Great Dark Spot was seen on Neptune during Voyager 2's flyby in 1989 [1]. It abated and disappeared in the years following and was replaced by another similar storm at different latitude. These dark storms are thought to occur deeper in the Neptunian atmosphere than the bright clouds.

Image [2] shows that the white clouds sit well above the planet's blue disc. The width of the cloud streaks varies between 50 and 200 kilometres.

A high-altitude haze layer is seen [3] as the surrounding red glow in this image taken with visual and infrared wavelengths. In visible light this haze layer is virtually transparent.

[4] Springtime on Neptune

These three portraits of Neptune taken over six years capture snapshots of the planet's southern hemisphere as it enters springtime. A build-up of clouds can be seen, brightening the entire hemisphere of the planet. Six years is barely the beginning for spring. Because the planet orbits the Sun only once every 165 years, each season lasts more than 40 years.

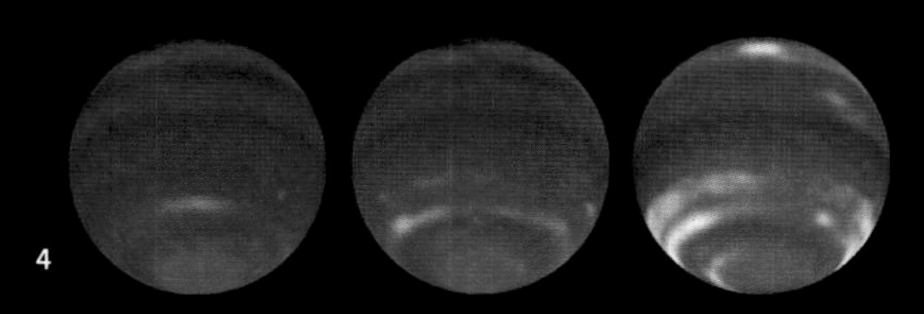

DISTANCE	DIAMETER	MASS	ROTATION PERIOD	ORBITAL PERIOD	MEAN CLOUD TOP TEMPERATURE
4.5	49	17.1	16	165	55
BILLION KM	THOUSAND KM	EARTHS	HOURS	YEARS	KELVIN

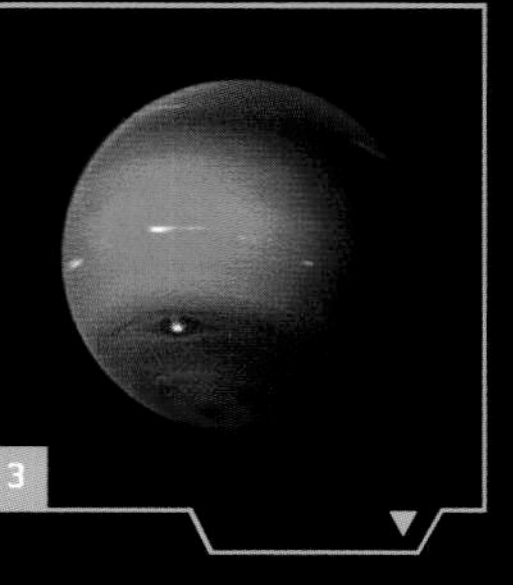

NEPTUNE'S INTERIOR
A dense core of rocks and ice supports a mantle of strongly compressed ices. This becomes a dense ice-rich atmosphere containing hydrogen and helium, topped off by the visible cloud layer.

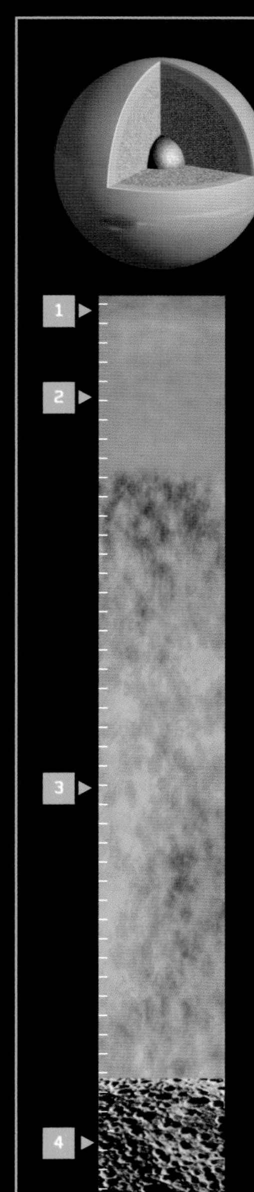

[1] Visible atmosphere and clouds, containing hydrogen, helium and methane.

[2] Deeper atmosphere where the gases become denser with depth.

[3] Ices of methane, ammonia and water, all compressed by the pressure.

[4] A compacted core of rock and ice, some metals.

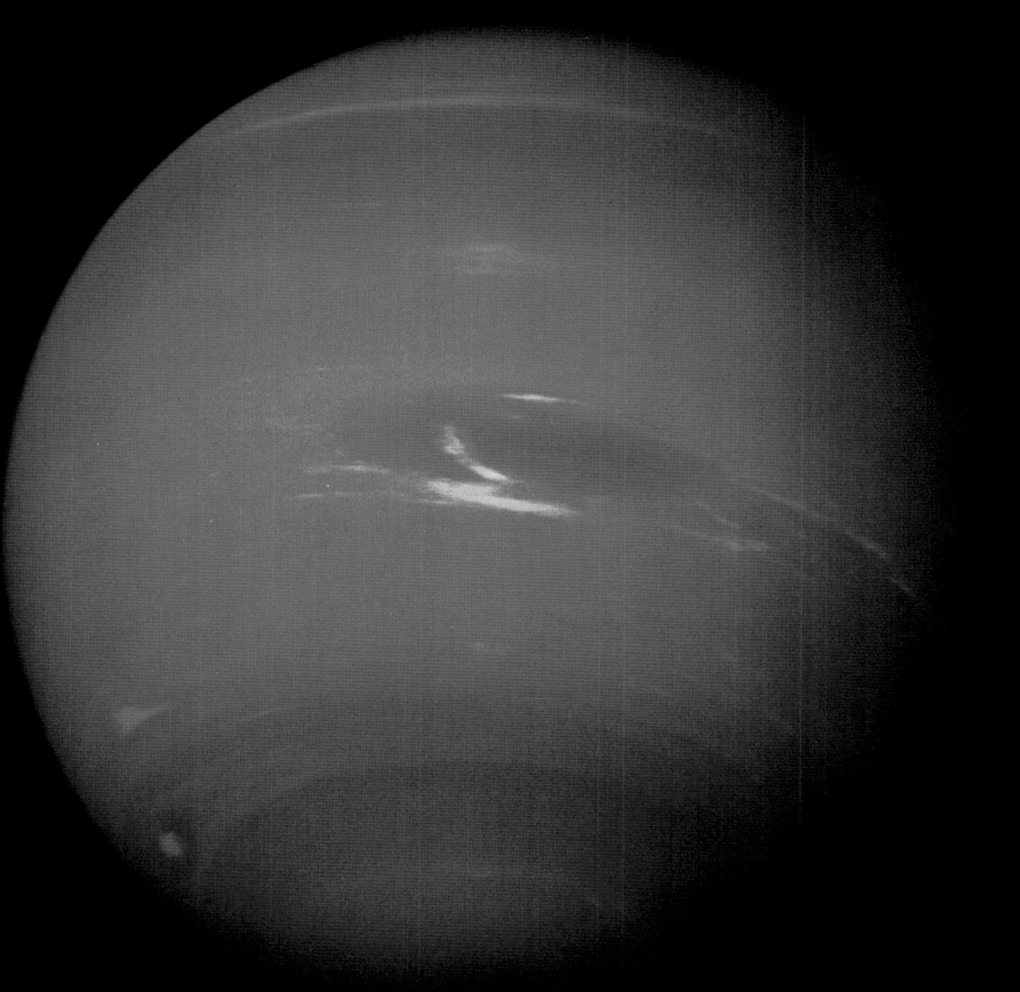

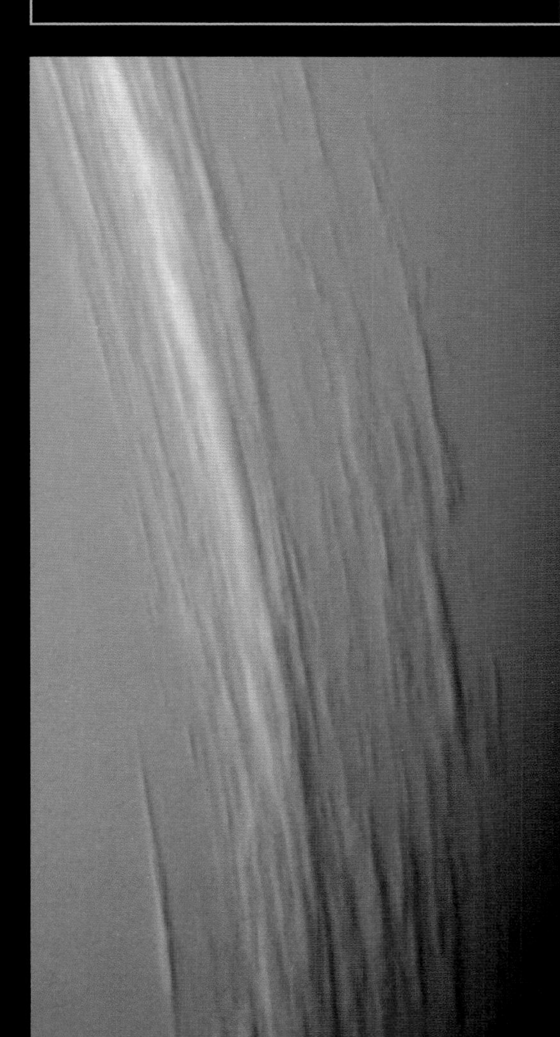

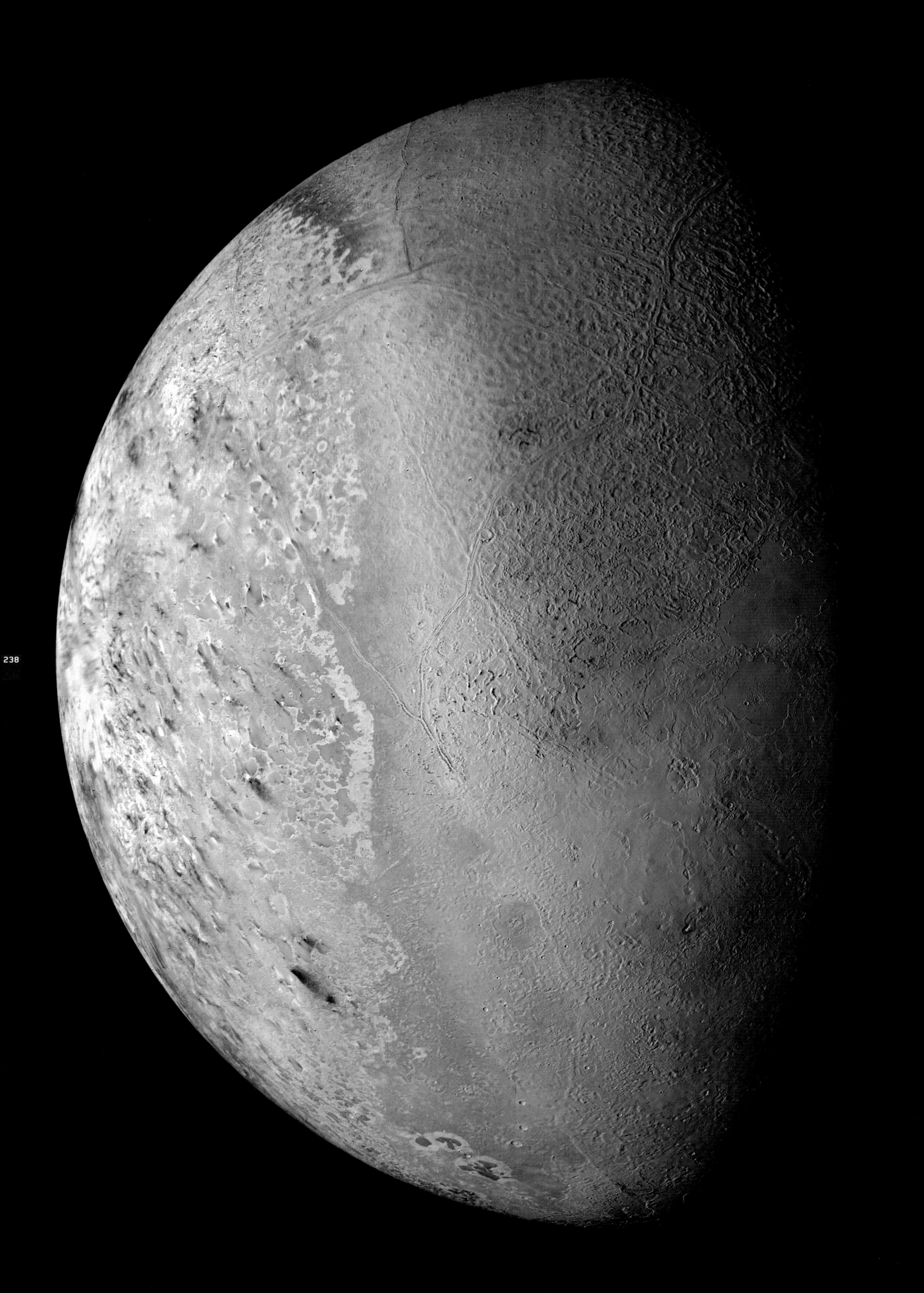

The moons of Neptune

Neptune plays host to 13 moons, of which most are small rocky objects. This could be because the largest moon Triton is an interloper captured by Neptune's gravity. Its arrival probably perturbed the other moons, causing them to collide and fragment into the bodies we see today.

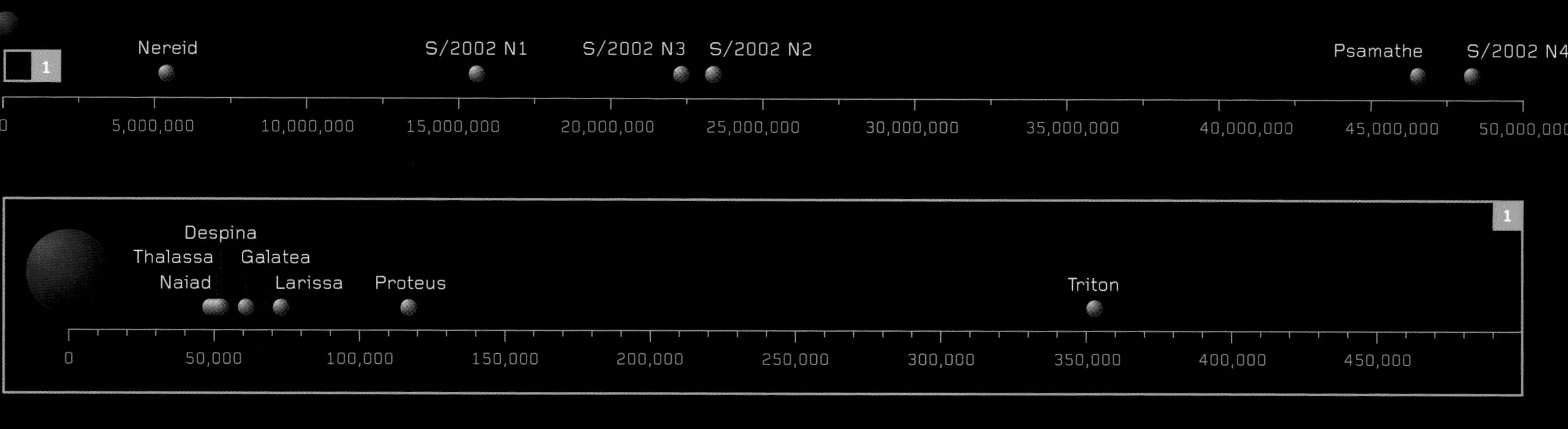

[1] Triton

Triton is bizarre because it orbits Neptune the wrong way. Most satellites orbit their parent world in the same direction as the planet is spinning. This is because they all formed out of the same swirling disc of matter. Only a number of smaller, outer moons orbit the other gas giants in this opposite – or retrograde as astronomers call it – sense. So could Triton have once been a dwarf planet orbiting the Sun, rather like Pluto, which strayed too close to Neptune and was captured? If so, that would explain another mystery about Neptune: Triton is its only large moon.

This is unusual – the other three gas giants have retinues of larger satellites. Perhaps, on its arrival in the Neptunian system, Triton's gravitational influence expelled the other large moons, leaving only the little ones in place.

Triton is one of only three moons in the Solar System known to be volcanically active. The other two are Io and Enceladus. The effect of Triton's geysers can be seen opposite as dark stains trailing downwind in the lower half of the sunlit hemisphere. Over time this cryovolcanism has resurfaced Triton, erasing its craters and giving it the varied terrain seen today.

This process is captured here [1], where two larger impact basins can be seen undergoing the slow geological process of 'melting away', whilst a small fresh crater sits in the middle of the right-most one. This gradual decay of the craters is driven by the internal warmth of the moon, which allows the ice to flow slowly back towards smoothness over millions of years.

DISTANCE FROM NEPTUNE	DIAMETER	MASS	ROTATION PERIOD	ORBITAL PERIOD	MEAN CLOUD TOP TEMPERATURE
355	2.7	3	6	6	38
THOUSAND KM	THOUSAND KM	milliEARTHS	DAYS	DAYS	KELVIN

1

[2] Nereid

Nereid loops around Neptune in a highly elliptical orbit, perhaps the orbit it was exiled into by Triton's arrival in the system. It is a tiny dot of a world, little bigger than an asteroid.

DISTANCE FROM NEPTUNE	DIAMETER	MASS	ROTATION PERIOD	ORBITAL PERIOD	MEAN CLOUD TOP TEMPERATURE
5.5	340	5	0.5	360	50
MILLION KM	KILOMETRES	microEARTHS	DAYS	DAYS	KELVIN

2

[3] Proteus

One of Neptune's inner moons, and therefore tightly bound to the planet by gravity, Proteus is also little more than an asteroid. Its stony face is covered in a multitude of small craters.

DISTANCE FROM NEPTUNE	DIAMETER	MASS	ROTATION PERIOD	ORBITAL PERIOD	MEAN CLOUD TOP TEMPERATURE
118	440	7.37	1.1	1.1	51
MILLION KM	KILOMETRES	microEARTHS	DAYS	DAYS	KELVIN

3

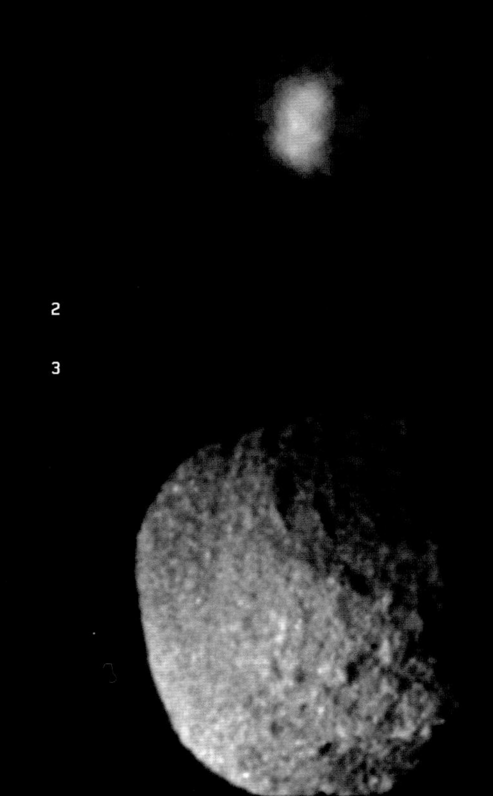

OUTER LIMITS_

Far beyond the gas giants is a large volume of space that contains the icy debris left over from the formation of the planets. These are the comets, giant icebergs in space, most of which are a few kilometres or even tens of kilometres in size.

The gravitational fields of the gas giants, particularly Jupiter, conspired to throw the comets into their gargantuan orbits. Most of them are on orbits that stretch about one light year off into space, which is 50,000 times further from the Sun as the Earth or approximately a quarter of the way to the nearest star.

In addition to the comets that sweep in and out of the Solar System, there are permanent residents in the outer limits, celestial bodies that spend all their time in the dark depths. Similar to asteroids, they are sub-planetary objects that, as well as being rocky, are almost certainly rich in ices.

They are found in an area known as the Kuiper belt, named after Gerard Kuiper, a Dutch American astronomer who talked about such a disc in the 1950s. Interestingly, Kuiper believed that any such ring of debris would have been dispersed by the gravity of Pluto, because in those days it was assumed to be the size of the Earth.

As astronomers gradually refined their estimates of Pluto's mass, each time reducing it, so the possibility of a Kuiper belt became established. Yet, it was not until the 1990s that telescopes achieved sufficient power to actually detect Kuiper belt objects.

As the discoveries have continued, Kuiper's suggestion of a scattered population of outer debris has also come true. Beyond the Kuiper belt is what astronomers refer to as the scattered disc with objects in highly elongated and inclined orbits. The question is, if Pluto is too small to push the objects out there, what did? The answer appears to be Neptune.

Studying the orbits of the scattered disc objects and running the simulations of the formation of the Solar System, points to Neptune and Uranus having originally formed much closer to Saturn. Then, over the course of millions of years, interactions with the remains of the dusty disc from which they condensed, boosted their orbit, sending them into the Kuiper belt, which originally began much closer to the Sun.

As the giant planets, particularly Neptune, encroached so they flung out the smaller bodies, forming the scattered disc of objects that astronomers are just beginning to see today.

In fact, modern astronomers find themselves in the same situation where their colleagues were at the start of 19th century when the asteroids were discovered. They are trying to make sense of all the new discoveries and deciding just how many more there are to find.

Unlike the asteroids, comets have been known about since antiquity. This is because they sometimes re-enter the inner Solar System. For some, it is the first time they have returned to the realm of the planets since their original expulsion. As they cross the orbit of Jupiter, the Sun's heat begins to work on the icy surface and transform it into gas. This streams off into space, dislodging dust and grit as well, and creating ghostly tails that hang in veils across the night sky. No wonder that astronomers call their appearances apparitions.

There are Chinese records of Comet Halley stretching back to around 240 BC. Halley appears again in the Bayeux Tapestry, which depicts the Norman Conquest of England in 1066. At the time, the different apparitions were always thought to be new objects but late in the 17th century, English astronomer Edmund Halley used Isaac Newton's newly published laws of gravity to show that some apparitions were return visits by the same

comet. Upon his successful prediction of that comet's next pass, in 1758, the comet was named in Halley's honour, even though he did not live long enough to see it himself.

Dusty showers

The dust thrown off by a comet can create meteor showers on Earth, if our planet happens to pass through its orbit. Halley itself contributes two faint meteor showers, the Eta Aquarids in May and the Orionids in October. One of the most spectacular meteor showers is the August Perseids. These are the remnants of a comet called Swift-Tuttle.

There are currently around 3500 known comets. They can be split into two distinct groups: those with short periods and those with long periods. Short-period comets are those that complete a single passage of the Sun in less than 200 years. At present there are approximately 300 short-period comets known. Due to the relatively recent date of some discoveries, one third of them have so far been observed to travel close to the Sun only once. These short-period comets are all thought to have had their orbits altered by Jupiter's gravity, pulling them into their short-period configurations.

The long-period comets are those with periods greater than 200 years, or single visit comets that gain enough speed on their long inward fall, again due to the action of Jupiter's gravitational field, that they will escape the Sun's gravitational hold altogether and journey back into the dark tracts of deep space, never to return.

Other planets?

The outer limits of the Solar System also contain larger objects as well. The best known of these is Pluto. Discovered in 1930, it was originally designated as a planet in its own right as, although it was the smallest planet, it was more than double the size of even the nearest asteroid, and hundreds of times larger than a typical comet. In recent years, however, astronomers with better telescopes have discovered a number of objects in the outer Solar System similar in size to Pluto. One of them, now called Eris, is even bigger.

For a while it seemed as if these objects too would have to be designated planets but at the August 2006 meeting of the International Astronomical Union, astronomers decided to downgrade Pluto from its status as a planet. Instead it became the prototype for a new class of celestial object: the dwarf planet. This remains a controversial decision.

In 2008 the Interna
Union, which has been
celestial objects since
a name for objects sin
on they will be known

Some astronomers
Mars and even Earth-
found in the outer limi
Computer models of h
suggest that worlds o
been thrown onto larg
after close encounters
giants during the peal
four and a half billion

Because these plan
own light, they would
reflecting little but a f
that falls on their surf
survey telescopes cur
prove sufficiently sens
orphaned planets - if

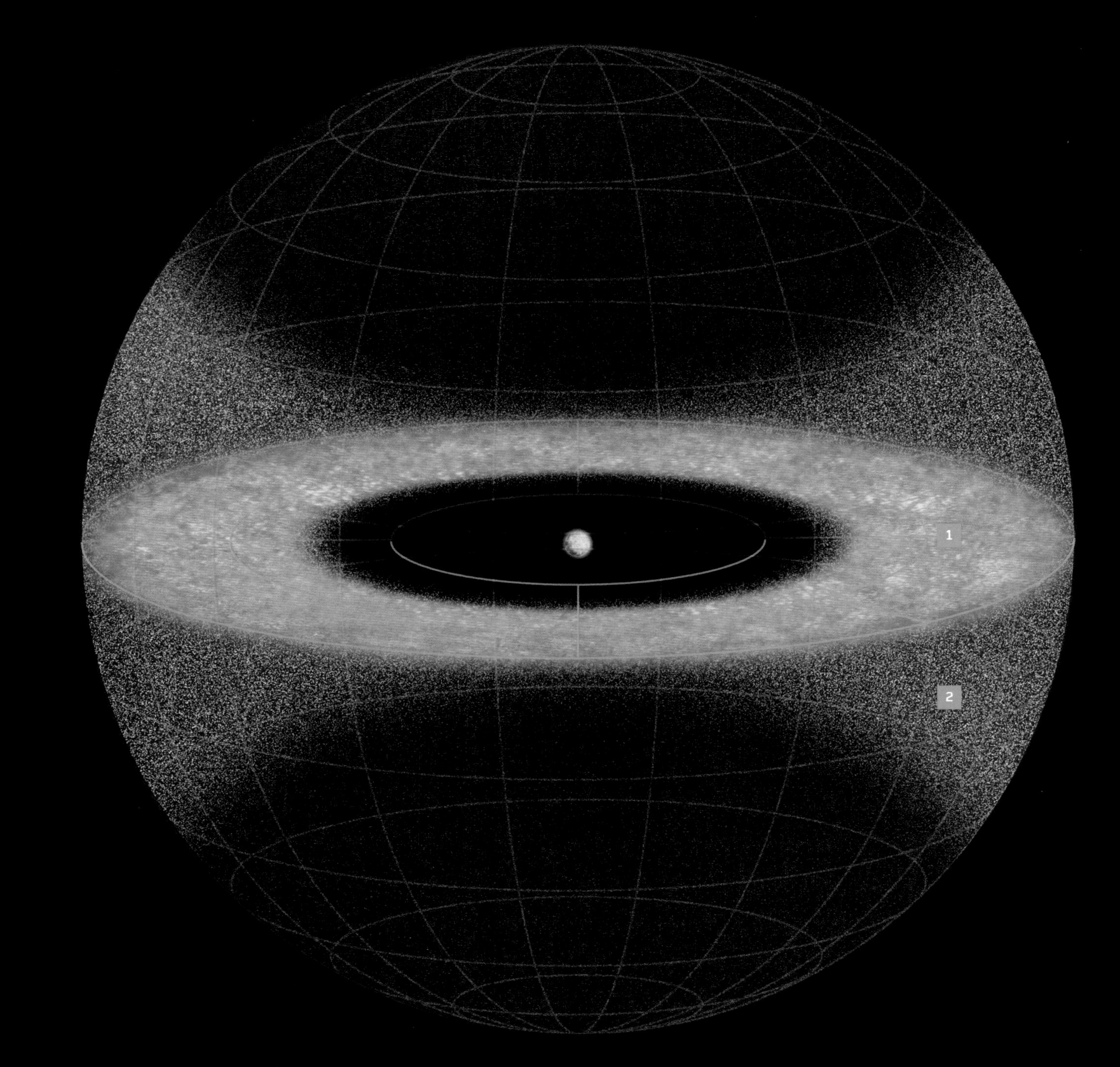

The Kuiper belt

Out on the ragged edge of the Solar System is the place where the familiarity of the planets and the dominance of the Sun fade away. Despite their relative proximity, these regions are only now coming within visual reach of astronomers and their telescopes.

The Kuiper belt [1] is similar to the asteroid belt in that it contains a large number of smaller celestial objects. It is 20 times wider than the asteroid belt, extending from just beyond the orbit of Neptune to almost double this distance. Most of the objects are in the form of icy 'asteroids' composed of water, ammonia and methane.

The first Kuiper belt object (KBO) was discovered in 1992 and since then the number has increased to more than a thousand. Astronomers now estimate that at least 70,000 KBOs greater than 100km in diameter exist and that their combined mass is some 20–200 times the amount found in the asteroid belt.

KBOs resemble comets in their composition but studies have shown that they are mostly in stable orbits and so cannot fall inwards to become the comets we see. So, the long-period comets must come from even further afield. Some come from a more unstable population of objects beyond the Kuiper belt called the scattered disc [2]; others from the Oort cloud, an even larger reservoir of cometary bodies.

The heliosphere

Somewhere near the boundary between the Kuiper belt and the scattered disc, the Sun loses its electromagnetic influence over space. This position is thought to be purely a coincidence. The vast solar eruptions that drive the space weather propel electrically charged particles through space in all directions. These finally lose their momentum at around 100 times the distance of the Earth from the Sun and become entrained in the general sweep of such particles that fills deep space. The Sun's region of influence, known as the heliosphere, is a three-dimensional structure, roughly spherical in shape. It can temporarily inflate when the Sun goes through a particularly active phase.

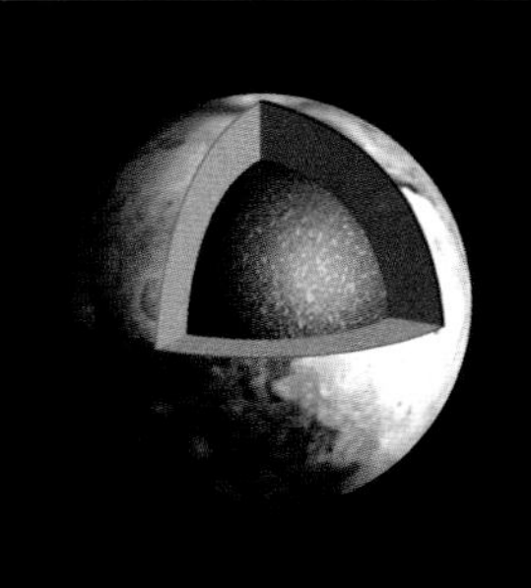

INTERIOR OF A KBO
Kuiper Belt Objects are thought to have a core of rocky material surrounded by an icy mantle and a solid icy crust. This picture awaits confirmation by the New Horizons mission.

3

4

[3, 4] Pluto
134340 PLUTO

Until recently, Pluto was the icy ninth planet of the Solar System. Its surface is 98 percent nitrogen ice and the best map we have [3] is derived from computer analysis of the way light dimmed from the planet's surface as Charon, one of its moons, passed repeatedly in front of it during a recent sequence of eclipses. The colours in this map are approximately correct, giving Pluto a somewhat ruddy complexion.

Pluto is a surprisingly complicated planet, having a large moon Charon, and two smaller moons: Nix and Hydra [4]. These last two moons were discovered in 2005 during a telescopic campaign designed to study the dwarf planet in anticipation of the flyby of NASA's New Horizon Pluto probe in 2015.

Although thought of as the prototype dwarf planet because of its relative proximity, Pluto is no longer the largest dwarf planet. That honour belongs to Eris.

PERIHELION	APHELION	DIAMETER	ORBITAL PERIOD
4.4	7.3	2.4	248
BILLION KM	BILLION KM	THOUSAND KM	YEARS

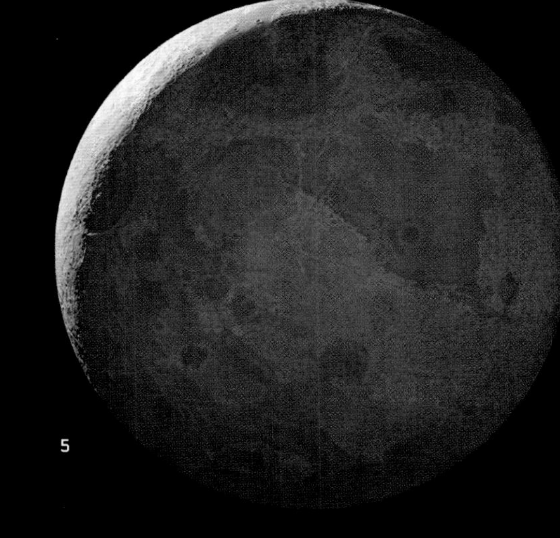

5

6

[5, 6] Eris
2003 UB313

Whereas Pluto orbits in the Kuiper belt, Eris follows a path within the scattered disc. Its orbit is tilted by over 44 degrees from the average orbital plane of the planets, indicating that Eris probably formed closer to the Sun and was then banished to the farther reaches, perhaps by Neptune.

The dwarf planet was discovered in January 2005 and in October of the same year was found to have a tiny moon, now called Dysnomia. Eris's discovery ignited the whole argument over how to define a 'planet' that ultimately led to the demotion of Pluto from the planetary club. For a while after its discovery, the object was nicknamed Xena. When the International Astronomical Union decided that it was a dwarf planet, however, a name derived from creation mythology had to be found. Appropriately, Xena was renamed Eris, after the Greek goddess of discord.

The image at the top of the page [5] is an artist's imression, while the sharpest view we currently have of Eris is below [6].

PERIHELION	APHELION	DIAMETER	ORBITAL PERIOD
5.7	14.6	2.6	557
BILLION KM	BILLION KM	THOUSAND KM	YEARS

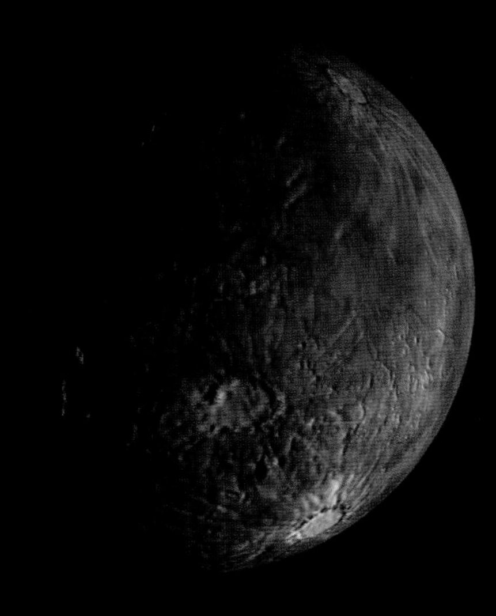

7

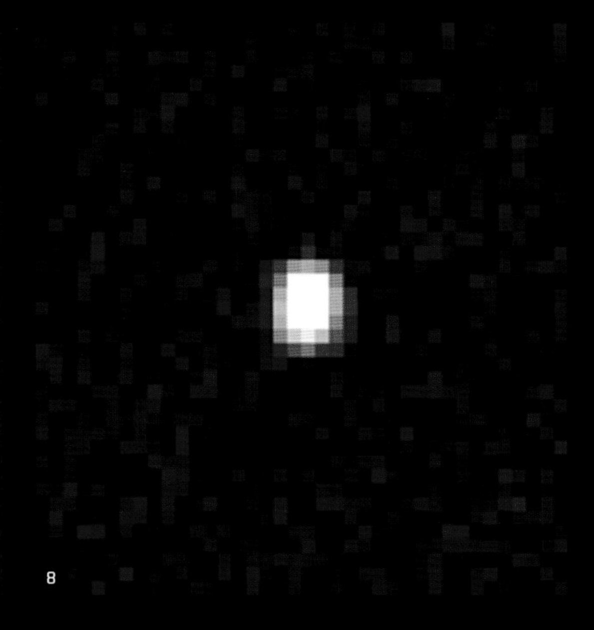

8

[7, 8] Quaoar
2002 LM60

Quaoar was the first Kuiper Belt Object to be discovered that had an appreciable size. It was found in 2002 and, although it was half the size of Pluto, it signalled to astronomers that objects comparable to Pluto could exist in the Kuiper belt and scattered disc.

Quaoar is a dark, reddish object, reflecting only 10 percent of the already feeble sunlight that falls upon it. A small moon, probably some 100 kilometres in diameter, was discovered in 2007. It has yet to be named.

Image [7] is an artist's impression of Quaoar, while image [8] is our best actual view to date. Such pixellated images may compare unfavourably with the crisp images we have of galaxies many millions of light years distant, but the comparative sizes of these objects makes imaging KBOs the more noteworthy optical feat – one that has been likened to trying to spot a football from a thousand kilometres away.

PERIHELION	APHELION	DIAMETER	ORBITAL PERIOD
6.2	6.7	1.3	288
BILLION KM	BILLION KM	THOUSAND KM	YEARS

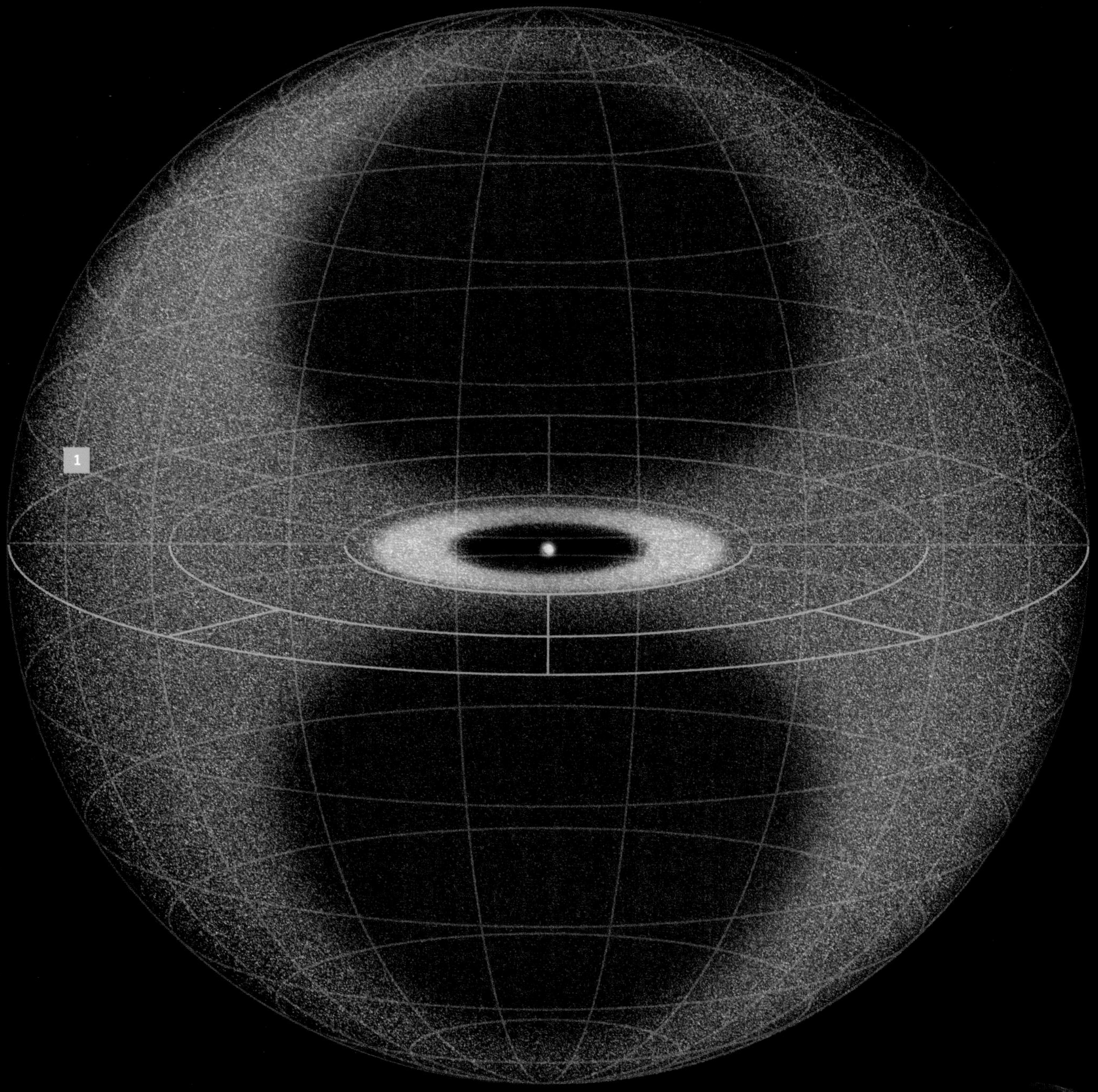

1

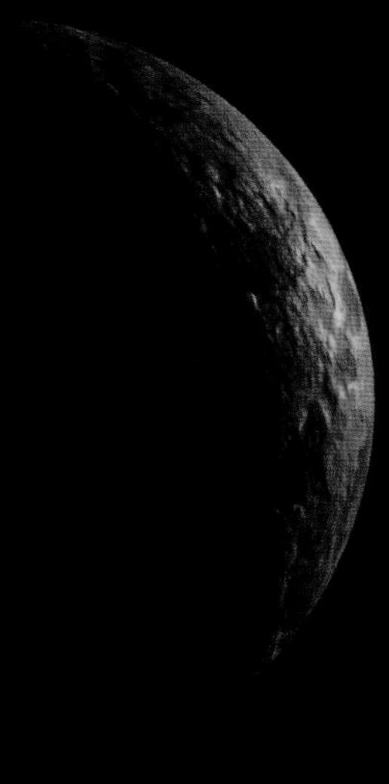

The Oort cloud

The outermost boundary of the Solar System is the Oort cloud. Here are the true outcasts of the Solar System, the mountain-sized chunks of rock and ice that were discarded during its formation.

2

The Oort cloud [1] is thought to be a vast but tenuous store of comets that surrounds the Solar System. It has never been observed directly but is theorized to exist because of the random directions from which the long-period comets approach the Sun. Estimates place over a billion comets in this vast collection, all of them bound to the Sun by the most delicate of gravitational threads. At these vast distances their motions are inchworm-like and they can be easily dislodged by the passage of other celestial objects, such as wandering stars.

It is suggested that if a star passed closely enough, it could cause a shower of comets to rain down into the Solar System, colliding with Earth and the other planets. Such a devastating bombardment would probably cause a mass extinction on our world.

Halley's Comet is thought to be typical of the objects that originated in the Oort cloud. Where it would once have had an orbit lasting for millions of years, close passes of Jupiter at some time in the past have reduced this to just 76 years. Halley's origin in the Oort cloud is betrayed by the steep angle at which it passes through the Solar System. Some comets have been trapped into even smaller orbits.

Although the Oort cloud is vast in extent, it is not thought to contain that much in the form of mass. Assuming Halley's comet is representative of the population of Oort cloud objects, there is probably only about five times the mass of the Earth out there.

[2] 2003 VB12

Sedna

Sedna is the most distant Solar System object ever observed. It was discovered in 2003 when it was 90 times further from the Sun than the Earth. Its orbit is highly elliptical and it will bring it to within 76 times the Earth's distance from the Sun before returning it to almost one thousand times as far from the Sun as Earth. These distances are so great that Sedna may be the first permanent inhabitant of the Oort cloud to be discovered.

PERIHELION	APHELION	DIAMETER	ORBITAL PERIOD
11 BILLION KM	146 BILLION KM	1.8 THOUSAND KM	12 THOUSAND YEARS

[3] 73P/ SCHWASSMANN-WACHMANN 3

Discovered in 1930, this short-period comet began to break up in 1995, splitting into four chunks. By 2006 it had disintegrated into more than a dozen fragments. Astronomers do not know if comet 73P will survive its next swing past the Sun.

PERIHELION	APHELION	DIAMETER	ORBITAL PERIOD
140	776	1.1	5.4
MILLION KM	MILLION KM	KILOMETRES	YEARS

[4] P1/HALLEY

Comet Halley

The most famous comet of them all, Halley is currently approaching its furthest point, just beyond the orbit of Neptune. It will return to the inner Solar System in 2061. This view from the European Giotto spacecraft was the first view humans received of a comet's nucleus and shows the jets of gas and dust lifting from the nucleus to create the tail.

PERIHELION	APHELION	DIAMETER	ORBITAL PERIOD
88	6.7	16	76
MILLION KM	BILLION KM	KILOMETRES	YEARS

[5] 19P/BORRELLY

Comet Borrelly

This comet was widely observed during January 1905, following its discovery the previous month by the French astronomer Alphonse Louis Nicolas Borrelly. Approaching close to Jupiter in 1936 nudged the comet into an unfavourable orbit for further observations until 1972, when another Jovian encounter placed it back on a more observable path.

PERIHELION	APHELION	DIAMETER	ORBITAL PERIOD
875	203	8	6.8
MILLION KM	MILLION KM	KILOMETRES	YEARS

[6] 9P/TEMPEL

Comet Tempel 1

Comet Tempel 1 was the subject of an audacious experiment on 4 July 2005, as a projectile launched by NASA's Deep Impact spacecraft smashed into the comet's nucleus. The collision threw up a large dust cloud but did not spark a new site of jetting activity as had been hoped.

PERIHELION	APHELION	DIAMETER	ORBITAL PERIOD
225	705	3.5	5.5
MILLION KM	MILLION KM	KILOMETRES	YEARS

[7] 81P/WILD

Comet Wild 2

In 1974, Jupiter pushed comet Wild 2 into the inner Solar System. Instead of following a 40-year orbit, the comet suddenly found itself circling the Sun in just 6.4 years. NASA's Stardust mission returned samples of comet Wild 2's tail to Earth. These have been shown to contain a large number of carbon-bearing molecules. This increases the belief that comets brought the chemical ingredients for life to Earth.

PERIHELION	APHELION	DIAMETER	ORBITAL PERIOD
239	796	4	6.4
MILLION KM	MILLION KM	KILOMETRES	YEARS

3

4

5

6

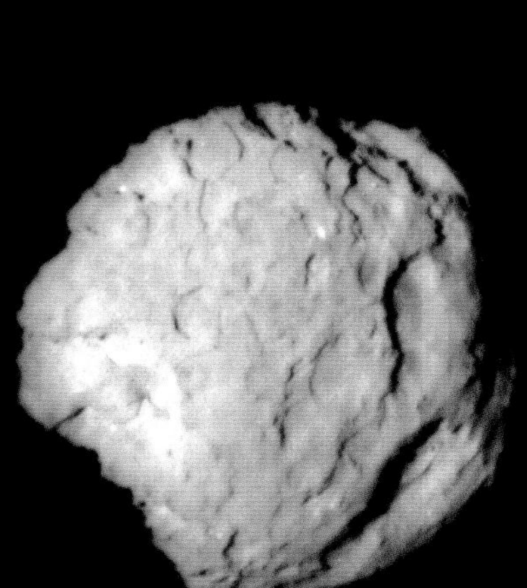

7

1

C/2001 Q4

Comet NEAT

Discovered by one of the robotic telescopes that patrol the night sky as part of the Near Earth Asteroid Tracking (NEAT) programme, comet NEAT fell into the sights of human observers. It arrived at the inner Solar System from almost overhead in the southern hemisphere, travelling in the opposite direction to the planets. In May 2004, it crossed inside the orbit of the Earth, rounded the Sun and began its retreat back into the outer Solar System and beyond. It will never return, having picked up enough speed to break its gravitational bonds with the Sun.

PERIHELION	APHELION	DIAMETER	ORBITAL PERIOD
180 MILLION KM	~ MILLION KM	7 KILOMETRES	~ YEARS

17P/HOLMES

Comet Holmes

Discovered in 1862, comet Holmes was a relatively undistinguished member of the Solar System until 2007 when it started to grow. Flinging dust and gas into space, the comet's girth surpassed first the Earth's, then Jupiter's and finally the Sun's. On the scale of this picture from the Canada-France-Hawaii Telescope, the Sun would fit into the brightest circular region surrounding the comet. The sphere overwhelmed any tail the comet may have produced. Soon afterwards comet Holmes faded, and astronomers still don't know how or why the eruption occured.

PERIHELION	APHELION	DIAMETER	ORBITAL PERIOD
308	777	3.4	6.88
MILLION KM	MILLION KM	KILOMETRES	YEARS

What next?

The study of the Universe is a never-ending search for knowledge. As complete as our understanding appears to be, there may be some new discovery made tomorrow that will prove how little we really do perceive of the celestial puzzle. With this in mind, shedding light on the dark Universe is one of the astronomers' biggest tasks. The dark universe consists of two components: dark matter and dark energy. Of these astronomers think they know what the dark matter is, but they still have few firm ideas about what dark energy might be.

Dark matter is assumed to be present in the Universe whenever astronomers see some kind of motion that they do not understand. In theory, dark matter could solve the problems because its mass brings extra gravity into play and this allows the celestial objects to move correctly. They also think such extra gravity catalysed the formation of galaxies in the early Universe.

However, astronomers are having trouble understanding the precise properties of dark matter and seek help from particle physicists. There are now a number of experiments around the world that are reaching the extraordinary sensitivities needed to trap the odd particle of dark matter. In addition, the newly upgraded particle accelerator at CERN in Switzerland, called the Large Hadron Collider, may naturally create particles of dark matter during its experiments.

Some astronomers, however, do not believe that the existence of dark matter is the right answer. They think instead that the anomalous motions they see are telling us that our understanding of gravity is awry. If so, then both Isaac Newton's and Albert Einstein's theories of gravity must be amended, and that will be a massive undertaking.

In the case of dark energy, there is a growing belief that this highlights an even more serious gap in our understanding of the Universe. To explain why the expansion of space is accelerating instead of decelerating, astronomers can choose to believe that a previously undiscovered energy permeates all of space. The trouble is that would wreck our understanding of the Universe at its smallest scales, because there seems to be no place for it in the quantum theory.

Another choice is that perhaps the dark energy is actually a so-far unidentified force of nature. Yet that is scarcely better, because there is presently no theoretical basis for such a force, which leads astronomers to wondering whether it is not a new force at all, but an unanticipated facet of gravity. Just as with the proposal to replace dark matter, this is a rocky road to travel because it involves so much tinkering with what has always been considered to be the bedrock of physics.

However astronomers explain the composition of the dark universe, it will mark a radical shift in our understanding. In this regard, it cannot fail.

On the smaller scale, there are other areas of research that offer enormous rewards. In the hunt for planets around other stars, so-called extrasolar planets, the big prize will be to find Earth-sized worlds. In 2009, NASA plan to launch the space telescope Kepler. This mission will continually monitor the brightness of 100,000 stars for between 3.5 and 6 years. It will be looking for the drop in brightness caused by a planet passing across the face of the star and blocking a small fraction of its light.

Kepler has been designed with a sensitivity capable of detecting the drop in starlight caused by an Earth-sized planet and many astronomers are hoping that it will become the spacecraft that makes the first detection of our 'sister' world around another star.

Once Earth-sized planets have been discovered, the ultimate quest will be to determine whether any of them could be habitable or even inhabited. The best way to do this is to collect the light bouncing off the atmosphere of each planet and look for the signature of the gases it contains. Astronomers, and their astrobiology colleagues, will be looking for the presence of reactive gases such as oxygen and methane.

These are prevalent in Earth's atmosphere because of animal metabolism. Such gases are highly reactive and, left to their own devices, would bond with other chemicals and disappear from the atmosphere of the planet within a relatively short time. So, if a planet were to be found with a similar cocktail of unstable gases, it would be a tell-tale sign that life was present on that world and constantly replenishing the atmosphere.

The beauty of this approach is that it increases the chances of finding life because, unlike the radio search for extraterrestrial signals, even the simplest life forms pollute their atmosphere with metabolic gases, which can be detectable. So, whereas humans have been spilling radio communications into space for less than a century, life has been changing Earth's atmosphere for billions of years.

Astrobiologists are also working in labs to see if they can come up with other combinations of unstable atmospheric gases, based on metabolisms unlike those found in the predominant life forms of Earth.

With the exploration of our own Solar System, we face a crossroads. Do we continue to rove the planets using robotic spaceprobes? Or do we largely abandon this endeavour and focus our resources on the much more expensive proposal of sending humans into space to perform the investigations in person?

There are arguments for both courses of action. For the same price as a manned mission to the Moon, or particularly to Mars, we could send many robotic spaceprobes across the Solar System and gather much more data. However, is science just about gathering large quantities of data?

Proponents of manned spaceflight argue that a living, breathing geologist on Mars would be able to spot things, to follow human intuition in their personal exploration that might make all the difference in finding a breakthrough. Great discoveries often come from concentrating on the unknown occurrence or the oddity that does not quite fit. Robots, some say, do not have this capacity even if there are incredible advances taking place in artificial intelligence. The debate is lively, with good arguments and expressive champions on both sides.

Then of course, in all of this, there will be the surprises; the serendipitous discoveries that no one anticipates but rewrite the textbooks. The acceleration of the Universe, discovered in 1998, is a recent example. These are perhaps the events that make astronomy so fascinating. No matter how much we think we know, the Universe is always ready to spring another wonder on us. Throughout history, people have been tricked into thinking that they were closing the loop on natural knowledge. Every time this idea has gained credence, it has been subsequently destroyed by a new observation or happening. From our perspective at the beginning of the 21st century, we still have an awful lot to understand about the Universe – and that's a good thing; it will drive us forward.

GLOSSARY_

ASTEROID
A small rocky body orbiting the Sun, each up to 600 miles (1000 km) in diameter. Most are found in the asteroid belt between Mars and Jupiter but some have more elliptical orbits and swing past the inner planets.

ASTRONOMICAL ICES
The collective term for water, ammonia and methane, predominantly found beyond the asteroid belt. These substances are so far from the Sun that they are found in solid form.

ASTROPHYSICS
The study of the nature of celestial objects.

ATMOSPHERE
A shell of gas around a planet or moon, atmospheres exist with a variety of compositions and densities.

AURORA
The lights in the sky produced when incoming solar particles excite a planet's atmosphere, usually near the poles of the planet.

BARRED SPIRAL GALAXY
A galaxy with spiral arms that are joined to its nucleus by a straight bar of stars.

BIG BANG
The event that marks the origin of the Universe, 13.7 billion years ago. At this point in time, the Universe exploded into existence and has been expanding ever since.

BILLION
10^9 or 1,000,000,000 (a thousand million).

BLACK HOLE, SUPERMASSIVE BLACK HOLE
A concentration of mass, with an overwhelming gravitational field from which not even light can escape. Particularly massive stars form black holes when they collapse at the end of their lives. Much larger black holes, called supermassive black holes, are found at the centres of galaxies.

BOK GLOBULE
A dark, dense cloud of dust and gas where star formation takes place.

CALDERA
The central vent of a volcano, sometimes referred to as a volcanic crater.

COMET
An icy leftover from the formation of the Solar System. Comets are kilometres-wide chunks of dust and ice. Those that orbit the Sun in less than 200 years are termed short-period comets; long-period comets can take millions of years to return.

CORE
The dense centre of a moon, planet or star.

CORONA
The outer, rarefied gas around the Sun or other star, usually only visible during a total eclipse.

CRATER
The bowl-shaped depression left by an impact on the surface of a rocky body.

CRUST
The uppermost solid layer on a rocky body.

CRYOVOLCANISM
Volcanic activity involving astronomical ices rather than molten rock.

DARK ENERGY
A theoretical energy that permeates all of space, or an unidentified force of nature, employed to explain the acceleration of the Universe.

DARK MATTER
A hypothetical form of matter thought to outweigh normal atoms by ten times. The effect of its gravity on visible matter infers its presence, but it cannot be easily detected by emitted radiation.

DARK NEBULA
A cloud of dust and gas dense enough to block the visible light from the objects they obscure. Also known as absorption nebula.

DUST
Tiny particles of chiefly silicates and carbon found in space alongside gases. Dust absorbs visible light but infrared can pass through it more easily.

DWARF PLANET
A round planetary body that fails to clear its orbit of other celestial objects. Ceres, the largest asteroid, is dwarf planet, as is Pluto. In the case of Pluto and the other outer dwarf planets, the additional term, plutoid, has been coined.

DWARF GALAXY
A small, faint galaxy,either irregular or elliptical in structure.

ELECTROMAGNETIC RADIATION
Energy that is emitted at many different wavelengths, collectively known as the electromagnetic spectrum. Radio wavelengths are the longest. Infrared is invisible to human eyes but sensed as heat. Visible wavelengths are detected by the human eye as light. Ultraviolet radiation has a shorter wavelength than violet in the visible spectrum. X-rays are higher-energy than ultraviolet radiation but less energetic than gamma rays, which have the shortest wavelengths of all.

ELLIPTICAL GALAXY
Roughly spherical galaxies with no specific internal structure. The orbits of its stars are randomly inclined.

FACULAE
Luminous hydrogen filaments found near sunspots, or where sunspots have been or are about to appear. Faculae help give the Sun a mottled appearance.

GALACTIC HALO
The area around a galaxy, thought to contain a rarefied collection of stars and gas, and large quantities of dark matter.

GALACTIC NUCLEUS
The very centre of a galaxy, thought to contain a supermassive black hole.

GALAXY
A gravitationally bound system of dust, gas and stars, as small as a few hundred light years across or up to hundreds of thousands of light years in diameter. They can be spirals, barred spirals, elliptical, lenticular or irregular in shape.

GAS GIANT
A large planet with an extraordinarily thick atmosphere.

GLOBULAR CLUSTER
A densely packed ball of mostly old stars that orbits a galaxy.

GRANULATION
Pockets of convecting gas that can be seen on the Sun's surface.

GRAVITY
A mutual attraction between masses that manifests itself as a force of nature. It is proportional to the product of the masses and the inverse square of the distance between them.

HELIOPAUSE
The boundary within the far reaches of the Solar System where the Sun's magnetic influence fails and electrically charged particles are swept up in the general flow of the interstellar medium.

HERBIG-HARO OBJECT
A type of emission nebula produced when jets from newborn stars collide with the interstellar medium.

HERTZSPRUNG-RUSSELL DIAGRAM
A graph used by astronomers to illustrate the general properties of large numbers of stars. It compares luminosity on the vertical axis to surface temperature on the horizontal axis.

ICE GIANTS
Gas giant planets with a high proportion of astronomical ices in their make-up.

INTERSTELLAR MEDIUM
The extremely rarified 'atmosphere' of space, typically consisting of 90 percent hydrogen, 9 percent helium and 1 percent dust.

IRREGULAR GALAXY
Galaxies lacking the structure to be otherwise classified.

KELVIN
A scale of temperature that places zero as the coldest possible temperature. This is 273 degrees below the freezing point of water. To convert to Celsius, subtract 273.

KUIPER BELT, KUIPER BELT OBJECTS (KBOS)
A disc of icy bodies, including Pluto and Eris, that stretches from Neptune's orbit out to about 24 billion kilometres from the Sun.

LENTICULAR GALAXY
A galaxy with a central nucleus and a disc but lacking spiral arms.

LIGHT YEAR
The distance travelled in a year by light in a vacuum: 9.5 trillion km.

LIMB
The edge of a moon, planet or star as it turns into or away from the line of sight.

LOCAL GROUP OF GALAXIES
A collection of about 40 galaxies spread over an area of 10 million light years and dominated by the Milky Way and the Andromeda Galaxy.

LUNAR MARIA
Solidified lava plains on the Moon termed seas when they were first observed and catalogued.

MAGMA
Hot material shot up from under the crust of a body during a volcanic eruption.

MAGNETIC FIELD
The region of influence of the magnetic force of a body.

MAIN SEQUENCE
A band across a Hertzsprung-Russell diagram, where most stars can be placed. Massive stars appear towards the left.

MANTLE
An intermediate shell of material covering the core but beneath the crust of a rocky body.

MASS
In astronomy there is a careful distinction between mass, the amount of matter in a body, and weight, defined as the force acting on a body in a gravitational field.

MESSIER, CHARLES
A French astronomer who, between 1758 and 1781, compiled a catalogue of about 100 nebulous-looking astronomical objects. Most were later identified as galaxies or gaseous nebulae; a few as star clusters.

METEORITE
A piece of celestial rock that falls onto a planet.

METEOR SHOWER
The lights in the sky created by the Earth's atmosphere travelling through debris left by a comet, as the particles burn up.

MILKY WAY
Our galaxy, a large barred spiral galaxy spanning 100,000 light years and containing around 200 billion stars. Its name is derived from our perception of it as a misty band of stars that divides the night sky. Our Solar System lies about two-thirds of the way towards the edge of its disc, in a truncated spiral arm.

MILLION
10^6 or 1,000,000 (a thousand, thousand).

MOLECULAR CLOUD
An accumulation of dust and gas, significantly denser than the interstellar medium, which spans hundreds of light years and is the site of star formation.

MOON
A moon is a natural satellite of a planet. There are more than 140 in the Solar System of which the Moon orbits Earth. Shepherd moons affect rings around a planet.

NEBULA
A nebula is a cloud of dust and gas in space. Absorption nebulae are sufficiently dense to block light. Emission nebulae shine with their own light, re-emitting absorbed radiation at visible wavelengths. Reflection nebulae scatter the light from nearby stars.

NGC (NEW GENERAL CATALOGUE)
An index of 7,800 astronomical objects published in 1888. A two-part supplement to the New General Catalogue, the Index Catalogue (IC), was added in 1895 and 1908.

NEUTRON STAR
The extremely dense remnant of a supernova explosion created when huge gravitational forces compress electrons and protons to produce neutrons.

NOVA
Novae occur in binary systems where one component is a white dwarf that collects material from its companion until explosive nuclear reactions are triggered, resulting in a hundredfold increase in brightness.

NUCLEAR FUSION
Stars are powered when two or more atomic nuclei are forced together, forming a single larger nucleus and releasing energy. Most stars spend the majority of their lives converting hydrogen into helium; more massive, hotter stars can fuse heavier elements.

OORT CLOUD
Studies of long-period comets suggest there is a swarm of comets surrounding the Solar System at a distance of half to one light year from the Sun.

OPEN STAR CLUSTER
A loose accumulation of stars born at the same time from the same cloud.

ORBITAL PERIOD
The time it takes one body to travel all the way around another, pulled by gravity.

PLANET
A large body in orbit around a star.

PLANETARY NEBULA
A shell of debris, flung out by a red giant star as it becomes unstable, that fades over 100,000 years as the remaining white dwarf star cools. Misnamed because of their appearance through early telescopes.

PROMINENCE
A gargantuan eruption of relatively cool gas that hangs suspended in the Sun's atmosphere.

PULSAR
A rotating neutron star that emits a sweeping beam of high-energy radiation from its magnetic poles.

ROCKY WORLDS
Planets formed predominantly from rock, sometimes with an atmosphere around them.

ROTATION PERIOD
The time it takes a body to spins once on its axis.

ROVER
A manmade remote controlled vehicle landed on another planet or moon for exploratory purposes.

SAGITTARIUS A*
The purported black hole at the centre of our Galaxy, it is a source of intense radio waves and X-rays.

SATELLITE
Any body in orbit about another body.

THE SCATTERED DISC
The home of the plutoids and cometary material, out beyond the Kuiper belt in the Solar System.

SOLAR–
Anything associated with our Sun: a solar mass of 1.98 trillion, trillion tonnes, is used as a unit to express the mass of other stars: the Solar System includes all the bodies in orbit around the Sun; and the solar wind is a stream of plasma flowing from the Sun.

SPECTRAL ANALYSIS
The recording and study of light split into a spectrum, often concentrating on the location and identification of particular spectral lines that indicate certain elements or molecules within, for example, a star's atmosphere.

SPIRAL GALAXY
Having a spherical central bulge of older stars and surrounded by a flattened disc containing a spiral pattern of young, hot stars. The Milky Way is a spiral galaxy.

STAR
A massive ball of hydrogen and helium bound together by gravity and shining for most of its life with the light of nuclear fusion. Stars of many different sizes are born in nebulae and open clusters, and spend most of their lives, sometimes in pairs, fusing hydrogen into helium before evolving into red giants. A Wolf–Rayet star is a particularly massive, short-lived star, usually containing more than 25 solar masses of material. Wolf–Rayets have powerful stellar winds that strip away the outer layers of their own atmospheres, leaving their interiors exposed. Depending on their mass stars die as planetary nebulae or supernovae. The stellar remnants they leave behind may be white dwarfs, neutron stars or black holes. White dwarfdom awaits all but the most massive stars. It is the dense, cooling ember of a star that has exhausted its nuclear fuel and collapsed under the force of its own gravity.

STAR FORMATION
The process by which stars gravitationally condense from molecular clouds.

SUN
The star at the centre of our Solar System.

SUNSPOTS
Darkened cooler areas on the Sun's surface identifying increased magnetic activity.

SUPERNOVA
The explosive demise of a star, a supernova can be one of two kinds: Type Ia that involves the collapse of an existing white dwarf, or Type II, the explosion that marks the demise of a star at least eight solar masses in size. Depending on the mass of the star, either a neutron star or a black hole is left at the centre of the conflagration.

SUPERNOVA REMNANT
An expanding shell of dust and gas produced by a supernova. As it is flung outwards into space, it mixes together with swept-up interstellar matter.

TRANSIT
The celestial alignment that occurs when a smaller celestial object passes in front of its parent body, blocking some of the light from our line of sight.

TRILLION
10^{12} or 1,000,000,000,000 (a million, million).

UNIVERSE
The entirety of space, time and everything that it contains.

YARDANG
A wind-cut ridge usually found in a desert environment; many can be seen on Mars.

INDEX_

Underlined figures indicate images.

1 Ceres 196, 196
2 Pallas 196
3C 10 131, 131
3C 461 144, 144
4 Vesta 196
9P/Tempel 245, 245
10 Hygiea 196
17P/HOLMES 247, 247
19P/Borrelly 245, 245
34 Tauri 200
51 Pegasi 151
73P/Schwassmann-Wachmann 3 245, 245
81P/Wild 245, 245
433 Eros 196, 196, 197
2002 LM60 243, 243
2003 UB313 243, 243
2003 VB12 244, 244
134340 Pluto 243, 243

A
A Ring 216
Abell 1656 16, 16
Abell 1689 14, 14
Abell 2151 20, 20
Abell 3627 18, 18
Al Sufi, Abd al-Rahman: Book of Fixed Stars 41
Alpha Canis Majoris B 130, 130
aluminium-26 154
Amalthea 201
Amalthea group 206, 206
Andromeda Galaxy 34, 34, 37, 77, 251
Ant Nebula 120, 120
Antares 59, 59
anti-protons 143
antimatter 143
Apollo spacecraft 179, 180, 182
Apophis 155
arachnoids 168, 168
Ariel 234, 234
Armstrong, Neil 182, 183
Asteroid Belt 154, 155, 196-9, 242, 250
asteroids 152, 155, 167, 250
astronomical ices 200, 250
Au Microscopii 152, 152
Aureum Chaos 189, 189
aurorae 201, 202, 214, 214, 250

B
B Ring 216
Barnard, Edward Emerson (E.E.) 79
Barnard 33 83, 83
Barnard 68 78, 79
Barnard 72 78, 79
Barnard 163 79, 79
BD+602522 star 109
Bernard's galaxy 37, 37
Beta Pictoris 152, 152
Biblis Patera 187, 187
Big Bang 10, 12, 68, 250
black holes 48, 49, 64, 66, 67, 74, 74, 113, 119, 139, 139, 250, 251, 252
black smokers 177, 177
Blinking Nebula 121, 121
Blish, James: Solar Plexus 200
Bode, Johann Elert 154
Bode's galaxy 27, 27
Bok, Bart 81
Bok globules 80, 81, 81, 250
Boomerang Nebula 120, 120
Borrelly, Alphone Louis Nicolas 245
Bow-tie Nebula 120
Brahe, Tycho 72, 131
bright giants 117
brown dwarfs 74, 97, 97, 105
Bubble Nebula 109, 109
Bunsen, Robert 72
Butterfly Nebula 124, 124

C
C Ring 216
C/2001 Q4 246, 246
C/2006 P1 240-41, 241
caldera 187, 187, 209, 209, 250
Callisto 206, 212, 213, 213
Caloris basin 162, 163
Carina Nebula 90-91, 91, 92-3, 93, 132, 133
Carme group 206
Cassini, Giovanni Domenico 205
Cassini Division 216, 217, 221
Cassini probe 223
Cassini Regio 231
Cassiopeia A 144, 144
Cat's Eye Nebula 121, 121
Cat's Paw Nebula 100, 100
Centaurus 18
Cerberus 185, 185
Ceres 160, 196, 196, 250
CERN, Switzerland 248
Chandra X-ray telescope 139
Chandrasekhar limit 74, 119
Charon 243
Chasma Boreale 194, 195
chlorofluorocarbons 175
CHNOPS elements (carbon, hydrogen, nitrogen, oxygen, phosphorus and sulphur) 143
Cigar galaxy 32, 33
Clarke, Arthur C 171
Coma cluster 16, 16
Coma Supercluster 16
Comet Borrelly 245, 245
Comet Halley 240-41, 244, 245, 245
Comet Holmes 247, 247
Comet McNaught 240-41, 241
Comet NEAT 246, 246
Comet Tempel 1 245, 245
Comet Wild 2 245, 245
comets 126, 155, 205, 240-41, 241, 242, 244, 250, 251
common envelope 105
computer processing 86, 86, 87
computer simulations 10, 14, 68, 68-9, 119, 150, 178, 196, 241
Conamara Chaos 211
Cone Nebula 82, 82, 110, 111
continental drift 172
convective zone 156, 156
Copernicus Crater 180, 180, 181
Coprates Catena 189, 189
Corona Australis Complex 59, 59
coronae 157, 157, 250
coronae (Venus) 168, 168
cosmological distance ladder 11
Crab Nebula 140-41, 141
craters 160, 163, 163, 165, 196, 213, 230, 235, 235, 239, 250
Crescent Nebula 135, 135
cryovolcanism 223, 239, 250
Cygnus 130
Cygnus Loop 143, 143

D
D Ring 216
Dactyl 198, 199
dark energy 11, 12, 248, 250
dark matter 11, 49, 68, 68-9, 248, 250
Deep Impact spacecraft 245
Deimos 185, 185
dense cloud 60, 60
Descartes 180
deuterium 76
Dickinson Crater 166, 167
diffuse stellar medium 142
Dione 219, 225, 227, 227
Dragon Storm 215, 215
dwarf planets 160, 241, 243, 243, 250
Dysnomia 243

E
E Ring 216
Eagle Nebula 86, 86-7
Earth 154, 154, 160, 161, 168, 170-78, 178, 180
Earthrise 179, 179
Einstein, Albert 14, 248
Eistle Regio 166-7, 167
electromagnetic radiation 11, 250
electromagnetic spectrum 6, 250
electrons 143, 251
Elephant Trunk Nebula 85, 85
Enceladus 222, 223, 223, 239
Encke Division 217
Epimetheus 221, 221
Eris 155, 241, 243, 243, 250
Eros 196, 196, 197
Eskimo Nebula 122, 122
ESO 594-4 38, 38
Eta Aquarids 241
Eta Carinae 91, 93, 132
Europa 201, 210, 211, 211

F
F Ring 221
faculae 156, 250
Far Arm 50
Flame Nebula 95, 95
Flaming Star 106, 107
Flamsteed, John 144, 200
Fornax 32
Fox Fur Nebula 110, 111
Fra Mauro 180

G
galactic core 64, 64-5, 67
galactic disc 143
Galactic Snake 60, 60
galaxies 6, 10, 11, 250
  barred spiral 22, 23, 26, 27, 27, 41, 136, 136, 250, 251
  classification 22, 22-3
  clusters 10, 11, 12, 14, 16, 17, 20
  dwarf 38, 38, 57
  elliptical 20, 22, 22, 30, 31, 31, 34, 250
  field 16
  groups of 20
  irregular 32, 32, 33, 37, 37, 40-41, 41, 250
  lenticular 22, 28, 29, 131, 250
  orbit of 11
  satellite 34, 34, 38, 39, 64
  spiral 16, 20, 22, 22-3, 24, 24, 25, 36, 37, 48, 48-9, 49, 50, 56, 57, 136, 136, 251
  superclusters 10, 12, 16
Galileo Galilei 6, 48, 206, 216
gamma rays 6, 68, 72, 142, 143, 250
Ganymede 201, 212, 212
gas giant planets 151, 151, 161, 200-229, 240, 241, 250
Gaspra 198, 199
Geminga 142
giants 117
Gila Mons 166, 167
Giotto spacecraft 245
globular star clusters 49, 52, 112, 112-13, 113, 250
GO-15-0.05 132, 132
'Goldilocks orbit' 154
Gomez's Hamburger 123, 123
Gould's Belt 73, 73
Grand Canyon, Arizona 184, 235
Grand Erg Oriental 175, 175
granulation 157, 157, 250
gravity, laws of 11, 68, 154, 240
Great Attractor 18
Great Dark Spot 237
Great Orion Nebula see Orion Nebula
Great Red Spot 200, 201, 202, 204, 205, 205
Guabonito 228, 228

H
habitable zone 154-5
Hadley-Apennines 180
Halley, Edmund 155, 240, 241
Halley's Comet see Comet Halley
halos 49, 52, 72, 126, 143, 163, 163, 250
HD 12545 132, 132
HD 44179 124, 124
HD 107146 152, 152
HD 189733 151
HE2-104 129, 129
heliopause 154, 155, 250
heliosphere 242
Helix Nebula 118-19, 119, 126, 126-7
Hellas impact basin 185
HEN-1357 128, 128
Herbes Chasma 189, 189
Herbig-Haro objects 105, 106, 106, 110, 111, 250
Hercules Cluster 20, 20
Herschel, William 118, 154, 200
Herschel 36 103, 103
Herschel Crater 221
Hertzsprung-Russell diagram 117, 117, 250, 251
HH-32 106, 106
HH-34 106, 106
HH-47 106, 106
Homunculus Nebula 132, 132
Horsehead Nebula 83, 83, 95, 95
Hourglass Nebula 129, 129
Hubble, Edwin 22
Hubble Space Telescope 12, 72, 196
Hubble Ultra Deep Field 10-11
Hubble's Variable Nebula 106, 106
Humboldtianum Basin 178
Hurricane Ivan 174, 174

Huygens, Christiaan 185
Huygens spacecraft 228
Hydra (a moon) 243, 243
Hydra constellation 18
Hyperion 230, 230

I
Iapetus 231, 231
IC405 106, 107
IC418 125, 125
IC443 138, 138, 145, 145
IC1396 79, 85, 85
IC1590 81
IC2118 58, 59
IC2944 81
IC4406 124, 124
IC4592 59, 59
IC4593 122, 122
IC4812 59, 59
IC5070 102, 103
ice giants 200, 201, 232-9
Ida 198, 199
infrared
- cirrus clouds 60, 60
- dust lanes 62-3, 63
- images 144, 144, 175, 228, 228, 230
- light 6, 84, 84, 85, 85, 202
- radiation 34, 34, 175
- wavelengths 27, 28, 29, 34, 34, 43, 60, 64, 76, 97, 111, 111, 125, 125, 126, 126, 141, 141, 202, 228, 233, 237, 250

Inner Solar System 240, 245, 246
International Astronomical Union 196, 241, 243
International Space Station 174
Io 201, 206, 207, 208, 209, 209, 223, 239
IRAS 18059-3211 123, 123
Ithaca Chasma 224, 224

J
Janus 218, 218, 221
Jellyfish Nebula 145, 145
Jupiter 6, 105, 151, 154, 196, 200-213, 203, 240, 241

K
Kepler space telescope 248
Kirchhoff, Gustav 72
Kuiper, Gerard 240
Kuiper Belt 152, 155, 240, 242, 243, 250, 251
- Objects (KBOs) 242, 242, 243, 243, 250

L
Lagoon Nebula 103, 103
Large Hadron Collider 248
Large Magellanic Cloud 38, 40-41, 41, 43, 44, 64, 65, 137
Latona Corona 168, 168
lava tubes 182, 183, 187
lenticulae 211
Leo cluster 16
Libya Linea 211
light
- bending 14
- emissions 177, 177
- speed of 6

light years 6, 16, 251
Little Ghost Nebula 123, 123
LL Ori stellar bow shock 106, 106
LMC irregular galaxy 40-41, 41
Local Bubble 142
Local Group of galaxies 20, 21, 34, 35, 37, 251
Local Supercluster 18, 19
look-back time 6, 10
Loops I, II and III 142
Lunar Command Module 'Falcon' 182, 183
lunar maria 251

M
M1 140-41, 141
M1-67 132, 132
M2-9 124, 124
M4 112, 112
M8 103, 103
M16 84, 84-5
M20 88, 89, 89
M31 34, 34
M33 36, 37
M35 116, 116
M42 94-5, 95
M45 111, 111
M51 24, 25
M57 125, 125
M74 24, 24
M78 76-7, 77
M80 112, 112
M81 27, 27
M82 32, 33
M83 27, 27
M101 48-9, 49
M104 28, 29
Maat Mons 167, 167
Magellan, Ferdinand 41
magnesium-26 154
magnetic fields 104, 156, 159, 160-61, 170, 201, 213, 214, 251
Mangala Valles 194, 194
Mare Crisium 178, 178
Mare Imbrium 178, 178, 182, 183
Mare Serenitatis 178, 178
Mare Tranquillitatis 178, 178, 180
Marginis Basin 178
Mariner 9 probe 184
Mars 154-5, 154, 160, 161, 184-95, 252
Mars Reconnaissance Orbiter 191
mass 16, 251
Mathilde 198, 198
Melas Chasma 188, 188
Menzel 3 120, 120
Mercury 154, 160-63, 162, 163
Messi Chasma 235
Messier, Charles 251
meteor showers 241, 251
meteorites 154, 198, 231, 251
microwaves 6, 12
military satellites 72
Milky Way 6, 7, 10, 18, 34, 37, 38, 41, 46-69, 105, 105, 136, 251
Mimas 218, 218, 220, 220, 221, 221
Miranda 234, 234
molecular clouds 76-7, 79, 83, 86, 86, 142, 145, 251
Moon, composition 6, 178, 178, 180, 180, 181, 182, 182-3
Mount Everest 173, 173, 187
Mountains of Creation 84, 84
MYCN18 129, 129

N
N90 44, 44
N132D 145, 145
NASA 151, 184, 191, 236, 243, 245, 248
NC 281 80, 81
Near Arm 50
Near Earth Asteroid Tracking (NEAT) programme 246
nebulae
- absorption (dark) 78, 79, 79, 81, 81, 82, 82, 83, 83, 85, 85, 251
- emission 42-3, 43, 60, 61, 72, 73, 73, 79, 80, 81, 84, 84, 86, 86-7, 88, 89, 90-91, 91, 92-3, 93, 94-5, 95, 98, 98, 100, 100, 101, 101, 102, 103, 103, 106, 107, 109, 109, 110, 111, 132, 132, 134, 134, 135, 135, 251
- planetary 120-29, 251
- reflection 58, 59, 59, 81, 88, 89, 106, 106, 251
- spiral 24

Neptune 154, 154, 161, 200, 201, 223, 236-9, 240, 250
Nereid 239, 239
neutralinos 68
neutron stars 64, 74, 74, 117, 119, 138, 138, 139, 139, 141, 143, 161, 251, 252
neutrons 119, 251
New Horizons mission 242, 243
Newton, Isaac 11, 154, 240, 248
NGC 346 45, 45
NGC 602 44, 44
NGC 604 36, 37
NGC 628 24, 24
NGC 1132 31, 31
NGC 1300 26, 27
NGC 1316 30, 31
NGC 1350 27, 27
NGC 1427 32, 32
NGC 1559 136, 136
NGC 1569 32, 32
NGC 1999 81, 81
NGC 2070 42-3, 43
NGC 2158 118, 118
NGC 2237 60, 61, 98, 98
NGC 2238 60, 61, 98, 98
NGC 2239 60, 61, 98, 98
NGC 2244 60, 61, 98, 98
NGC 2246 60, 61, 98, 98
NGC 2261 106, 106
NGC 2264 82, 82, 110, 111
NGC 2346 128, 128
NGC 2359 134, 134
NGC 2371 129, 129
NGC 2392 122, 122
NGC 2403 136, 136
NGC 2440 130, 130
NGC 2467 99, 99
NGC 2736 146-7, 147
NGC 2770 136, 136
NGC 3132 122, 122
NGC 3372 90-91, 91, 92-3, 93, 132, 133
NGC 3582 101, 101
NGC 3603 73, 73, 75, 75
NGC 3682 72, 73
NGC 4013 24, 24
NGC 4214 32, 32
NGC 4526 131
NGC 5139 112-13, 113
NGC 5194 24, 25
NGC 6334 100, 100
NGC 6357 108, 108
NGC 6369 123, 123
NGC 6397 114, 114
NGC 6537 128, 128
NGC 6543 121, 121
NGC 6726 59, 59
NGC 6727 59, 59
NGC 6729 59, 59
NGC 6751 123, 123
NGC 6822 37, 37
NGC 6826 121, 121
NGC 6888 135, 135
NGC 6960 143, 143
NGC 7293 118-19, 119, 126, 126-7
NGC 7635 109, 109
Nix 243, 243
Noctis Labyrinthus 188, 188
Norma Arm 50
Norma Cluster 18, 18
Nova Cygni 1992 130, 130
novae 72, 74, 119, 130, 130, 145, 251
Nu Scorpii 59
nuclear fusion 104, 118, 119, 131, 200, 251

O
OB associations 77
Oberon 235, 235
Oceanus Procellarum (Sea of Storms) 180
Odysseus basin 224, 224
OH231.8+4.2 125, 125
Olympus Mons 186, 187, 187, 191
Omega Centauri 112-13, 113
Oort Cloud 155, 242, 244, 244, 251
open star clusters 49, 75, 75, 110, 111, 111, 116, 1
Opportunity (NASA rover) 191
optical images 138, 138
optical wavelengths 95, 95, 141, 141, 168
Orion molecular cloud complex 83, 95
Orion Nebula 43, 94-5, 95, 96-7, 97, 106, 153, 153
Orion Spur 50, 50
Orionids 241
Outer Arm 50
outer limits 240-47
Oval BA storm 205
ozone hole 175, 175

P
P1/Halley 245, 245
Pacman Nebula 80, 81
Palus Putredinus (the Marsh of Decay) 182, 183
pancake domes 168, 168
Pandora 218, 218, 219, 221, 221
Pangaea 172
Panthalassa 172
parallax 11
Parsons, William, Third Earl of Rosse 24
Pavonis Mons 187, 187
Pelican Nebula 102, 103
penumbra 157, 157
Perseids 241
Perseus Arm 50
PGC 3074547 120, 120
Phobos 185, 185
phytoplankton bloom 176, 177
Piazzi, Giuseppe 196
Pillan Patera 209, 209
Pinwheel 27, 27, 48-9, 49
Pismis 24-1 108

Pistol Nebula 132, 132
planet formation 150-51
planetars 150
planetary arrangement 155
planetary embryos 150, 151
planetary nebulae 120-29, 251
planetesimals 150
planets 10, 11, 148-249, 154, 160, 251
  around other stars 151
Pleiades 111
Pluto 154, 160, 240, 241, 243, 243, 250
plutoids 241, 250, 251
polar cap (Venus) 168
polycyclic aromatic hydrocarbons 97, 101
population I stars 50
population II stars 50, 52, 53
positrons 143
Prometheus 209, 221
prominences 158, 158, 251
Promothei Planum 192, 192
Proteus 239, 239
protons 143, 251
protostars 76, 77, 85, 89, 104
PSR B1257+12 161
pulsars 141, 251
Pwyll 211

Q
quantum theory 248
Quaoar 243, 243
quarks 119, 143
quasars 12

R
R Monocerotis 106
radiative zone 156, 156
radio wavelengths 67, 67, 142, 250
radio waves 6, 27, 215, 251
radioactive elements 142-3
RCW57 101
red dwarf stars 104, 126, 152, 152
red giant stage 73, 105, 118
red giants 74, 74, 105, 112, 112, 117, 119, 123, 128, 132, 132, 251
Red Rectangle 124, 124
Red Spider Nebula 128, 128
Red Spot Junior 205, 205
redshift 11
Retina Nebula 124, 124
Rhea 226, 226, 227, 227
Rho Ophiuchi Complex 59, 59
Rigel 59
Ring Nebula 125, 125
robotic spaceprobes 248
Rosette Nebula 60, 61, 98, 98
rotation period 251
Rotten Egg Nebula 125, 125
rovers 182, 191, 251
Rub Al Khali Desert, Saudi Arabia 175, 175
RX J0822-4300 139, 139

S
Sagittarius A* 66, 67, 251
Sagittarius Arm 50
sand dunes 175, 175, 191, 191
Sandage 96 star cluster 136
Sapas Mons 166, 167
Saturn 154, 200, 214-31, 240
scattered disc 155, 240, 242, 243, 251
Schiaparelli, Giovanni 185
Schiaparelli region 185, 185
Schmidt, Harrison 182
Scutum-Centaurus Arm 50
SDSS J1004+4112 12, 12
Sedna 154, 244, 244
seismometers 182
Seven Sisters 111, 111
Shapley, Harlow 49
shepherd moons 221, 251
Shoemaker-Levy 9 205
Shorty Crater 182, 182-3
Sigma Orionis 83
silicon 143
Sir Mons 167, 167
Sirius A 130
Sirius B 130, 130
Skull and Crossbones 99, 99
Small Magellanic Cloud 38, 44, 44, 45, 64, 65
SMC irregular galaxy 44, 44

Smythii Basin 178
SN 1006 145, 145
SN 1984J 136
SN 1986L 136
SN 1987A 137, 137
SN 1994D supernova Type IA 131, 131
SN 2004dj 136, 136
SN 2005df 136, 136
SN 2007uy 136, 136
SN 2008D 136, 136
Snake Nebula 78, 79
solar cycle 157, 157
solar eruptions 242
solar radiation 175
solar systems 148-59
solar wind 73, 251
Sombrero galaxy 28, 29
Southern Crab Nebula 129, 129
Southern Ring Nebula 122, 122
spectral analysis 72, 251
spiral arms 22, 24, 27, 29, 48, 49, 50, 52, 57, 64, 250, 251
  density waves 57, 57
  gaseous arms 56, 57
spiral galaxies see under galaxies
Spirograph Nebula 125, 125
Spitzer Space Telescope 151
star clusters 45, 45, 49, 81, 89, 99, 99, 111, 111, 136, 251
Stardust mission 245
stars 54, 54-5, 70-147, 251
  binary 105, 108
  birth 10, 76-103, 252
  blue 34, 48, 49, 50, 67, 67
  blue straggler 1123
  death of 72, 73, 74, 117, 142, 145
  double 105
  dwarf 64, 72
  elliptical orbits 57, 57
  exploding 41, 43, 72-3, 132
  life cycle 72-5
  main-sequence 152, 152
  maturity 104-17
  new 24, 48, 57, 60, 72, 74, 75, 75
  old age and death 118-41
  raw constituents of 48-9
  rebirth 142-7
  red 59, 59, 67, 67, 72, 105, 105
  size 10-11
  speed of 68
  starbursts 77
  supergiant 72
  variable 105
  Wolf-Rayet 132, 135, 251
  yellow 34, 116
  young 34, 81, 86, 95, 103, 106, 106, 107
  see also neutron stars; red dwarfs; red giants; white dwarfs; yellow dwarfs
stellar bow shock 106, 106
stellar classification 117, 117
stellar corpses 138, 138, 139-41
stellar mergers 114, 114-15
Stingray Nebula 128, 128
subgiants 117
Sun 6, 37, 49, 52, 53, 100, 104, 109, 154, 156-9, 206, 241, 246, 252
sunspots 156, 156, 157, 157, 159, 159, 250, 252
superearths 161
supergiant stars 117, 132-5, 132-7
  red 119, 135
supernova remnants 74, 74, 131, 131, 138, 138, 142-5, 143-7, 147, 252
supernovae 77, 119, 132, 136-8, 142, 143, 154, 251, 252
  Type I 74, 74
  Type Ia 252
  Type II 74, 74, 119, 252
Swift-Tuttle 241
Syrtis Major region 185, 185

T
Tarantula Nebula 42-3, 43
Taurus-Littrow 180
telescopes 6, 10, 11, 14, 37, 67, 98, 99, 105, 121, 123
  Chandra X-ray 139
  Hubble Space Telescope 12, 72, 196
  infrared 60, 63, 76
  and planets around nearby stars 151
  radio 37
  robotic 196, 246
  space 12, 20, 72, 151, 196, 248
  Spitzer Space Telescope 151
  survey 155, 241
Telesto 224, 224
Tethys 218, 218, 219, 224, 224
Tethys Ocean 173
Thackeray's Globules 81, 81
Tharsis region 187, 188
Thera 211, 211
Thor's Helmet 134, 134
Thrace 211, 211
'tiger stripes' 223
Titan 212, 219, 228, 228, 229
Titania 235, 235
Tithonium Chasma 188, 188
Titius, Johann Daniel 154
Titius-Bode law 154
transits 207, 252
Trapezium 97
Triangulum galaxy 36, 37
Triffid Nebula 88, 89, 89
Triton 223, 236, 236, 239, 239
Tsiolkovsky crater 180, 181
Tui Regio 228
Tunguska meteorite 155
Tupan Patera 209, 209
Tvashtar Patera 209, 209
Tycho's supernova remnant 131, 131

U
ultraviolet
  light 37, 82, 89, 109, 205, 228
  radiation 6, 126, 132, 135, 250
  views 168, 230
  wavelengths 157, 158, 214, 214
umbra 157, 157
Umbriel 234, 234
Universe 252
  acceleration of 11, 250
  distances 6
  evolution of 10, 14
  expansion of 10, 11, 18, 248
  origin of 10
  structure 12, 13
Uranus 118, 154, 154, 161, 200, 232-5, 240

V
V380 Orionis 81
V838 Monocerotis 114, 114-15
Valhalla Crater 213
Valles Marineris 184, 184, 188, 188-9, 189
Veil Nebula 143, 143
Vela Supernova Remnant 146-7, 147
Venera 13 lander 165
Venus 145, 154, 154, 160, 161, 164, 164-9, 165, 167, 168
Vesta 198, 198
Victoria crater 190-91, 191
Virgo Cluster 18, 20, 20
visible-wavelength images 228, 229, 230
voids 14, 15, 18
volcanoes 160, 166-7, 167, 168, 168, 182, 184, 186, 187, 187, 209, 209
Voyager 2 spacecraft 236, 237

W
W5 84, 84
War and Peace Nebula 108, 108
water vapour 175, 175
Whirlpool Galaxy 24, 25
white dwarfs 74, 74, 112, 117, 117, 118, 126, 128, 130, 130, 131, 251, 252
Witch Head Nebula 58, 59
Wolf-Rayet stars 132, 135, 251
WR 124 132

X
X-rays 6, 20, 28, 29, 31, 64, 65, 66, 67, 81, 130, 130, 131, 131, 136, 138, 138, 139, 141, 141, 144, 144, 145, 145, 158, 250, 251
Xena 243
XX Triangulum 132, 132

Y
yardangs 191, 191, 252
yellow dwarfs 152, 152

Z
zone of avoidance 18

CREDITS_

p2: 2MASS/J. Carpenter, T. H. Jarrett, & R. Hurt; p5: Robert Gendler; p7: K. Don and NOAO/AURA/NSF; p10-11: NASA, ESA, S. Beckwith (STScI) and the HUDF Team; p12: [1] NASA/WMAP Science Team; ESA, NASA, K. Sharon (Tel Aviv University) and E. Ofek (Caltech); p13: Jurgen Ziewe; p14: NASA, N. Benitez (JHU), T. Broadhurst (Racah Institute of Physics/The Hebrew University), H. Ford (JHU), M. Clampin (STScI), G. Hartig (STScI), G. Illingworth (UCO/Lick Observatory), the ACS Science Team and ESA; p15: Jurgen Ziewe; p16: [1] NASA, ESA, and the Hubble Heritage Team (STScI/AURA), acknowledgment: D. Carter (Liverpool John Moores University) and the Coma HST ACS Treasury Team; [2] Canada-France-Hawaii Telescope/Coelum/J.-C. Cuillandre & G. Anselmi; p17: Wally Mammoth; p18: European Southern Observatory; p19: Jurgen Ziewe; p20: Canada-France-Hawaii Telescope/Coelum/J.-C. Cuillandre & G. Anselmi; p21: Jurgen Ziewe; p22-23: NASA/JPL-Caltech/K. Gordon (Space Telescope Science Institute) and SINGS Team; p24: [1] NASA, ESA, and the Hubble Heritage (STScI/AURA)-ESA/Hubble Collaboration, acknowledgment: R. Chandar (University of Toledo) and J. Miller (University of Michigan); [2] NASA and The Hubble Heritage Team (STScI/AURA), acknowledgment: J.C. Howk (Johns Hopkins University) and B.D. Savage (University of Wisconsin-Madison); p25: [3] NASA, ESA, S. Beckwith (STScI), and The Hubble Heritage Team (STScI/AURA); p26: [1] NASA, ESA, and The Hubble Heritage Team (STScI/AURA), acknowledgment: P. Knezek (WIYN); p27: [2] NASA, ESA, and The Hubble Heritage Team (STScI/AURA); [3] NASA/JPL-Caltech/S. Willner (Harvard-Smithsonian Center for Astrophysics); [4] ESO; [5] NASA/JPL-Caltech/VLA/MPIA; p28-29: NASA and The Hubble Heritage Team (STScI/AURA); [1] NASA/JPL-Caltech and The Hubble Heritage Team (STScI/AURA); [2] NASA/UMass/Q.D.Wang et al; p30: [1] NASA, ESA, and The Hubble Heritage Team (STScI/AURA), acknowledgment: P. Goudfrooij (STScI); p31: [2] NASA, ESA, and the Hubble Heritage (STScI/AURA)-ESA/Hubble Collaboration, acknowledgment: M. West (ESO, Chile); [3] X-ray: NASA/CXC/Penn State/G. Garmire; Optical: NASA/ESA/STScI/M. West; p32: [1] NASA, ESA, and The Hubble Heritage Team (STScI/AURA), acknowledgment: M. Gregg (Univ. Calif.-Davis and Inst. for Geophysics and Planetary Physics, Lawrence Livermore Natl. Lab.); [2] ESA, NASA and P. Anders (Göttingen University Galaxy Evolution Group, Germany; [3] NASA and The Hubble Heritage Team (STScI); p33: [4] NASA, ESA, and The Hubble Heritage Team (STScI/AURA), J. Gallagher (University of Wisconsin), M. Mountain (STScI), and P. Puxley (National Science Foundation); p34: [1] Robert Gendler; [2] NASA/JPL-Caltech/P. Barmby (Harvard-Smithsonian CfA); [3] NASA/JPL-Caltech/P. Barmby (Harvard-Smithsonian CfA); [4] NASA/JPL-Caltech/K. Gordon (University of Arizona); p35: Wally Mammoth; p36: [1] T.A. Rector (NRAO/AUI/NSF and NOAO/AURA/NSF); [2] NASA and The Hubble Heritage Team (AURA/STScI); p37: [3] NRAO/AUI; [4] NRAO/AUI and NOAO/AURA/NSF; [5] NRAO/AUI; [6] P. Massey (Lowell Obs.), G. Jacoby, K. Olsen, C. Smith (NOAO/AURA/NSF) & T.A. Rector (NRAO/AUI/NSF); p38: NASA, ESA, and The Hubble Heritage Team (STScI/AURA), acknowledgment: Y. Momany (University of Padua); p39: Jurgen Ziewe; p40-41: NASA/JPL-Caltech/M. Meixner (STScI) & the SAGE Legacy Team; p42-43: ESO; [1] C. Smith, S. Points, the MCELS Team and NOAO/AURA/NSF; p44: [1] ESA/Hubble and Digitized Sky Survey 2, acknowledgements: Davide De Martin (http://www.skyfactory.org); [2] NASA, ESA and the Hubble Heritage Team STScI/AURA)-ESA/Hubble Collaboration; p45: [3] NASA, ESA and A. Nota (STScI/ESA); p48-49: NASA and ESA, acknowledgment: K.D. Kuntz (GSFC), F. Bresolin (University of Hawaii), J. Trauger (JPL), J. Mould (NOAO), and Y.-H. Chu (University of Illinois, Urbana); p50-51: Jurgen Ziewe; p52-53: Jurgen Ziewe; p54-55: Atlas Image courtesy of 2MASS/UMass/IPAC-Caltech/NASA/NSF/G. Kopan, R. Hurt; p56: NRAO/AUI and Fabian Walter, Max Planck Institute for Astronomy; p57: NASA, ESA, S. Beckwith (STScI), and The Hubble Heritage Team (STScI/AURA); p58: [1] Image Data: Digitized Sky Survey; Color Composite: Noel Carboni; p59: [2] Robert Gendler, Jim Misti, Steve Mazlin; [3] Robert Gendler, Martin Pugh; [4] Robert Gendler, Jim Misti, Steve Mazlin; p60: [1] MSX/IPAC/NASA/J. Keller; [2] NASA/JPL-Caltech/S. Carey (SSC/Caltech); p61: [3] Nick Wright (UCL) and the IPHAS collaboration; p62-63: NASA/JPL-Caltech/S. Stolovy (SSC/Caltech); p64-65: 2MASS/J. Carpenter, T. H. Jarrett, & R. Hurt; p65: [4] NASA/UMass/D. Wang et al; p66: [1-4] NASA/CXC/Caltech/M.Muno et al.; p67: [5] ESO; [6] NRAO/VLA F.Zadeh et al.; p68: [1] J. Dieman, M. Kuhen and P. Madu; p68-9: M.Kuhen, J. Diemand and P. Madau; p72-73: NASA, ESA, and the Digitized Sky Survey 2, acknowledgment: Davide De Martin (ESA/Hubble); p73: [3] NASA/JPL-Caltech/L. Allen (Harvard-Smithsonian CfA) & Gould's Belt Legacy Team; p74: Grade Design; p75: NASA, ESA, and the Hubble Heritage (STScI/AURA)-ESA/Hubble Collaboration, acknowledgment: J. Maíz Apellániz (Institute of Astrophysics of Andalucia, Spain); p76-77: T. A. Rector/University of Alaska Anchorage, H. Schweiker/WIYN and NOAO/AURA/NSF; p78: [1] Robert Gendler and Jim Misti; [2] European Southern Observatory; [3] Canada-France-Hawaii Telescope/Coelum/J.-C. Cuillandre & G. Anselmi; p79: [4] T.A. Rector/University of Alaska Anchorage, H. Schweiker/WIYN and NOAO/AURA/NSF; p80: [1] T.A. Rector/University of Alaska Anchorage and WIYN/NOAO/AURA/NSF; [2] NASA, ESA, and The Hubble Heritage Team (STScI/AURA), acknowledgment: P. McCullough (STScI); p81: [3] NASA and The Hubble Heritage Team (STScI); [4] NASA and The Hubble Heritage Team (STScI/AURA); p82: NASA, H. Ford (JHU), G. Illingworth (UCSC/LO), M.Clampin (STScI), G. Hartig (STScI), the ACS Science Team, and ESA; p83: T.A.Rector (NOAO/AURA/NSF) and Hubble Heritage Team (STScI/AURA/NASA); p84: [1] NASA/JPL-Caltech/L. Allen (Harvard-Smithsonian CfA); [2] DSS; p85: [3] NASA/JPL-Caltech/W. Reach (Caltech); T.A. Rector (University of Alaska Anchorage) and WIYN/NOAO/AURA/NSF; p86: [1] NASA, ESA, and The Hubble Heritage Team (STScI/AURA); [2] NASA, Jeff Hester and Paul Scowen Arizona State University; p86-87: T.A. Rector and B.A. Wolpa (NRAO/AUI/NSF); p88: [1] Robert Gendler and Jim Misti; [2-4] NASA/JPL-Caltech/J.Rho(SSC/Caltech); p89: [5] NASA, ESA, and The Hubble Heritage Team (AURA/STScI), acknowledgment: F. Yusef-Zadeh (Northwestern Univ.); [6] NASA and Jeff Hester (Arizona State University); p90-91: NASA/JPL-Caltech/N. Smith (Univ. of Colorado at Boulder); p91: [1] NOAO/AURA/NSF; p92-93: NASA, ESA, N. Smith (University of California, Berkeley), and The Hubble Heritage Team (STScI/AURA); p93: [inset] Nathan Smith, University of Minnesota/NOAO/AURA/NSF; p94-95: NASA,ESA, M. Robberto (Space Telescope Science Institute/ESA) and the Hubble Space Telescope Orion Treasury Project Team; p95: [1] Infrared Processing and Analysis Center, Caltech/JPL; [2] Robert Gendler; p96-97: NASA/JPL-Caltech/T. Megeath (University of Toledo) & M. Robberto (STScI); p97: [1] K.L. Luhman (Harvard-Smithsonian Center for Astrophysics, Cambridge, Mass.); and G. Schneider, E. Young, G. Rieke, A. Cotera, H. Chen, M. Rieke, R. Thompson (Steward Observatory, University of Arizona, Tucson, Ariz.) and NASA/ESA; p98: T.A. Rector, B.A. Wolpa & M. Hanna (NOAO/AURA/NSF); p99: ESO; p1: T.A. Rector/University of Alaska Anchorage, T. Abbott and NOAO/AURA/NSF; p101: T.A. Rector/University of Alaska Anchorage, T. Abbott and NOAO/AURA/NSF; p102: [1] University of Colorado, University of Hawaii and NOAO/AURA/NSF; p103: [2] Robert Gendler; [3] A. Caulet (ST-ECF, ESA) and NASA; p104-105: NASA, ESA, K. Sahu (STScI) and the SWEEPS science team; [1] ESO; p106: [3] J. Morse/STScI, and NASA; [2] NASA and The Hubble Heritage Team (AURA/STScI); [4] NASA and The Hubble Heritage Team (STScI/AURA); [5] NASA and The Hubble Heritage Team (AURA/STScI); p107: T.A.Rector and B.A.Wolpa/NOAO/AURA/NSF; p108: NASA, ESA and Jesús Maíz Apellániz (Instituto de astrofísica de Andalucia, Spain). Acknowledgement: Davide De Martin (ESA/Hubble); p109: T.A. Rector/University of Alaska Anchorage, H. Schweiker/WIYN and NOAO/AURA/NSF; [1] NASA, Donald Walter (South Carolina State University), Paul Scowen and Brian Moore (Arizona State University); p110: [1] T.A. Rector (NRAO/AUI/NSF and NOAO/AURA/NSF) and B.A. Wolpa (NOAO/AURA/NSF); p111: [2] NASA, ESA and AURA/Caltech; [3] NASA/JPL-Caltech/J. Stauffer (SSC/Caltech); [4] NASA/ESA and The Hubble Heritage Team (STScI/AURA), George Herbig and Theodore Simon (University of Hawaii); p112: [1] NOAO/AURA/NSF; [2] The Hubble Heritage Team (AURA/STScI/NASA/ESA); p112-113: NASA, ESA, and the Hubble Heritage Team (STScI/AURA), acknowledgment: A. Cool (San Francisco State University) and J. Anderson (STScI); p114-115: [1] NASA, ESA, and H. Bond (STScI); p114: [3] NASA and the Hubble Heritage Team (AURA/STScI); p115: [2] NASA and The Hubble Heritage Team (AURA/STScI); p116: Canada-France-Hawaii Telescope/Coelum/J.-C. Cuillandre & G. Anselmi; p117: Grade Design; p118-119: NASA, NOAO, ESA, the Hubble Helix Nebula Team, M. Meixner (STScI), and T.A. Rector (NRAO); p120: [1] NASA, ESA and The Hubble Heritage Team (STScI/AURA); [2] R. Sahai and J. Trauger (JPL), NASA/ESA; p121: [3] NASA, ESA, HEIC, and The Hubble Heritage Team (STScI/AURA); [4] Bruce Balick (University of Washington), Jason Alexander (University of Washington), Arsen Hajian (U.S. Naval Observatory), Yervant Terzian (Cornell University), Mario Perinotto (University of Florence, Italy), Patrizio Patriarchi (Arcetri Observatory, Italy) and NASA; p122: [1] Hubble Heritage Team (STScI/AURA/NASA); [2] NASA, Andrew Fruchter and the ERO Team [Sylvia Baggett (STScI), Richard Hook (ST-ECF), Zoltan Levay (STScI)]; [3] NASA, ESA, and The Hubble Heritage Team (STScI/AURA); p123: [4] NASA and The Hubble Heritage Team (STScI/AURA); [5] NASA, The Hubble Heritage Team (STScI/AURA); [6] NASA and The Hubble Heritage Team (STScI/AURA); p124: [1] NASA and The Hubble Heritage Team (STScI/AURA); [2] NASA; ESA; Hans Van Winckel (Catholic University of Leuven, Belgium); and Martin Cohen (University of California, Berkeley); [3] Bruce Balick (University of Washington), Vincent Icke (Leiden University, The Netherlands), Garrelt Mellema (Stockholm University), and NASA; p125: [4] Hubble Heritage Team (AURA/STScI/NASA); [5] NASA/JPL-Caltech/J. Hora (Harvard-Smithsonian Center for Astrophysics); [6] NASA and The Hubble Heritage Team (STScI/AURA); [7] ESA/NASA & Valentin Bujarrabal (Observatorio Astronomico Nacional, Spain); p126-127: NASA, NOAO, ESA, the Hubble Helix Nebula Team, M. Meixner (STScI), and T.A. Rector (NRAO); p126: [1] NASA/JPL-Caltech/ J. Hora (Harvard-Smithsonian CfA); [2] J. L. Hora (Harvard Smithsonian Center for Astrophysics); W. B. Latter (NASA/Herschel Science Center); M. Marengo (Harvard Smithsonian Center for Astrophysics); G.G. Fazio (Harvard Smithsonian Center for Astrophysics); H.A. Smith (Harvard Smithsonian Center for Astrophysics); p128: [1] Matt Bobrowsky (Orbital Sciences Corporation) and NASA; [2] Garrelt Mellema (Leiden University) et al., HST, ESA, NASA; [3] NASA and The Hubble Heritage Team (AURA/STScI); p129: [4] Raghvendra Sahai and John Trauger (JPL), the WFPC2 science team, and NASA; [5] NASA, ESA, and the Hubble Heritage Team (STScI/AURA); [6] Romano Corradi, Instituto de Astrofisica de Canarias, Tenerife, Spain; Mario Livio, Space Telescope Science Institute, Baltimore, Md; Ulisse Munari, Osservatorio Astronomico di Padova-Asiago, Italy; Hugo Schwarz, Nordic Optical Telescope, Canarias, Spain; and NASA; p130: [1] NASA, ESA, and K. Noll (STScI), acknowledgment: The Hubble Heritage Team (STScI/AURA); [2] NASA, H.E. Bond and E. Nelan (Space Telescope Science Institute, Baltimore, Md.); M. Barstow and M. Burleigh (University of Leicester, U.K.); and J.B. Holberg (University of Arizona); [3] NASA/SAO/CXC; [4-5] F. Paresce, R. Jedrzejewski (STScI), NASA/ESA; p131: [6] NASA/CXC/Rutgers/J.Warren & J.Hughes et al.; [7] NASA, ESA, The Hubble Key Project Team, and The High-Z Supernova Search Team; [1] Yves Grosdidier (University of Montreal and Observatoire de Strasbourg), Anthony Moffat (Universitie de Montreal), Gilles Joncas (Universite Laval), Agnes Acker (Observatoire de Strasbourg), and NASA; [2] Don F. Figer (UCLA) and NASA; p132: [3] K. Strassmeier, Vienna, NOAO/AURA/NSF; [5] Jon Morse (University of Colorado), and NASA; p133: [4] Nathan Smith, University of Minnesota/NOAO/AURA/NSF; p134: Canada-France-Hawaii Telescope/Coelum/J.-C. Cuillandre & G. Anselmi; p135: T.A. Rector (NRAO/AUI/NSF and NOAO/AURA/NSF); p136: [1] ESO; [3] NASA, ESA, A.V. Filippenko (University of California, Berkeley), P. Challis (Harvard-Smithsonian Center for Astrophysics), et al.; [5-8] NASA/Swift Science Team/Stefan Immler; p137: Hubble Heritage Team (AURA/STScI/NASA); [9] NASA, P. Challis, R. Kirshner (Harvard-Smithsonian Center for Astrophysics) and B. Sugerman (STScI); p138: [main, 1] Chandra X-ray: NASA/CXC/B.Gaensler et al; ROSAT X-ray: NASA/ROSAT/Asaoka & Aschenbach; Radio Wide: NRC/DRAO/D. Leahy; Radio Detail: NRAO/VLA; Optical: DSS; p139: [2-3] Chandra: NASA/CXC/Middlebury College/F.Winkler et al; ROSAT: NASA/GSFC/S.Snowden et al.; Optical: NOAO/AURA/NSF/Middlebury College/F.Winkler et al.; [4] Ute Kraus, Physics education group Kraus, Theoretische Astrophysik Tübingen Tempolimit Lichtgeschwindigkeit; p140-141: NASA, ESA, J. Hester and A. Loll (Arizona State University); p141: [1] NASA/CXC/ASU/J. Hester et al. And NASA/HST/ASU/J. Hester et al.; [2] X-ray: NASA/CXC/ASU/J.Hester (ASU); Optical: NASA/ESA/J.Hester & A.Loll (ASU); Infrared: NASA/JPL-Caltech/R.Gehrz (Univ. Minn.); p142-143: T. Rector/University of Alaska Anchorage and WIYN/NOAO/AURA/NSF; p143: [1] NASA, ESA, the Hubble Heritage (STScI/AURA)-ESA/Hubble Collaboration, and the Digitized Sky Survey 2, acknowledgment: J. Hester (Arizona State University) and Davide De Martin (ESA/Hubble); p144: [main] NASA, ESA, and the Hubble Heritage (STScI/AURA)-ESA/Hubble Collaboration, acknowledgment: R. Fesen (Dartmouth College) and J. Long (ESA/Hubble); [1] NASA/JPL-Caltech/O. Krause (Steward Observatory); p145: [2] NASA, ESA, and The Hubble Heritage Team (STScI/AURA), acknowledgment: J.C. Green (Univ. of Colorado) and the Cosmic Origins Spectrograph (COS) GTO Team; NASA/CXO/SAO; [3] NASA/SAO/CXC; [4] Canada-France-Hawaii Telescope/Coelum/J.-C. Cuillandre & G. Anselmi; [5] NASA/CXC/Rutgers/J.Hughes et al; p146-147: Anglo-Australian Observatory/David Malin Images; p150-151: NASA/JPL-Caltech/Cornell; p151: [1] NASA/JPL-Caltech/H. Knutson (Harvard-Smithsonian CfA); p152: [1] Mark McCaughrean (Max-Planck-Institute for Astronomy), C. Robert O'Dell (Rice University), and NASA; [2] NASA, J. Bally (University of Colorado), H. Throop (SWRI), C.R. O'Dell (Vanderbilt University); [3] NASA, ESA, D. Golimowski (Johns Hopkins University), D. Ardila (IPAC), J. Krist (JPL), M. Clampin (GSFC), H. Ford (JHU), and G. Illingworth (UCO/Lick) and the ACS Science Team; [4] NASA, ESA, D.R. Ardila (JHU), D.A. Golimowski (JHU), J.E. Krist (STScI/JPL), M. Clampin (NASA/GSFC), J.P. Williams (UH/IfA), J.P. Blakeslee (JHU), H.C. Ford (JHU), G.F. Hartig (STScI), G.D. Illingworth (UCO-Lick) and the ACS Science Team; [5] NASA, ESA, J.E. Krist (STScI/JPL); D.R. Ardila (JHU); D.A. Golimowski (JHU); M. Clampin (NASA/Goddard); H.C. Ford (JHU); G.D. Illingworth (UCO-Lick); G.F. Hartig (STScI) and the ACS Science Team; p153: NASA,ESA, M. Robberto (Space Telescope Science Institute/ESA) and the Hubble Space Telescope Orion Treasury Project Team; p154-155: Grade Design; p156: [main] NSO/AURA/NSF; [inset] Pikaia Imaging; p157: [1] Göran Scharmer, Kai Langhans, Mats Löfdahl, ISP, SST, Royal Swedish Academy of Sciences; [2] SOHO(EIT)/NASA/ESA; [3] SOHO(EIT)/NASA/ESA; p158: [1] NASA(TRACE); [2] SOHO(EIT)/NASA/ESA; [3] SOHO(EIT)/NASA/ESA; p159: SST, Royal Swedish Academy of Sciences; p160-161: NASA/Johns Hopkins University Applied Physics Laboratory/Carnegie Institution of Washington; p162: [main] NASA/Johns Hopkins University Applied Physics Laboratory/Carnegie Institution of Washington; [inset] Pikaia Imaging; p163: [1] NASA/Johns Hopkins University Applied Physics Laboratory/Carnegie Institution of Washington; [3] NASA/Johns Hopkins University Applied Physics Laboratory/Carnegie Institution of Washington; [2] NASA/JPL-Caltech; [4] NASA/Johns Hopkins University Applied Physics Laboratory/Carnegie Institution of Washington; p164: [main] Mattias Malmer/NASA; [inset] Pikaia Imaging; p165: [1] NASA/JPL-Caltech; [2] NASA/JPL-Caltech; [3] NASA/JPL-Caltech; [4] NASA/JPL-Caltech; [5] Soviet Planetary Exploration Program, NSSDC; p166-167: [1] NASA/JPL-Caltech; p166: [2] NASA/JPL-Caltech; [3] NASA/JPL-Caltech; p167: [4] NASA/JPL-Caltech; p168: [1] NASA/JPL-Caltech; [2] NASA/JPL-Caltech; [3] NASA/JPL-Caltech; p169: [4] ESA/MPS/DLR-PF/IDA; [5-8] ESA/VIRTIS/INAF-IASF/Obs. de Paris-LESIA/Univ. of Oxford; p170: [main] NASA; [inset] Pikaia Imaging; p171: [1] Wally Mammoth/Blue Marble: Next Generation Earth dataset by Reto Stöckli, NASA Earth Observatory (NASA Goddard Flight centre); [2-4] Wally Mammoth/Blue Marble: Next Generation Earth dataset by Reto Stöckli, NASA Earth Observatory (NASA Goddard Flight centre); p172: [1-3] The Maltings Partnership; [4] R. Dietmar Mueller, University of Sydney/NOAA-NESDIS-NGDC; p173: Image Analysis Laboratory/NASA Johnson Space Center (ISS4-E-8852); p174: Image Analysis Laboratory/NASA Johnson Space Center (ISS9-E-22187); p175: [1] F. Hasler et al., (NASA/GSFC) and The GOES Project; [2] METI/ERSDAC; [3] METI/ERSDAC; [4] METI/ERSDAC; [5] Fritz Hasler and Hal Pierce/NASA/Goddard Space Flight Centre; p176: [1] ESA; p177: [2] Wally Mammoth; [3] NASA Landsat Project Science Office and USGS National Center for EROS; [4] David Batson/DeepSeaPhotography.com; p178: [1] NASA/JPL-Caltech; [2] NASA/JPL-Caltech; [inset] Pikaia Imaging; p179: NASA; p180: Pikaia Imaging; p181: Pikaia Imaging; [1] NASA/JPL-Caltech; [2] NASA; p182-183: [1] Tom Dahl/NASA; [2] Mike Constantine/NASA; p183: [3] NSSDC/NASA; [4] NASA Johnson Space Center (NASA-JSC); p184: [1] USGS Astrogeology Research Program; [inset] Pikaia Imaging; p185: [2] USGS Astrogeology Research Program; [3] USGS Astrogeology Research Program; [4] USGS Astrogeology Research Program; [5] NASA/JPL-Caltech/University of Arizona; [6] NASA; p186: [1] NASA/JPL-Caltech; p187: [2] MOLA/NASA; [3] ESA/DLR/FU Berlin (G. Neukum); [4] ESA/DLR/FU Berlin (G. Neukum); [5] ESA/DLR/FU Berlin (G. Neukum); p188-189: NASA/JPL/Arizona State University; p188: [1] ESA/ DLR/ FU Berlin (G. Neukum); [2] ESA/ DLR/ FU Berlin (G. Neukum); [3] ESA/DLR/FU Berlin (G. Neukum); p189: [4] ESA/ DLR/ FU Berlin (G. Neukum); [5] ESA/DLR/FU Berlin (G. Neukum); [6] ESA/DLR/FU Berlin (G. Neukum); p190: [2-3] NASA/JPL/University of Arizona; p191: [1] NASA/JPL-Caltech/Cornell; [4] ESA/DLR/FU Berlin (G. Neukum); [5] NASA/JPL/University of Arizona; [6] NASA/JPL/Malin Space Science Systems; [7] NASA/JPL/Malin Space Science Systems; p192: ESA/ DLR/ FU Berlin (G. Neukum); p193: [1-2] NASA/JPL/University of Arizona; [3] NASA/JPL/Malin Space Science Systems; [4] NASA/JPL-Caltech; [5] ESA/DLR/FU Berlin (G. Neukum); p194: [1] ESA/DLR/FU (G. Neukum); [2] NASA/JPL/University of Arizona; p195: [3] NASA/JPL-Caltech/Univ. of Arizona; p196: [1] NASA, ESA, J. Parker (Southwest Research Institute), P. Thomas (Cornell University), L. McFadden (University of Maryland, College Park), and M. Mutchler and Z. Levay (STScI); [2] NASA/JPL-Caltech; p197: [3] NASA/JPL-Caltech; p198-199: [1] Ben Zellner (Georgia Southern University), Peter Thomas (Cornell University) and NASA; [2, 4] NASA/JPL-Caltech; [3] NASA/JPL-Caltech; [5] NASA/JPL-Caltech; [6] NASA/JPL-Caltech; p2-201: NASA/JPL/Space Science Institute; p202: [inset] Pikaia Imaging; [1] NASA/JPL-Caltech; [2] Gemini Observatory/AURA; [3] NASA/JPL-Caltech; p203: NASA/JPL/Space Science Institute; p204: [1] NASA/JPL-Caltech; p205: [2] Reta Beebe, Amy Simon (New Mexico State Univ.), and NASA; [3] NASA, ESA, A. Simon-Miller (Goddard Space Flight Center) and I. de Pater (University of California, Berkeley); [4] Hubble Space Telescope Comet Team and NASA; p206: [from left] NASA/JPL-Caltech; NASA/JPL-Caltech; NASA/JPL-Caltech; NASA/JPL-Caltech; Grade Design; p207: NASA/JPL/University of Arizona; p208: NASA/JPL-Caltech; p209: [1-2] NASA/JPL-Caltech; [3] NASA/JPL-Caltech; [4] NASA/JPL-Caltech; [5] NASA/JPL/University of Arizona; [inset] Pikaia Imaging; p210: NASA/JPL-Caltech; p211: [1] NASA/JPL-Caltech; [2] NASA/JPL/University of Arizona/University of Colorado; [3] NASA/JPL/University of Arizona; [4] NASA/JPL-Caltech; [inset] Pikaia Imaging; p212: NASA/JPL-Caltech; [inset] Pikaia Imaging; p213: NASA/JPL-Caltech; [inset] Pikaia Imaging; p214: [1] NASA, ESA, J. Clarke (Boston University), and Z. Levay (STScI); p214-215: NASA/JPL/Space Science Institute; [2] NASA/JPL/Space Science Institute; Pikaia Imaging; p216: [1] NASA/JPL/Space Science Institute; p216-217: [2] NASA/JPL/Space Science Institute; p217: [3] NASA and The Hubble Heritage Team (STScI/AURA), acknowledgment: R.G. French (Wellesley College), J. Cuzzi (NASA/Ames), L. Dones (SwRI), and J. Lissauer (NASA/Ames); p218: NASA/JPL/Space Science Institute; p219: [1] NASA/JPL/Space Science Institute; Grade Design; p220: NASA/JPL/Space Science Institute; p221: [1] NASA/JPL/Space Science Institute; [2] NASA/JPL/Space Science Institute; [3] NASA/JPL/Space Science Institute; p222: NASA/JPL/Space Science Institute; p223: [1] NASA/JPL/Space Science Institute; [2] NASA/JPL/Space Science Institute; [inset] Pikaia Imaging; p224: [1] NASA/JPL/Space Science Institute; [2] NASA/JPL/Space Science Institute; [3] NASA/JPL/Space Science Institute; [4] NASA/JPL/Space Science Institute; p225: NASA/JPL/Space Science Institute; p226: NASA/JPL/Space Science Institute; p227: [1] NASA/JPL/Space Science Institute; [2] NASA/JPL/Space Science Institute; [3] NASA/JPL/Space Science Institute; [4] NASA/JPL/Space Science Institute; [5] NASA/JPL/Space Science Institute; p228: [1] Cassini Radar Mapper, JPL, ESA, NASA; [2] NASA/JPL; [3] NASA/JPL/Space Science Institute; [4] NASA/JPL/Space Science Institute; [inset] Pikaia Imaging; p229: NASA/JPL/Space Science Institute; p230: NASA/JPL/Space Science Institute; p231: NASA/JPL/Space Science Institute; p232: NASA/JPL-Caltech; p233: NASA/JPL-Caltech; Pikaia Imaging; p234: Grade Design; p235: [1] NASA/JPL-Caltech; [2] NASA/JPL-Caltech; [3] NASA/JPL-Caltech; [4] NASA/JPL-Caltech; [5] NASA/JPL-Caltech; p236: Voyager 2, NASA; p237: [1] NASA/JPL-Caltech; [2] NASA/JPL-Caltech; [3] NASA/JPL-Caltech; [4] NASA, L. Sromovsky, and P. Fry (University of Wisconsin-Madison); [inset] Pikaia Imaging; p238: NASA/JPL-Caltech; p239: Grade Design; [1] NASA/JPL; [2] NASA/JPL-Caltech; [3] NASA/JPL; p240-241: Sebastian Deiries (ESO); p242: [main] Pikaia Imaging; [inset] Pikaia Imaging; p243: [3] Eliot Young (SwRI) et al., NASA; [4] NASA, ESA, H. Weaver (JHU/APL), A. Stern (SwRI), and the HST Pluto Companion Search Team; [5] NASA, ESA, and A. Schaller (for STScI); [6] NASA, ESA, and M. Brown (California Institute of Technology); [7] NASA and G. Bacon (STScI); [8] NASA, ESA and M. Brown (Caltech); p244: [main] Pikaia Imaging; [2] NASA/JPL-Caltech/R. Hurt (SSC-Caltech); p245: [3] NASA, ESA, H. Weaver (APL/JHU), M. Mutchler and Z. Levay (STScI); [4] ESA; [5] NASA/JPL; [6] NASA/JPL/UMD; [7] NASA/JPL-Caltech; p246: NASA, NOAO, NSF, T. Rector (University of Alaska Anchorage), Z. Levay and L.Frattare (Space Telescope Science Institute); p247: Canada-France-Hawaii Telescope/Coelum/J.-C. Cuillandre & G. Anselmi; p249: NASA, ESA and H. Richer (University of British Columbia); Endpapers: NASA/JPL-Caltech/S. Stolovy (SSC/Caltech).

This 2008 edition published by Fall River Press, by arrangement with Quercus Publishing Ltd

Book design: Grade Design Consultants, London

Fall River Press
122 Fifth Avenue
New York, NY 10011

ISBN 978-1-4351-0938-4

Printed and bound in China

3 5 7 9 10 8 6 4 2